Molecular Biology

Molecular Biology

A Structural Approach

C. U. M. SMITH

The MIT Press
Massachusetts Institute of Technology
Cambridge, Massachusetts

NORTHEASTERN JUNIOR COLLEGE
STERLING, COLORADO 30981

© *C. U. M. Smith 1968*

All rights reserved. No part of this book may be
reproduced or utilized in any form or by any
means, electronic or mechanical, including photo-copying,
recording, or by any information storage and retrieval
system, without permission in writing from the publisher.

Library of Congress catalog card number: 69-16774

Printed in Great Britain

'. . . Praxiteles and Phidias and all the other statuaries used merely to decorate their material on the outside, insofar as they were able to touch it; but its inner parts they left unembellished, unwrought, unaffected by art or forethought, since they were unable to penetrate therein and to reach and handle all portions of the material. It is not so, however, with Nature.'

GALEN, *On the Natural Faculties*, Book 2, 1, 3.
Translated by A. J. Brock.

Acknowledgements

The subject which this book outlines has been put together by the painstaking work of many gifted men and women. In preparing this book, as in writing the original from which it grew, my debt to them has been total.

More specifically I am most grateful to copyright holders for permission to reproduce micrographs and drawings. The photographs here reproduced from printed half-tone copy inevitably show a loss of detail and the quality of the results is not representative of the originals. Plate 10(*d*) is reproduced from *Molecular Biology of Bacterial Viruses* by Gunther S. Stent, W. H. Freeman & Company, Copyright © 1963.

Finally I am greatly indebted to my wife for much help in typing, proofreading and in the preparation of the index.

Contents

CONTENTS

CONTENTS

11

CONTENTS

CONTENTS

List of Figures, Plates and Tables

FIGURES

13

FIGURES, PLATES AND TABLES

15

FIGURES, PLATES AND TABLES

FIGURES, PLATES AND TABLES

PLATES

17

FIGURES, PLATES AND TABLES

TABLES

18

Introduction

'A book,' wrote I. A. Richards, 'is a machine for thinking with.' It is hoped that this book will help students and the interested general reader to think about, and gain some understanding of, molecular biology.

The present volume has grown from an attempt to prepare a second edition of *The Architecture of the Body*. The earlier book set out to provide a popular exposition of molecular biology as that subject existed towards the end of 1961. However, so rapid has been the development of knowledge in this field, and so exciting has been the consequent increase in understanding that it soon became apparent that nothing less than a complete rewriting was appropriate. Furthermore, in order to display the unity in diversity of the subject, it became necessary to treat the material at somewhat greater depth than in the previous book. It was felt that the book which emerged from so radical and far-reaching a revision was in fact a new book. In consequence it became necessary to find a new title.

The quest for a new title was not an easy one. The intention and orientation of the book remain the same as those of *The Architecture of the Body*. An attempt is made to describe and discuss the materials of which living bodies, chiefly animal bodies, are fabricated. The title finally fixed upon—*Molecular Biology: a Structural Approach*—emphasises this anatomical treatment of the subject matter. Some might argue, however, that a book with this title should contain some account of the fascinating and many-faceted field of virus morphology. It was felt that an adequate discussion of this topic would have diverted attention too far from the central theme of this book. Consequently viruses are mentioned only in connection with their rôle as tools for furthering our understanding of molecular genetics. The present volume, like its predecessor, restricts itself to

19

an outline discussion of the structure and function of animal bodies at the molecular level.

It has already been mentioned that the subject matter of molecular biology is treated with rather less superficiality than in the previous book. The loss of superficiality is, of course, only comparative. The present text remains an introduction to an introduction. Inevitably, however, reduction in superficiality has led to a certain concomitant reduction in simplicity. Nevertheless, an attempt has been made to ensure that the slightly increased sophistication does not place the book beyond the reach of the general reader.

It is difficult to know exactly what criteria distinguish a book intended solely for the student from one intended also for the informed general reader. Scholarly works on history, literature, and even sociology frequently circulate widely outside the narrow world inhabited by academics. This, however, is seldom, if ever, the case with a book on some aspect of natural science. The highly developed language of science makes the subject matter opaque to the uninitiated. Any form of mathematical treatment—and, after all, mathematics has been said to be the language of science—immediately diminishes the potential readership.

Molecular biology has emerged from an intermingling of biology, chemistry and physics. Its subject matter is life; its experimental techniques and intellectual concepts are frequently mathematical and physical. Its language, like the language of all science, becomes increasingly unnatural, precise and mathematical.

In this book an attempt is made to define, either explicitly or implicitly, the technical terms as the text develops. The number of these terms, moreover, is kept as small as is consonant with clarity and reasonable precision. Mathematics, in addition, except for the most elementary type has been eschewed altogether. By these means it is hoped that the book remains accessible to the general reader who wishes to know what all the excitement is about.

Stephen Toulmin[1] has pointed out that a study of the history of science shows that a principal trend in scientific thought since the Renaissance has been a continuing attempt to explain function in terms of underlying structure. Toulmin's historical insight is well borne out by the last fifteen years' work in fundamental biology.

[1] Toulmin, S. and Goodfield, J., *The Architecture of Matter*, Hutchinson, London, 1962, p. 21.

INTRODUCTION

It is a strong characteristic of molecular biology that function is founded on, and emerges from, structure. The functions of proteins, of genes, of organelles, of cells themselves are being increasingly explained in terms of their detailed structures.

In this book, as its title suggests, this aspect of the subject is emphasised. Starting at the level of atoms we ascend 'through all the gyres of form' to the threshold of multicellularity.

We see, first, how our modern understanding of the structure of atoms allows us to explain their chemical properties. These properties manifest themselves most importantly in the ability of atoms to join with others to form stable systems. Such semi-permanent groups of atoms are, of course, known as molecules.

Molecules vary very greatly in size and complexity. The simplest and smallest is the hydrogen molecule. The largest and most intricate are nucleic acids and proteins. As the size and complexity of a molecule increases its shape becomes more and more important to its activity. L. E. R. Picken[1] maintains that 'a zoologist is an amateur of plastic form'. If this is true a zoologist should feel more at home in the world of giant molecules than almost anywhere else.

At the next level of magnitude we find molecules associating together to form assemblies. These assemblies are often very delicate and easily disrupted. In consequence they are often extremely difficult to study. Nevertheless, the effort is well worth while as it is found that these assemblies often have new and unsuspected properties: properties not shown by their constituent molecules.

Beyond the level of the molecular assembly we find the world of organelles. Molecular biologists are just beginning to achieve the glimmerings of an understanding of how these vital structures may spontaneously form from molecules and molecular assemblies if the ambient physico-chemical conditions are right. Once again organelles exhibit properties distinctively different from those of the molecules and molecular assemblies of which they are formed.

Organelles, by definition, are parts of cells. The complexity of even the simplest cell still defeats the imagination of the molecular biologist. It is possible to see that molecular assemblies arise automatically from the conjunction of appropriate molecules in the correct physico-chemical conditions; it is possible to imagine similar mechanisms to be responsible for the self-assembly of certain organelles; the organisation of cells, however, remains beyond the

[1] In *The Cell and the Organism*, Cambridge University Press, 1961, p. 90.

21

present-day horizons of molecular biology. It is at this level too, a level of interacting molecules in a narrow space, that the great triumphs of molecular genetics have their full significance. The structure and activity of the living cell is determined to a large extent by the information inscribed in the structure of its nucleic-acid molecules. Notice the adjective—living. It is probable that cells are the simplest entities in the continuous series of natural forms to which this adjective, with its usual meaning, can be applied.

The final level, in this book, is the level of the multicellular organism. This level, moreover, is only touched upon, or alluded to, in a discussion of the possible molecular mechanisms underlying the differentiation of cells in the multicellular body.

The properties characteristic of each level seem to emerge from the interaction of units in the level immediately below. This is, perhaps, clearest at the molecular level. The properties of a molecule such as, say, water are strikingly different from those of its constituent atoms. This, of course, is no new idea: it was propounded, for example, by both Smuts and Alexander.[1] Molecular biology, originating as it so largely did in the Cavendish Laboratory at Cambridge, provides an ironic recompense to the latter philosopher for Rutherford's slighting remark:[2]

'When you come to think of it, Alexander, all that you have said, and all that you have written during the last thirty years: what does it all amount to? Hot air! Hot air!'

The existence of a hierarchy of structures or, to use a more classical expression, the existence of a 'great chain of being', is, of course, not only a feature of the architecture of the body but also, viewed in its temporal aspect, a reflection of the evolutionary history of that body. The science of molecular biology has been of great help to scientists interested in the origins of life on Earth. Fundamental to recent discussions of this problem has been the gathering realisation that life is but a supremely interesting and awe-inspiring feature of the planet's geochemistry. In other words, it emerges from the chemical properties of the elements which happen to be present at the globe's interface with the Universe. Furthermore it is no 'strange' coincidence that the elements which are maximally present in living forms should have been distributed on the Earth's surface: it turns out that

[1] Alexander, S., *Space, Time and Deity*, London, 1920.
[2] Quoted in *Rutherford* by A. S. Eve, Cambridge, 1939, p. 240.

carbon, hydrogen, oxygen and nitrogen are amongst the commonest atoms in the Universe.

As every student of comparative anatomy knows, the past is often preserved, for the instructed eye, in the anatomies of the present. The incipient science of comparative molecular anatomy may thus help scientists not only to understand more clearly the evolutionary relationships of existing organisms, but also to perceive a little of the form of things long past. Perhaps students of this branch of molecular biology will find vital clues to the nature of the so-called Urey-Miller 'soup' in which, it is suggested, life originated some three or four billion years ago. This type of study has already given a new dimension to biochemistry: that of the evolutionary relationships of molecules and reactions.

At a higher level, it may well turn out that some of the organelles inhabiting the cytoplasms of animal and plant cells may, at some period in 'the vast backward and abysm' of evolutionary time, have possessed independent existence. It is interesting to find that several of these organelles retain the power of self-replication. Furthermore it is at the least suggestive to note that recent work[1] has shown that the structure of the DNA found in mitochondria more closely resembles that of bacterial DNA than that of the DNA of the 'home' cell's nucleus. Perhaps the modern commitment to the exploration of space will lead to the discovery of worlds containing living organisms which will bring reality to the speculations of the biopoets.

This is for the future. For the present we are confined to the Earth and to the deductions we can make from the phenomena which affect our senses. If the living state emerges from the properties of atoms and the forces between atoms, it is clear that in order to come to grips with it we have to grapple first with some of the elements of physics and chemistry: the sciences of energy and matter.

It has been clear for at least two millennia that an explanation of the phenomena of the physical world requires two major abstractions: matter and energy. Both the principal schools of philosophy in the immediate post-Aristotelian world—the Epicureans and the Stoics—realised this necessity. Perhaps, of the two, it was the Stoics who most firmly grasped this duality in things. Matter, for this school of philosophers, was merely passive and impressionable, and in itself

[1] Cummins, J. E., Rusch, H. P. and Evans, T. E. (1967), *J. Mol. Biol.*, *23*, 281.

quite incapable of accounting for the hard facts of experience. Another concept was essential: force. The Stoic interest in the causes of things, at root an ethical concern, resulted in much speculation about the nature of this second concept. Sambursky,[1] who is well qualified to judge, believes that in the Stoic philosophy we find the earliest intimations of the science of energetics, or thermodynamics.

Matter, although ultimately equally mysterious, is an easier concept to grasp than the concept of energy. Like Dr Johnson, we are all inclined to assert our familiarity with matter by reference to its unyielding existence. Energy, on the other hand, seems more abstract, more difficult to fully comprehend. Ultimately, like all physical concepts, it is based upon our physiological experiences. We all know what it is like to feel full, or drained, of energy. Yet it remains difficult to say exactly what it is that we feel full or drained of! Aristotle would have said that energy was not 'being' but 'potentiality'. When we are 'full of energy' we are full of a power to change things, to exert force; the situation is the reverse when we are enervated.

Helmholtz, in 1847, clarified the Stoic position by pointing out that matter and energy were both abstractions: two facets of the unending stream of 'happenings' which constitute our experience. 'The existence of matter itself', he writes,[2] 'is to us something tranquil and devoid of action. . . . Natural objects are not, however, thus passive; in fact we come to a knowledge of their existence solely from their actions upon our organs of sense, and infer from these actions a something which acts. When, therefore, we wish to make actual application of our idea of matter we can only do it by means of a second abstraction and ascribe to it properties which in the first case were excluded from our idea, namely, the capability of producing effects . . . of exerting force.'

This is the essence of the concept of energy. It is that property of a body, or more properly a system of bodies, in virtue of which it is able to exert a force, or to do work.

Some examples may make this clearer. No one will deny that work has to be done to raise a mass of one pound one foot. Now if we let the mass fall from this height work, useful or otherwise, will be done. For example, we could so arrange matters that another weight would

[1] Sambursky, S., *The Physical World of the Greeks*, Routledge & Kegan Paul, 1956, Chapter 6.

[2] *Ueber der erhaltung der kraft*, translated by John Tyndall, 1853.

be raised above the ground. Such a system of counterweights is made use of in the design of lifts. Furthermore, in an ideal world, we could regain in this way exactly the amount of work we put into raising the first weight.

The elevated body is said to have the potentiality of doing work. It is rather like a reservoir of stored work. Cutting the string from which it is suspended is rather like destroying the reservoir's dam. To be precise this *potential energy* is not a property of a body in isolation, but of the system of which it forms a part. In our example the system is composed of the body and the Earth, the gravitational attraction between which is responsible for the weight of the body and hence its movement.

It is easy to think of many other examples of potential energy. A watch spring fully wound possesses this sort of energy. It makes its presence felt by driving the clockwork. Compressed air, again, possesses this potentiality for doing work. In an airgun the energy is used for driving a bullet.

Now, in all the cases we have considered so far potential energy has exerted its effect by causing a body to move: a weight is raised, the hands of a clock revolve, a bullet is shot from a gun. At this point we make use of an all-important principle: the conservation of energy. This principle, too, was prefigured in the philosophical schools of Greek antiquity. 'Nothing', the Greeks asserted, 'can come of nothing' and vice versa. Its resurrection into modern physical science occurred in the seventeenth century. Both Descartes[1] and Leibnitz believed that what they termed 'quantity of motion' was conserved. Energy may be transformed from one form to another but its total quantity remains the same.[2]

If this is the case, and it seems hard to deny, we must draw the conclusion that in our examples the potential energy has been transformed into some other form. This second form in which energy may exist is called 'kinetic energy': the capacity for doing work which a body possesses in virtue of its movement. This energy may easily be

[1] 'As for the first cause, it seems to me evident that it is nothing other than God, Who by His Almighty power created matter with motion and rest in its parts, and who thereafter conserves in the universe by His ordinary operations as much of motion and of rest in its parts as He put in His first creation.' Descartes in *Principles of Philosophy*. Part 2, Section 36 (1644).

[2] Einstein, in showing that matter and energy are interconvertible ($e=mc^2$) broadened the conservation law. We have now to say that the *sum* of matter and energy remains constant.

25

NORTHEASTERN JUNIOR COLLEGE
STERLING. COLORADO 30981

measured by determining the amount of work necessary to stop the movement of the body.

Thus we have two sorts of energy, mutually interchangeable. One sort, potential energy, associated with a body or system of bodies in virtue of its position; the other sort, kinetic energy, associated with a body in virtue of its motion.

It was mentioned above that in an ideal world no energy would be 'lost' in a transformation from one type to another. In the example the weight at the moment of impact would possess a quantity of kinetic energy precisely equivalent to the quantity of potential energy possessed at the start of its fall. This if we think about it is bound to be the case. It is a matter of definition. The potential energy is *defined* as the quantity of work 'do-able' by the system. The only way in which this work can be *done* is by, in some way or other, making use of the kinetic energy of the body as it falls. Mathematical systems, however, are mental constructs: mathematics indeed may more properly be considered an art than a science. Now mechanics is a mathematical system par excellence. The world of events approximates only more or less closely to it. It is found that though in the harmonious world of mathematics potential and kinetic energy are exactly equivalent, in the imprecise, rough and ready world of everyday events potential energy always exceeds kinetic energy.

An explanation is readily found for this disparity: friction. As the weight falls through the air it encounters resistance. The molecules of air impede its progress and rub along its sides. Just as two sticks are heated by rubbing together, so the air molecules and the falling body are heated. Now heat is another form of energy.[1] Hence the reason for the disparity between kinetic and potential energy is easy to see. Some of the potential energy is transformed into heat energy in the air molecules and in the molecules of the weight. Only the remainder appears as kinetic energy. Thus, assuming the conservation law, although kinetic energy is always less than potential energy, potential energy is precisely equivalent to the sum of kinetic energy plus the heat energy produced by friction.

This leads on to a second great generalisation: that energy changes in nature are not, in fact, reversible. In the example we have been considering we have seen that if all the kinetic energy of the body at

---

[1] In fact the kinetic theory developed at the end of the last century shows that heat energy is due to molecular motion. It is thus a special case of kinetic energy.

the end of its fall were collected it would not be sufficient to raise the body back to its original height. To do this the energy transformed into heat by friction would also have to be collected—an impracticable task. This, in fact, rules out the possibility of perpetual motion machines.

The understanding that such machines are impossible has been the mark of the scientist since at least the sixteenth century. Clarification of exactly why this should be so had, however, to await the work of Carnot in the nineteenth century. Carnot shared the avid interest of his contemporaries in the heat engine. By analysing the precise sequence of events occurring in the working of such an engine he was able to show that in any natural system the amount of work done would always be less than the work potential of the system. This is, as can be seen, merely a restatement of what was said above about the disparity between potential and kinetic energy.

Carnot's achievement was to have put these qualitative ideas into a precise quantitative form. His generalisation has come to be called the second law of thermodynamics.

The science of thermodynamics is thus founded on two great laws: the first states that 'nothing can come of nothing' and the second indicates that there is a tide in natural affairs which cannot be reversed. It is the second law which is, perhaps, of the greatest interest and importance to the biologist as it is this law which points out the direction in which natural changes occur. And, after all, activity and change are probably the most obvious characteristics of living things. The second law notes, for example, the obvious fact that heat flows from a hot to a cold body and that after a short while both are in consequence lukewarm. It finds an analogous directionality in all other natural changes. Within an isolated system extremes tend to even out; the trend is towards a monotonous 'grey' uniformity. Just as it is unlikely to find that if a dozen dice are shaken in a bag six would, on being tipped out, show one spot uppermost and six six spots uppermost, so it is unlikely for a natural system to display energy differences between its parts. In short, natural systems tend to randomness, to 'mixed-upness'. The change in this property of randomness as a system moves from one state to another can be measured. It is called a change of *entropy*. In other words entropy, in natural processes, is found always to increase.

In that physicist's abstraction 'an isolated system' the total energy must remain constant. There can, by definition, be no exchange between the system and its environment. The internal parts of the system can, however, undergo any number of rearrangements. It follows from the second law that these parts will interact in such a way that the total energy is evenly spread. In other words those parts of the system initially possessing rather more than the average amount of energy will lose this energy to those parts initially possessing rather less than the average. Let us consider the intuitively obvious example of a falling weight once again. The initially high potential energy of the weight is converted first to thermal energy in the molecules of the air through which it falls, and then to various sorts of energy as it hits the ground. The entropy of the system 'earth-weight' increases; the energy associated with the weight itself is minimised. This aspect of the nature of things: that the available, or 'free' energy of an object is less in its final state than in its initial state is of great importance in biology as well as in physics. Indeed the architecture of the body itself, as of its smallest molecule, can be seen as the form which matter takes as it 'seeks' to achieve a state of minimal energy.

It is clear that in order to give these qualitative ideas quantitative precision *units* must be defined and used. This, of course, applies not only to thermodynamics but to any other branch of science. Hence the last section of this Introduction is devoted to a brief discussion and definition of the more important units used in the ensuing pages of this book.

Science is essentially quantitative and metrical. Until the advent of molecular biology the science of biology, or large tracts of it, seemed to escape this characteristic. Molecular biology, however, is a thoroughly quantitative science. We can assign a weight to a gene, an energy to a reaction, a size to a protein. Accordingly our descriptions can be more precise. A virus is no longer a filter-passing infective agent: we know precisely how small it is, and can compare it with a sugar molecule or a red blood cell. A protein is no longer merely a complicated and massive albuminous molecule: we know how it is constructed, out of how many units, and in some cases we are beginning to know how long it takes the cell to build it. Again we can compare it precisely with other proteins and with other types of molecule. In order to do this, in order to develop a deep and precise insight into the machinery of life, it is necessary to define and use units.

TABLE 1

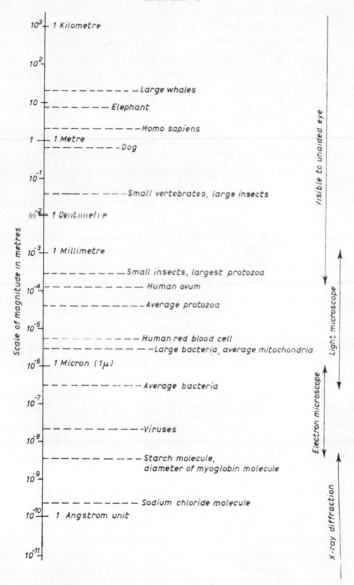

Fig. I.1 Magnitudes of some objects of biological interest.

INTRODUCTION

The units of length, mass and time used by biologists are centimetres, grams and seconds.

Most of the objects studied by the molecular biologist are, however, very much smaller than 1 cm. in length or diameter. Consequently three smaller units of length have been defined and are in common use. The micron (μ) is defined as 10^{-4} cm., the millimicron (mμ) is one thousand times smaller still at 10^{-7} cm. and the Angstrom unit (A) is yet another order of magnitude smaller, 10^{-8} cm. Fig. I.1 shows the linear dimensions of some objects of interest to the biologist.

Similarly, the unit of time—the second—is divided, for convenience, into smaller units; the millisecond (msec.) which is 10^{-3} sec. and the microsecond (μsec.), 10^{-6} sec.

In the same way the unit of mass—the gram—is inconveniently large for many of the entities in which the molecular biologist is interested. Hence two smaller units of mass, the milligram (mgm.)$=$ 10^{-3} gm. and the microgram (μgm.)$=10^{-6}$ gm., are commonly used.

However, perhaps the most important units of mass for the molecular biologist are the atomic and molecular weights. An atom's weight is determined by comparing it with the weight of a 'standard' atom—nowadays a particular isotope of carbon, ^{12}C, is chosen. ^{12}C is *defined* as having an atomic weight of twelve. The weights of all the other atoms are determined in comparison with this isotope. The weight of a molecule is quite simply the sum of the weights of all its constituent atoms.

The molecular weight of a substance in grams defines an important unit—the gram molecular weight, or *mole*. For example, it is easy to calculate, by adding together the atomic weights of sodium and chlorine, that the molecular weight of sodium chloride is approximately 58·4. It follows that 58·4 gm. is the mole or gram molecular weight of this molecule.

It should be clear from the above account that a mole of any substance contains the same number of molecules. It is not too difficult to determine what this number is; in fact it is known as Avogadro's number, symbolised by N, and has the value $6·023 \times 10^{23}$. If a mole of any substance is dissolved in 1 litre of a suitable solvent the resulting solution is said to be *molar* with respect to the solute. It follows that all molar solutions contain the same number (N) of molecules per unit volume.

Let us now pass on from this outline of the units of mass and consider, equally briefly, the units of force and energy. Physicists define the unit of force by reference to our intuition that it requires effort to displace a body either from a state of rest or from rectilinear motion. Consequently the unit of force is defined as that which must be applied to a mass of 1 gm. to accelerate it 1 cm./sec./sec. This force is defined as 1 *dyne*. Having defined a unit of force it is now possible to go on and define a unit of work. Again physicists appeal to our intuition. When we do work, for example when we push a spade into the ground, we exert a force through a certain distance. The point at which the force is applied moves. If it does not, if we just, to take another example, press the spade on to a concrete surface, we cannot be said to be doing work. Hence the physicists define the unit of work—the *erg*—as that which is accomplished when a force of 1 dyne is moved through a distance of 1 cm.

Energy, we saw in the previous section, may be regarded as the potentiality for doing work. Hence ergs are also the units of energy.

Now it is not difficult to show that if water is vigorously stirred its temperature rises. Consequently it is possible to obtain a relation between the work done in stirring and the observed rise in temperature of a known quantity of water. This relation was first determined by Joule in the nineteenth century, and is called the mechanical equivalent of heat. Accurate determinations of this parameter, usually symbolised in Joule's honour by J, show that 4.18×10^7 ergs are required to raise the temperature of 1 gm. of water from $14.5°$C to $15.5°$C. This quantity of energy defines the *calorie* (cal.). In contrast to the units of mass, length and time it is an inconveniently *small* unit. Hence most workers use a unit known as the kilocalorie (kcal.) which is defined as 10^3 cal.

By making use of the units defined in the above paragraphs it is possible to describe the energy changes occurring in biochemical reactions with precision. In order to systematise matters the quantities of reacting chemical species are invariably taken to be moles. Thus when, for example, we read the equation

$$C_6H_{12}O_6 + 6\ O_2 \rightleftharpoons 6\ CO_2 + 6\ H_2O - 686\ \text{kcal./mole}$$

we understand that one mole of glucose has reacted with one mole of oxygen to yield one mole of carbon dioxide and one mole of water. In this reaction 686 kcal. of energy are liberated. Hence the molecules on the right-hand side of the equation have less energy associated with them than those on the left-hand side. This fact is indicated by the minus sign in front of the energy term.

Finally it will be found that the worlds of biochemistry and molecular biology are very heavily populated by initials. These mostly stand for the cumbersome names of molecules. Readers will probably already be familiar with the initials DNA and RNA which stand, respectively, for deoxyribonucleic acid and ribonucleic acid. ATP is another frequently used set of initials standing for adenosine triphosphate. The suffix -*ase* after a name, or set of initials, indicates that the molecule referred to is an enzyme. Thus RN-ase, standing for ribonuclease, is an enzyme which catalyses the breakdown of RNA; similarly ATP-ase is an enzyme capable of hydrolysing ATP.

1

The Primary Substance

1

Gillespie, in his book on the history of Science, *The Edge of Objectivity*,[1] maintains that a cutting 'edge of objectivity' has, in historical times, moved through the various fields of human knowledge converting them from speculation into science. This edge has now penetrated deeply into the science of biology. In its wake have developed the sciences of biophysics and molecular biology.

It is probable that objectivity must have been present, in practical matters, since the beginnings of human history. Only with the Greeks, however, does this attitude to things first penetrate into the world of philosophy.

The great virtue of the Greek mind in the fifth century B.C. seems to have been a wide-ranging curiosity.[2] The earliest names in Greek, and thus European, philosophy—Thales, Anaximander, Anaximenes —are those of men possessed by a great desire to experience and understand all the objects and situations of their world. Their curiosity, moreover, did not stop short at the worlds of the smith, the sailor, or the herbalist. To a far greater extent than the theologians of Egypt and Babylon they searched for answers to their questions in the phenomena of the world around them. In Poynting's phrase the early Greek philosophers sought to explain 'the sensible in terms of the sensible'.

The temper of mind of many of these early thinkers may be judged from the following passage in which Lucretius[3] extols the virtues of natural philosophy:

'This terror then, this darkness of the mind [Lucretius is referring

---

[1] Gillespie, G. C., *The Edge of Objectivity*, Princeton University Press, 1960.
[2] Burnet, J., *Early Greek Philosophers*, A. & C. Black, London, 1892, p. 23.
[3] Lucretius, *On the Nature of Things*, Book 1, translated by C. Bailey.

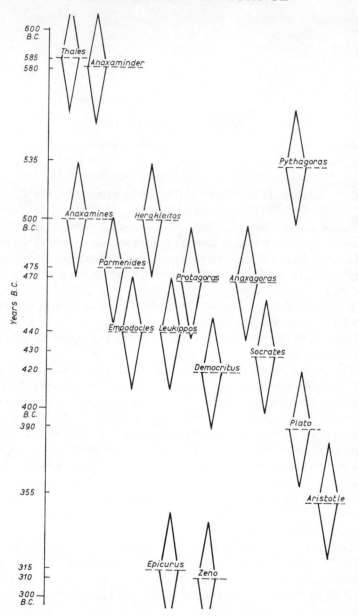

Fig. 1.1 The temporal relationships of the Presocratic philosophers.

to the religion of his time] must needs be scattered not by the rays of the sun and the gleaming shafts of day, but by the outward view and inner law of nature; whose first rule shall take its start from this, that *nothing is ever begotten of nothing by divine will.* Fear forsooth so constrains all mortal men, because they behold many things come to pass on earth and in the sky, the causes of whose working they can by no means see, and think that a divine power brings them about. Therefore, when we have seen that nothing can be created from nothing, then more rightly after that shall we discern that for which we search, both whence each living thing can be created, and in what way all things come to be created without the aid of the Gods.'

One of the principal endeavours of the classical schools of Greek philosophy was to determine the nature of the 'primary substance'.[1] Thales, for example, concluded that the enduring substance underlying the changeable world of experience was water: a conclusion which, according to Bertrand Russell,[2] has dampened the enthusiasm of generations of freshmen philosophers. Many other suggestions as to the nature of the primary substance were put forward. They need not detain us here. From this quest, however, arose, about half way through the fifth century B.C., the first clear statement of the atomic theory of matter.

That matter is ultimately constructed of minute indivisible particles is an heir to much of this early philosophising. For it emerged as a solution to a series of apparently insoluble paradoxes into which the search for the primary substance seemed to have led the philosophers of antiquity. These paradoxes concerned the nature of change. The famous riddles of Zeno—the race between the tortoise and the hare, the flight of an arrow—were invented to illustrate the difficulties into which the philosophy seemed to have fallen.

Parmenides, one of the greatest of the Presocratic philosophers, put the dilemma very clearly. Unlike the majority of the Presocratics Parmenides had been more strongly influenced by the power of pure reason than by experimentation and observation. If, of two

[1] The primary substance of the Presocratics was, according to Aristotle, 'That from which all particular things derive their existence, that from which they originally came into existence—the substance remaining unchanged underneath, though subjected to changes of form. . . .' *Metaphysica*, translated by W. D. Ross, 983^b, 6.
[2] Bertrand Russell, *A History of Western Philosophy*, Allen & Unwin, London, 1946, p. 43.

propositions, reason supported the first and the senses the second, Parmenides inclined to the first. This attitude may seem to be the opposite of scientific. It is not really so. Reason and observation have always been inextricably intermixed in the history of science. One of the great scientists of all time wrote as follows:

'I cannot sufficiently admire the eminence of those men's wits, that have received and held it to be true, and with the sprightlyness of their judgements offered such violence to their senses, as that they have been able to prefer that which their reason dictated to them, to that which sensible experiments represented manifestly to the contrary . . . I cannot find any bounds for my admiration, how that reason was able in Aristarchus and Copernicus, to commit such a rape upon the senses, as in despite thereof to make herself mistress of their credulity.'[1]

Nevertheless a complete preference for the dictates of his reason led Parmenides to what seems an absurd position. For he found himself forced to assert that in truth there was no change, no becoming and no passing away. These were illusions. What was real was a 'solid, uncreated, changeless, eternal, motionless, uniform sphere', an absolute fullness of being. How was Parmenides forced to so astounding a belief? Simple! He merely took the law of the excluded middle, a sound logical principle, seriously, and abided by the consequences.

The law of the excluded middle asserts that 'a thing either is or is not so-and-so', there is no halfway stage, no middle position: '"x" either is or is not "A"', where 'x', as usual, stands for an unknown. Other ways of stating this principle are: 'either "p" is true or "p" is false', 'either "q" exists or "q" does not exist', or, a classical formulation, 'it is impossible for anyone to believe the same thing to be, and at the same time not to be'.[2] A modern instance: 'Light either is or is not propagated as a wave.' And it is surely true to say that these formulae will appear self-evident, as all the best logical principles should, and be assented to by all thinking people.

Yet if we accept them, and abide by their consequences, we at once find ourselves faced with the Parmenidean dilemma. For to account for change, for growth, for dissolution, we must suppose that that which *is* comes to be mixed with that which *is not*. Clearly that which

---

[1] Galileo Galilei, *Dialogues concerning two great systems of the world* (London, 1661).
[2] Aristotle, *Metaphysica*, Translated by W. D. Ross, 1006ª, 7.

is not, just simply is not: it just does not exist. Nothing, certainly, is not a thing. Consequently it is impossible to mix it with that which is. Ergo, that which is cannot change. It must remain unto all eternity changeless and immutable.

But our senses inform us that the most noticeable and important feature of the world is, precisely, change and mutability. Certainly the Greek apprehension of this fact was particularly acute. There are many references in their literature to the sadness of the passing of youth to the transitoriness of things:[1] 'naught may endure but mutability'. Hence the dilemma. Parmenides, and the rest of the Eleatic school, chose to believe the world of the senses unreal, or illusory—that which was real was being: immutable, changeless, eternal. 'An absolute fullness, or plenum, of being' situated in empty space—the void.

The Parmenidean analysis of being and not-being, of the plenum and the void, made a profound impression on the philosophical schools of Greece and her colonies in the fifth century B.C. It was reflection on these ideas that led Leukippos, in about 420 B.C., to propose an atomic theory of the primary substance. Aristotle,[2] who took particular care to summarise the views of his predecessors, writes as follows:

'Leukippos, however, thought he had a theory which was in harmony with sense and did not do away with coming into being and passing away, nor motion, nor the multiplicity of things. He conceded this to experience, while he conceded on the other hand to those who invented the *One* that motion was impossible without the void, that the void was not real,[3] and that nothing that was real was not real. "For," said he, "that which is, strictly speaking, real is an absolute plenum; but the plenum is not one. On the contrary there are an infinite number of them and they are invisible owing to the smallness of their bulk. They move in the void, and by their coming together they effect coming into being, and by their separation passing away."'

Thus Leukippos was able to synthesise the truths of the senses with the truths of logic. Thus originated the atomic theory. The observed facts of change: growth and decay, the digestion and assimilation of

---

[1] Burnet, J., *loc. cit.*, p. 9.
[2] Aristotle, *De Generatione et Corruptione*, translated by H. H. Joachim, 325ª, 24.
[3] 'Real' for the Presocratics was equivalent to corporeal.

food, etc., found their explanation in the arrangement and re-arrangement, the coming together and separation, of invisible entities—the atoms. The atoms themselves could be dealt with in a Parmenidean manner: they were that which *is*, immutable, and eternal. Lucretius calls them 'solid, uncreated, eternal, changeless, uniform'. The atoms have their existence in the void. Lucretius gives this concept clear expression too. He found the idea necessary in order to explain how bodies could be cut or compressed: '. . . all things are not held close pressed on every side by the nature of the body; for there is a void in things . . . a void, mere space, untouchable, empty'.

Although Leukippos is nowadays given the credit for inventing the atomic theory, his close contemporary, Democritus, appears to have been responsible for its first comprehensive working out. The theory found its most powerful advocate in Lucretius in the second century B.C. It remained, however, in the ancient world a purely speculative theory, though one of the most powerful and compre-hensive explanations of the nature of the 'primary substance'.

2

A period of more than two thousand years was to elapse before the atomic theory was again taken up and developed beyond the stage at which the peoples of antiquity had left it. By this time, however, technology had advanced sufficiently for the hypothesis to be tested. Many and ingenious were the experiments devised to prove the theory, and in its main postulates it was not found wanting. This, surely, is one of the most splendid of tributes to the power of the human mind. The great insights of the philosopher and scientist into the nature of the world-stuff, like the great insights of the dramatist into the nature of man, have remained remarkably the same.

One of the principal reasons for the languishment of the atomic theory during the Dark and Middle Ages was a deeply held disbelief in the existence of the 'void'. This was a cardinal tenet of the Aristo-telian philosophy which had become more or less obligatory in the schools of European learning. Indeed the idea lingers on into our present-day thinking. Nature's supposed abhorrence of a vacuum seems to have become a belief imbibed almost with the mother's milk. Most of us, when a physicist points out that, in fact, Nature is largely void, nothingness, are surprised and perplexed. In our day-to-day business we seem to apprehend quite the opposite. If we are not philosophers or physicists, the thought has not worried us, and will not worry us long.

In 1643 Torricelli, by means of his barometer, showed that a vacuum could, and in certain circumstances did, exist. Inverting a glass tube filled with mercury over a trough of mercury he showed that the level of mercury in the tube fell to about 32 inches above the level of mercury in the trough. The space above the mercury column could contain, apart from a minute trace of mercury vapour, nothing. Thus the Aristotelian philosophy suffered a severe blow, and the air was cleared for a resurgence of atomism.

Pierre Gassendi, a younger contemporary of Torricelli, is usually given the credit for reviving the ancient atomic theory and initiating its modern development. Gassendi did not deviate from the ideas of classical antiquity: his atoms were still provided with hooks, eyes and antlers so that they could cling together to form the solid bodies of everyday experience. In spite of following so closely in the footsteps of his ancient masters he was nevertheless able to grasp the significance of Torricelli's experiments. In 1658 he described these experiments at length, and used them as evidence for the existence of vacua in Nature.

Following Gassendi came Boyle and then Newton. Newton added to his many other firsts by being the first to show that hooks, eyes and antlers were unnecessary encumbrances. He imagined 'hard' atoms, infinitesimal billiard balls, with merely attractive and repulsive forces between them. In one of his most famous passages[1] Newton described his conception of the atom:

'. . . God, in the beginning form'd Matter in solid, massy, hard, impenetrable, moveable particles. . . .'

Dalton,[2] the Manchester schoolmaster, who is generally given the honour, in spite of several precursors, of being the first to provide experimental backing for the atomic theory, was probably more strongly influenced by Newton than by the atomists of antiquity. It seems that he had begun to study Newton's writings as early as 1790 when schoolmastering in the Lake District. It was at this period in

[1] Newton, *Opticks*, London, 1717, Query 31.
[2] Dalton lived from 1766 to 1844. He began keeping a record of his meteorological observations in 1787, and continued to the end of his life. Altogether more than 200,000 observations were recorded. During 1808 to 1810 he published his *New System of Chemical Philosophy* outlining his ideas on the atomic theory.

his life, too, that he acquired the interest in meteorology from which the chemical evidence with which he backed up his theory was to be directly derived. For this evidence was based on experiments involving the mixture and combination of gases. From this work Dalton built up a theory in which each gas was pictured as being made up of atoms of a particular weight. This marked a considerable advance on previous thinking where the atoms had differed, if they had differed at all, only in shape.

It is interesting at this point to remark that three of the salient advances in our understanding of the nature of the primary substance derived directly from an interest in meteorology. Thales, at the origin of the whole tradition, observing the overwhelming importance of water to parched Miletos, noticing the transformations of mist into rain, and, apparently, water into earth as rivers silted up, asserted 'all things are water'. Dalton, at the recrudescence of the theory, walked the hills around Kendal, and wondered at the swirling mists and driving rain. Finally C. T. R. Wilson, at the opening of the theory's most modern phase, became fascinated by the atmospheric conditions over his native Scottish hills. Out of this interest in the clouds, the fogs, and the mists of Scotland he was able to conceive and develop the 'cloud chamber' by means of which physicists were able to follow for the first time the actual tracks of atomic and sub-atomic particles.

3

The break-through to our modern ideas about the nature of the atom came, however, from another unexpected direction. Towards the end of the nineteenth century a certain amount of interest gathered around the topic of the discharge of electricity through gases. At first sight little could be further removed from an investigation of the structure of atoms.

At ordinary pressures gases do not conduct electricity unless a very high voltage is applied, when a crackling discharge occurs, the most well-known example of which is lightning. If, however, a piece of apparatus, something like that shown in fig. 1.2, is constructed, and the pressure within the glass cylinder reduced, a 'discharge' can be made to occur between the two electric terminals. The walls of the tube begin to glow, and a metallic object, placed in front of the negative electrode, or cathode, produces a shadow, thus

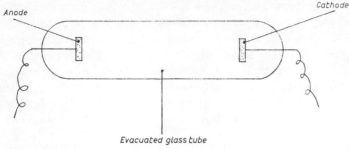

Fig. 1.2 Simple discharge tube.

showing that whatever it is that emanates from the cathode travels in straight lines.

In 1895 Perrin showed that these rays which emanated from the cathode, and which, in consequence, were called cathode rays, carried a negative charge. Two years later J. J. Thomson proved that these 'rays' were in fact volleys of negatively charged 'corpuscles'. These 'corpuscles' were later on to be renamed as electrons. In his paper on 'Cathode Rays' in the *Philosophical Magazine* of October 1897, J. J. Thomson, after giving an account of his experimental methods and calculations, goes on to suggest where the charged corpuscles he had discovered come from:

'If', he writes, 'in the very intense electric field in the neighbourhood of the cathode, the molecules of the gas are dissociated and are split up, not into the ordinary chemical atoms, but into the primordial atoms, which we shall for brevity call corpuscles; and if these corpuscles are charged with electricity and projected from the cathode by the electric field, they would behave exactly like cathode rays. . . .

'Thus on this view we have in the cathode rays matter in a new state, a state in which the sub-division of matter is carried very much further than in the ordinary gaseous state; a state in which all matter —that is, matter derived from different sources such as hydrogen, oxygen, etc., is of one and the same kind; this matter being the substance from which all the chemical elements are built up.'

For the first time the atom had been shown to have a structure. For Dalton as for the Greeks, the atom was, by definition, unsplittable. Indeed this is the literal meaning of the word 'atom'. Thomson had shown that this ultimate particle, this 'solid, uncreated, changeless, eternal, motionless, uniform sphere' was itself made up

41

of smaller units. This marks a considerable break with the classical tradition. Worse, as we shall find in the next chapter, was to follow.

The corpuscles which Thomson had discovered were negatively charged. Yet the atoms from which they had originated were electrically neutral. Hence within the atom these negative charges must be balanced up by equivalent positive charges. Two questions became pressing: first, how many negative charges were there in any given atom and, secondly, how were the positive and negative charges arranged within the atom?

It was fairly quickly established that the number of electrons was equivalent to half the atomic weight. Thus helium, with an atomic weight of four, was found to possess two electrons.

The query about the arrangement of the electrons within the atom proved, however, much harder to answer. J. J. Thomson was able to show that the mass of the electrons compared to that of the hydrogen atom was very small, so that it was obvious that the greater part of the mass of the atom was associated with the positive charge. Thomson arrived at a picture of the atom as a sphere of positive electricity in which the negatively charged electrons were embedded like currants in a bun.

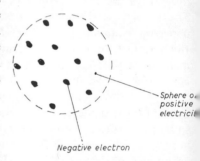

Sphere of positive electricity

Negative electron

Fig. 1.3 Thomson's 'currant-bun' atom.

It was at this point that the genius of Ernest Rutherford made itself felt. In New Zealand he had already shown great mathematical and experimental ability, and very soon after his arrival at Cambridge, as the first research student in the Cavendish Laboratory, he had established a reputation as a physicist. His interests, originally directed to the transmission and reception of radio signals, a topic which, because of its possible military and naval applications, brought him to the notice of the establishment, shifted, under the influence of J. J. Thomson, the Cavendish Professor, to atomic structure. He left the Cavendish Laboratory in 1898 for Montreal, and then in 1907 for Manchester. It was at Manchester as Professor of Physics that his greatest work was done. With Soddy he had shown in 1902 that the phenomenon of radioactivity, to which the Curies and others had devoted so much patient work, was due to the spontaneous breaking-up of the radioactive atoms. This was the first time the possibility of a spontaneous sub-atomic change had been suggested, and it has led, in the fullness of time, to the realisation of the alchemist's dream: the transmutation of the elements.

During radioactive disintegration three different sorts of emission are given off by the atom: these were designated alpha, beta and gamma rays. The next part of our story shows how Rutherford, having gained experience of the facts of radioactive breakdown, made use of the alpha rays to prove the size and structure of the atom.

First Rutherford, in collaboration with Geiger, showed that the alpha rays were in fact particles carrying two positive charges, and weighing four times as much as the hydrogen atom. In fact alpha particles, as they may now be called, are helium nuclei: they are emitted from the radioactive atom with a velocity of about 2×10^9 cm./sec.

Rutherford devised a simple, elegant and decisive experiment which established once and for all the manner in which the negative and positive charges are arranged within the atom. He designed a

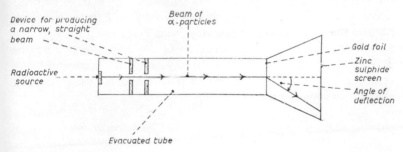

Fig. 1.4 Rutherford's apparatus.

piece of apparatus in which a thin 'pencil' of alpha particles was directed at a zinc sulphide screen. Each time an alpha particle hits such a screen a minute flash of light occurs. These scintillations are easily observed through a low-power microscope. Rutherford placed a piece of gold foil between the source of the alpha particles and the screen. Why gold? Not because it is expensive, or noble, but simply because very thin sheets of gold may be produced quite easily. The foil Rutherford used was about $\frac{1}{2000}$ mm. thick. In passing through the gold foil the alpha particles would be deflected. The extent and nature of the deflection indicated the structure of the gold atoms.

All that it was necessary to do was to observe the deflections of the alpha particles. This Rutherford and his assistant Geiger proceeded to do. It simply entailed going into a dark room, getting accustomed to the dark, and counting the scintillations on the zinc sulphide screen. A tedious procedure. Rutherford admitted in one of his letters that his patience soon became exhausted, but that Geiger, on the other hand, proved inexhaustible. The experiment was simple but the theory and calculations behind it demanded physical insight of the highest order. The upshot was that Rutherford was able to show[1] that the atoms of gold through which the alpha particles had passed and, presumably, all other atoms, must possess a central, heavy, positively charged nucleus, around which the electrons were distributed in some manner yet to be determined. Thomson's 'currant bun' atom was definitely out.

The picture of the atom which finally emerged from the work of Rutherford and his school was that of an infinitesimal solar system. The place of the sun was taken by the nucleus, that of the planets by the electrons. The planets are held in orbit, as Newton showed, by the force of gravity, which exactly balances the centrifugal forces which would otherwise cause them to fly off at a tangent. The electron, on the other hand, is prevented from flying off at a tangent by the electrostatic attraction between its negative charge and the positive charges on the nucleus. In any atom the electrostatic and centrifugal forces were supposed to exactly match each other. The electron, in consequence, is held in a stable orbit.

[1] Rutherford, E. (1911), *Philosophical Magazine*, *21*, 669.

2

Atoms

1

In the first chapter we traced the development of the atomic theory to the beginnings of the twentieth century A.D. We saw how the concentrated attack mounted by Rutherford and his co-workers succeeded in removing some of the mysteries surrounding the nature of the atom. Above all, Rutherford showed the atom not to be one and indivisible but to be made up of smaller units arranged in a particular manner. The 'unchanging, everlasting one' of the Eleatics had thus to be shifted a stage further back, from the entire atom, which the facts of radioactivity had shown to be mutable, to the sub-atomic particles—the electrons, the neutrons, the protons. In very recent times the immutable 'one' has been pursued to a further level of minuteness. It has been shown, for example, that the neutron itself has a structure. The quest shows signs of being endless. Perhaps the trouble is at root philosophical. Perhaps Parmenides was mistaken when he assumed the universal validity of the law of the excluded middle. Perhaps the 'one' is at the same time splittable and unsplittable, mutable and immutable, just as, and in the same way as, light is nowadays believed to be at once corpuscular and non-corpuscular.

To return to Rutherford. We saw that he pictured the atom as a miniscule solar system. The electrons, minute corpuscles bearing a charge of negative electricity, orbit round a central heavy positively charged nucleus. It was not long, however, before certain internal contradictions in this theory brought about its downfall.

Clerk Maxwell, Cavendish Professor at the end of the nineteenth century, had shown that when an electric charge is accelerated an electromagnetic wave is radiated away from it. Now it is a fact of elementary applied mathematics that any body orbiting another, whether or not the orbit is circular, has an acceleration directed towards the centre of the system. Hence, according to Rutherford's model, the circling electron would continuously emit electromagnetic radiation. Now electromagnetic radiation is a form of energy. Hence the electron would become less and less energetic. But, according to the planetary model, the electron is held in orbit by a delicate balance of forces. Electrostatic attraction between the positively charged nucleus and the negatively charged electron tends to draw the electron in towards the nucleus. Centrifugal force, equal and opposite in direction to the electrostatic force, tends to cause the electron to fly off at a tangent. Upset this balance and the unstable atom disintegrates. But centrifugal force depends on the rapidity with which the electron orbits the nucleus. If some of the electron's energy is tapped off then its velocity is bound to fall. Hence the

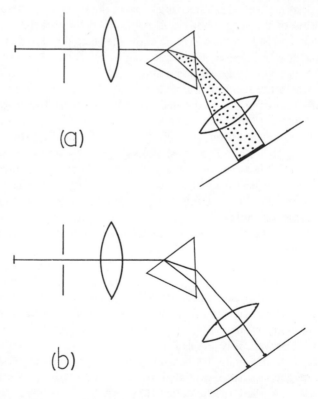

(a)

(b)

Fig. 2.1 (*a*) Continuous emission spectrum. (*b*) Line spectrum.

centrifugal force acting on it becomes less than the electrostatic force. Hence the electron would spiral in towards the nucleus. Hence the planetary atom is inherently unstable.

Worse still, not only was Rutherford's atom a theoretical paradox but it was unable to account for some very well known observations. For it is found that atoms *do* radiate electromagnetic waves and that these waves have some rather strange properties. We are all nowadays familiar with vapour lamps. The sodium lamps of our arterial roads, for example, contain incandescent sodium vapours which radiate a brilliant yellow light. To the naked eye this light does not seem different in kind from the light emanating from the tungsten filament of an ordinary electric light bulb. The naked eye, however, is badly mistaken. For it is found that if the light from a tungsten filament and from a sodium lamp is analysed by passing both through a glass prism two very different results are obtained. The light streaming away from an incandescent tungsten filament is split by the prism into a spectrum containing all the colours of the rainbow. The light emanating from a sodium vapour lamp, on the other hand, is split into just two narrow bands. In consequence we say that the light from our tungsten lamp, or, for that matter, from the sun gives a *continuous* spectrum, whereas that from a sodium lamp gives a *line* spectrum. These two different types of spectra are shown, diagrammatically, in fig. 2.1.

It turns out that different atoms produce different line spectra. By the end of the nineteenth century physicists had observed and recorded a great number of these different line spectra. Rutherford's model of the atom proved incapable of explaining these observations.

2

Before, however, pursuing the topic of line spectra further we must renew and sharpen our acquaintance with wave motion itself.

In Chapter 1 we saw that the belief that matter is ultimately composed of invisible unsplittable particles originated amongst Greek thinkers of the fifth century B.C. It is interesting to note that the first insights into the nature of wave motion may also be traced to this formative period. These initial insights are associated with the name of Pythagoras. The figure of Pythagoras is, of necessity, a shadowy one; he left no writings himself and is believed to have imposed a vow of secrecy on his followers. Nevertheless it seems probable that the central elements in the Pythagorean tradition— that number is the essence of all things, and that the relationships between numbers are 'harmonics'—derive from the master.[1]

Aristotle states[2] that the Pythagoreans had discovered that 'the attributes and ratios of musical scales were expressible in numbers'. The tradition suggests that the discovery was made by measuring off lengths of string on a musical instrument and observing how the resultant note varied. It is not difficult to imagine how significant the

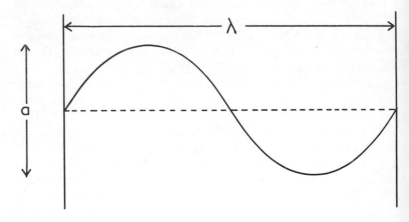

Fig. 2.2 Vibrating string.

discovery of a relation between a measurement and a sensation must have been to a sect fascinated by numerology.

The physical basis of this relationship is nowadays well understood. We recognise that sound can be regarded as a succession of alternate compressions and rarefactions in the atmosphere. These alterations in atmospheric pressure are readily produced by a vibrating string. It is easy to demonstrate that a given musical note is caused by a string vibrating a particular number of times per second. It is also easy to demonstrate that the frequency of vibration is, if the tension on the string is kept constant, dependent on the string's length. The shorter the string, the higher the frequency.

Now the vibration of a string is one of the simplest examples of

[1] Freeman, K., *The Presocratic Philosophers*, Macmillan, London, 1946.
[2] Aristotle, *Metaphysica*, translated by W. D. Ross, 985[b], 23.

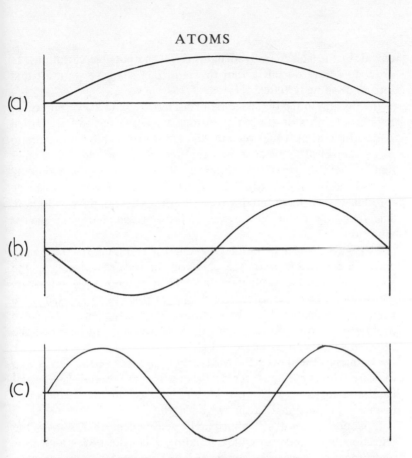

Fig. 2.3 Modes of vibration of a string fixed at both ends.

(*a*) Fundamental. Note that the wave-length is twice the length of the string.

(*b*) First harmonic. The wave-length is equal to the total length of the string. The frequency is thus twice that of the fundamental.

(*c*) Second harmonic. The wave-length is now two-thirds of the string's length. The frequency is thus $\frac{3}{2} \times 2$, or three times that of the fundamental.

wave motion. Let us, therefore, consider some of its characteristics in more detail.

In fig. 2.2 a string stretched tautly between two fixed points has been set vibrating. The vibration may, of course, take many forms other than that shown in fig. 2.2. Some of these other possibilities are shown in fig. 2.3. In all cases, however, one important feature remains the same. This is the obvious fact that the ends of the string, being fixed, remain stationary. Although obvious this fact is not trivial. For it fixes the wave-lengths of all the possible vibrations. In order to assure ourselves that this is in fact the case we must first introduce some technical terms.

In addition to the two fixed points in figs. 2.2 and 2.3 certain other regions of the string remain stationary. These regions are called nodes. In contrast other regions, the antinodes, exhibit a maximum of movement. The distance between one node and the next defines half the *wave-length* of the vibration. Wave-length is conventionally symbolised by lambda (λ). The *amplitude* (*a*) is the vertical distance through which the antinodes travel during one complete vibration. The *frequency* is the time required for the completion of such a vibration.

The wave shown in fig. 2.2 is called a standing, or stationary, wave. In contrast to it are the waves on the surface of water, or the sound waves in the atmosphere, which, in general, progress across the medium. In progressive waves it is not difficult to see that there is an inverse relation between wave-length and frequency. If a wave progresses with a constant velocity—and we have all heard of the speed of sound and the speed of light—then it is clear that the higher the frequency the shorter the wave-length and vice versa. This is also the case with standing waves. In these waves the motion is reflected back and forth between two fixed points. Again the frequency is inversely proportional to the wave-length.

It is perhaps not so immediately self-evident that during the reflection back and forth of a standing wave the nodes and antinodes remain always in the same position. That this is so can, however, be easily demonstrated by placing light paper riders on the vibrating string. If these are placed on the antinodes they are thrown violently off; if they are placed on the nodes they remain in position.

Now if the ends of the string are fixed they must inevitably form nodes. The vibration of the rest of the string must, in consequence, so arrange itself that nodes are retained at each end. It follows that an integral number of antinodes must develop between the ends. Hence only certain wave-lengths are possible. Some of these possibilities are shown in fig. 2.3. It is important to note that the case where there is only one antinode, the simplest case, is called the *fundamental* frequency of the string, and that higher frequencies are called *harmonics*.

Before leaving this outline of waves and wave motion it must be mentioned that the energy carried by a wave is proportional to the

NORTHEASTERN JUNIOR COLLEGE
STERLING. COLORADO 30981

square of its amplitude. That the energy should be related to the amplitude is probably intuitively obvious to anyone who has watched great seas pounding a beach. That it should be proportional to the square of the amplitude is easy enough to prove, but the proof is probably best left to the pages of elementary texts in physics.

3

Having familiarised ourselves with some of the important characteristics of wave motion we can now return to our account of the nature of atoms. It will be recalled that we broke off our discussion on reaching the problem posed by line spectra. These spectra, it will be remembered, are given by vapour lamps. In other words they are due to the incandescence of vapours consisting of atoms of just one type. It follows that line spectra are due to the atoms themselves. The line spectrum given by sodium atoms has already been mentioned: it consists of two lines in the yellow part of the spectrum. These lines are known as the sodium D lines and we can now say that they are caused by light having wave-lengths of 5896A and 5890A respectively. Mercury lamps produce a slightly more complex spectrum with lines produced by light of wave-length 4358A, 5460A, and 5780A.

The credit for seeing the beginnings of a way to explain the production of line spectra by atoms belongs to Niels Bohr. Bohr's theory was published in 1913. His proposals formed the first step on the road which has led physicists steadily away from the classical 'ping-pong ball' physics of the nineteenth century to the 'quarks', 'weak interactions' and 'non-conservation of symmetry' which perhaps mark the beginnings of a fresh understanding of the nature of things.

Niels Bohr was, as usual, not without forerunners. The concepts which he took up and used to explain the production of line spectra by atoms had been developed by earlier thinkers. The principal harbingers of the coming revolution were two German scientists— Max Planck and Albert Einstein.

For some years towards the end of the nineteenth century physicists had striven to make sense of the way in which energy was radiated away from a hot body. This simple-sounding problem appeared to be insoluble to scientists using orthodox concepts. However, Planck, in 1900, showed that if one assumed energy to be emitted from a hot body in a series of distinct packets, or quanta, rather like a hail of machine-gun bullets, then a solution to the problem was available. This was, in fact, a revolutionary development. The great developments in, for example, optics during the nineteenth century had seemed to prove, once and for all, that energy was radiated in the form of waves. Planck was proposing that, at least in the case of radiation from a hot body, energy was particulate, like matter, and was sprayed forth as a hail of quanta.

The radiant heat which Planck studied is a form of electromagnetic radiation and hence its velocity is constant, equal to the velocity of light. Now, according to Planck, the quantity of energy associated with each quantum is proportional to the frequency of the radiation of which it forms a part. The higher the frequency the greater the energy. Or, to put it the other way round, the shorter the wavelength the greater the energy. A simple-minded visualisation of Planck's proposition would be to imagine all quanta to have the same 'length', then the amount of energy carried by each would be proportional to the number of waves packable into this length. Evidently the shorter the wave-length the greater this number would be and hence, according to our picture, the higher the energy carried by the quantum.

Albert Einstein, in 1908, was able to show that an analogous theory was necessary if the effects of electromagnetic radiation on matter and on chemical reactions were to be explained. Thus in the early twentieth century it was beginning to be realised that energy, like matter, was not infinitely divisible. A little later on, in the nineteen-twenties, the French physicist, de Broglie, carried things to a logical conclusion by showing that just as energy possessed some of the characteristics of a particle, so matter possessed some of the features of a wave. For example, de Broglie was able to show that the interaction of electrons could in some circumstances produce diffraction patterns—a phenomenon whose explanation demands the existence of waves (see Chapter 6). However, this development was some way in the future when Bohr published his ideas on atomic structure in 1913.

Bohr took the essence of Planck's quantum theory and applied it to the Rutherford atom. In Bohr's atom the electron still moves in a circular orbit around the nucleus, but the distance of possible electron orbits from the nucleus is quantised. This makes electron orbits different in kind from the orbits of, say, artificial satellites around the

Earth. An artificial satellite can take up any of an infinite number of different orbits depending principally on the velocity with which it is fired from the ground. In complete contrast the number of orbits permitted for an electron circling the nucleus of a Bohr atom is strictly limited. In the simplest case, the hydrogen atom, Bohr showed that the permissible orbits were $1^2 \times 0.53$A, $2^2 \times 0.53$A, $3^2 \times 0.53$A . . . $n^2 \times 0.53$A distant from the nucleus. There are no intermediate values. The electron, if it exists, exists at certain specified distances from the nucleus and no others.

The second assumption of Bohr's theory was that the potential energy associated with an electron was determined by the orbit in which it found itself. The energy was greatest when the electron was in a distant orbit and least when it was in the lowest orbit. Furthermore just as distances of the orbits from the nucleus varied in an 'all-or-nothing' quantal fashion, so the energy associated with the electron varied in a step-wise manner from one orbit to the next.

Instead of imagining that the electron circles the atomic nucleus like a minute satellite we might, alternatively, regard it as held stationary at certain heights above the nucleus. Indeed, as we shall see below, this is a more realistic picture. The heights at which the electron can exist are, of course, quantised in exactly the same way as the orbits. This analogy to the gravitational situation is valuable as it makes it intuitively obvious that a high-placed electron possesses more potential energy than one at a low level. Indeed an electron is commonly regarded as occupying a certain 'energy level' and the higher this level the greater is its energy.

Again, just as in the gravitational analogy, if an electron falls from a high to a low level the energy difference has in some way to be dissipated. In the case of the electrons the energy is always dissipated in the form of an electromagnetic radiation. Furthermore, remembering Planck, the electromagnetic radiation will take the form of a quantum. Let us consider an example. If an electron falls from a very high to a very low level a large amount of energy will be liberated. It follows from what we have said that the energy will be dissipated in the form of a quantum consisting of particularly short wave-length radiation. On the other hand a fall from a low-lying level to the level immediately beneath results in the liberation of only a small amount of energy. Consequently a quantum consisting of long wave-length radiation is emitted.

The orbits permissible to electrons will, of course, differ in different atoms. In other words electron energy levels differ in different atoms. It follows that the energy liberated when electrons move from one level to another varies characteristically from one atom to the next. For example, the energy dissipated by electron movements in the sodium atom will vary markedly from that dissipated by electron movements in, say, the mercury atom. Thus each kind of atom emits electromagnetic radiation of a characteristic and diagnostic wave-length.

Atoms, however, are normally quite stable structures. Electron movements and the consequent radiation do not normally occur. Only when an atom is 'excited' is its characteristic radiation emitted. This excitation occurs in the incandescent vapour lamps we considered initially. When an atom is excited its electrons are raised from their usual or 'ground' states to higher levels. On falling back to their ground levels a quantum of electromagnetic radiation of a characteristic wave-length is emitted. It is this characteristic radiation which is, of course, responsible for line spectra. In this way Bohr's atom proved brilliantly successful in accounting for all the puzzling features of these spectra.

A natural corollary of the ability of Bohr's atom to account for emission spectra is its ability to account for absorption spectra. If, on falling from one level to another, an electron is responsible for the emission of a particular quantum, then it follows that a quantum of this, and only this, particular wave-length is able to raise the electron back from its lowly state to its original position. This follows because there are no intermediate stages between the electron levels. In order to ascend from one level to another a precise amount of energy is necessary. This can only be provided by a quantum possessing just this amount of energy. In other words by a quantum of electromagnetic radiation of a particular wave-length. Thus we see that Bohr's model also explains the observation that different atoms absorb radiation of characteristically different wave-lengths. In Chapter 10 we shall notice that the connection between energy, wave-length and absorption spectra is of considerable importance to the living world.

4

The preceding account shows that Bohr's model of the atom successfully explains the phenomena of absorption and emission spectra. It overcomes, in other words, the 'practical' deficiencies of the

Rutherford atom. It is not, however, a great theoretical improvement. The electron is still 'seen' as a miniscule electrostatically charged 'billiard ball'. Why this particle should not radiate electromagnetic energy whilst revolving in one of Bohr's quantised orbits is not explained. It is simply assumed that, whilst remaining in a given orbit, this just does not happen. It is clear, therefore, that Bohr's model, brilliant practical success though it was, could not satisfy for long the intellects of physicists. We can see today that it is a halfway-house between the classical Democritean concept and the deeper understanding of twentieth-century physics. The fault in Bohr's model, it was soon realised, lay in taking literally the simple pictorial idea of the electron as a very very small charged particle.

The break-through to our modern understanding of fundamental particles came with the enunciation by Heisenberg in 1927 of the 'uncertainty principle'. This principle draws attention to the fact that in the world of the very very small we come up against a basic interaction between the observer and the observed. In order to detect anything in the world we have to get it to act upon our senses. Our senses may, of course, be extended and sharpened by the use of microscopes, scintillation counters, bubble chambers, etc.—it makes no difference. If an entity cannot make its presence felt then we have no means of knowing the first thing about it. This is obvious enough when we are concerned with the everyday objects with which we are surrounded. Dr Johnson, we remember, sought to refute the idealists by vigorously kicking at a boulder. There was no doubt in his commonsensical mind that the stone, in making its presence felt, confirmed its existence. Similarly when a solar photon is reflected from a stone into our eyes we should have to employ very subtle arguments to prove that the stone was not where we saw it. Let us see what happens, however, when we try to apply this epistemological principle at the level of fundamental particles.

It is plain that we cannot kick an electron, nor can we feel it, see it, or hear it. We have to get it to interact with something which does affect our senses. In the previous paragraph we saw that the presence of a stone could be ascertained through its ability to reflect photons. Similarly we have seen that electrons are also able to interact with electromagnetic photons. But, and here's the rub, photons do not leave the electron unchanged as, to all intents and purposes, they did the stone. They are likely, as we have seen, to knock the electron way off course. It is rather like trying to discover, blindfold, where a

55

football is by giving it a vigorous kick. You know it exists, for you have just kicked it, but where it *is*, is now anyone's guess.

In order to observe a fundamental particle one is bound to use probes—photons etc.—of approximately the same dimensions as the particle. The act of observation displaces the particle. In consequence one is left with a built-in uncertainty about its position. Heisenberg's principle, in fact, states that we cannot simultaneously determine the exact position *and* the exact momentum of a particle.[1] If we determine either parameter with precision the other becomes quite imprecise; we can only attain an approximate knowledge of both at once.

Now how does all this affect the Bohr atom? The effect is shattering, for, unfortunately for Bohr, his model defines a precise momentum for each of the electrons in each of his orbits. It follows from the uncertainty principle that we are in consequence *completely* in the dark about where in its orbit each electron is!

The German physicist Schroedinger provided an escape from this seeming impasse by developing a theory which has come to be known as wave mechanics. It will be remembered that earlier in this discussion it was mentioned that de Broglie had shown that just as energy must, in order to explain some observations, be considered particulate, so matter, to explain other observations, must be assumed to have wave-like properties. In particular, as we saw, the *electron* could be shown to possess wave-like properties. Thus the advance made by Schroedinger was to demonstrate that Bohr's electron orbits could be better treated as positions in which the electron could exist as a stationary wave.

This development results in a great clarification of the nature of the atom's structure. Bohr's energy levels, though of great practical value in the explanation of absorption and emission spectra, were, as we saw, arbitrary and theoretically inconsistent. Schroedinger's theory removes both the arbitrariness and the inconsistency.

5

It will be recalled from our discussion earlier in this chapter that stationary waves are bound to possess one of a strictly limited

---

[1] Heisenberg's principle is expressed quantitatively by the following equation:
$$\Delta p \times \Delta q \geqslant h$$
where Δp and Δq are the uncertainties of momentum and position, and h is Planck's constant: 6.6252×10^{-27} erg.sec.

number of wave-lengths or, to put it the other way round, they are bound to possess a strictly limited number of frequencies. These frequencies are all simple multiples of the fundamental frequency (fig. 2.3). Thus if the electron can be considered as a stationary wave, then it immediately becomes evident why it can only exist at certain 'heights' above the nucleus. These heights, it will be remembered, are merely pictorial representations of the different energies which the electron may possess. This, after all, is the observational reality. If, however, we suppose that the quantity of energy associated with an electron is governed by its wave-length, or frequency, and suppose further that the wave-lengths which it can possess are limited, as they are in the case of stationary waves, then the reason why the electron is associated with certain quantities of energy, and no others, is immediately apparent.

One point in Schroedinger's theory, however, remains obscure. We have replaced the 'billiard-ball' electron by a stationary wave—but a wave of what? The waves of our everyday experience all occur in or on some medium. Sound waves occur in the atmosphere, water waves occur on the surface of water, etc. But what can be the material substrate of an electron wave? This is indeed a puzzle, and it receives a rather astonishing answer. It seems that the best interpretation is to regard the wave as a probability wave. The wave represents the chance of discovering an electron at any particular point in its orbit.

Indeed at this point, if anywhere, one is inclined to agree with Heisenberg when he asserts that it is a mistake to try to translate the complex mathematics of wave mechanics into pictorial terms.[1] We have travelled some distance from the science of the nineteenth century when men of the stature of Lord Kelvin were able to maintain that, in order to genuinely understand a theory, it was necessary to first build a real working model of it. 'I never satisfy myself until I can make a mechanical model of a thing', wrote Kelvin.[2] 'If I can make a mechanical model I can understand it.'

Let us, however, continue with our effort to understand the science of the twentieth century. We saw earlier in this chapter that the energy of a wave is proportional to the square of its amplitude. In Schroedinger's theory the square of the amplitude (Ψ) of the electron

---

[1] Heisenberg, W., *The Physical Basis of the Quantum Theory*, translated by Eckhart & Hoyt, Chicago, 1930.

[2] Quoted in Hesse, M. B., *Forces and Fields*, Nelson, London, 1961, p. 5.

wave is proportional to the likelihood of finding an electron at that point.

In fig. 2.4 a diagrammatic representation of an electron wave is shown. According to Schroedinger the chances of finding an electron at points A and C are very remote; on the other hand the chances of finding an electron at B and D are good. The chances of finding it between A and B, B and C, C and D are intermediate between the two extremes. Accordingly it makes sense to talk about electron density. The density is very high at B and D, and very low at A and C.

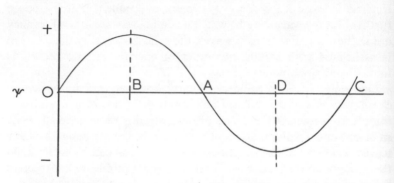

Fig. 2.4 Representation of an electron wave. For explanation see text.

The preceding brief discussion shows how very fundamental and all-pervading is the idea of wave-particle duality in the physics of fundamental particles. To interpret certain experimental results the electron is treated as a wave, to interpret others it is treated as a particle.

6

In our discussion of stationary waves we considered, as a simple example, the waves occurring in a vibrating string. The string was regarded as vibrating up and down in one spatial dimension. This simplicity is unfortunately lost in Schroedinger's electron waves. Electron waves are considered to vibrate in all three dimensions of space.

Reference back to fig. 2.3 will remind us that the frequencies permitted to the vibrating string are all simple multiples of the fundamental frequency. Thus if x c/s is the frequency of the fundamental, then $2x$ c/s, $3x$ c/s, $4x$ c/s . . . nx c/s are the frequencies of the first, second, third . . . $(n-1)$th harmonics. Thus one can specify any harmonic in the string by specifying a single integral number. The situation for electron waves, though fundamentally the same, is rather more complicated. To be exact, three times more complicated. For because electron waves vibrate in the three dimensions of space, three separate parameters are required to specify any harmonic. These parameters are conventionally designated 'n', 'l' and 'm'.

Assignment of whole number values to n, l and m specifies a particular harmonic. To put it another way, specific values for n, l and m define a particular electron *orbital*. Notice the word. In order to show that we have passed beyond the naivety of believing the atom to resemble a miniature solar system we use the word *orbital* in place of orbit.

The parameters n, l and m are called quantum numbers. The theory of wave mechanics shows that n, the *principal quantum number*, may have any positive integral value starting from, and including, 1; l, the *azimuthal quantum number*, may have any positive integral value less than n and including 0; and finally, m, the *magnetic quantum number*, may have any integral value including 0 from $+l$ to $-l$. By making use of this recipe one can work out for oneself the number of possible orbitals associated with different values of the principal quantum number. The modes of vibration, or orbitals, associated with the first three values of 'n' are set out in Table 2.1.

TABLE 2.1

Electron orbitals for the first three principal quantum numbers

Principal quantum number (n)	1		2			3	
Azimuthal quantum number (l)	0	0	1	0	1	2	
Magnetic quantum number (m)	0	0	$-1, 0, +1$	0	$-1, 0, +1$	$-2, -1, 0, +1, +2$	
Total number of orbitals in each shell	1		4			9	

Table 2.1 shows that, for example, when $n=2$ the rules of wave mechanics specify that $l=0$, or 1. If $l=0$, then $m=0$, whilst if $l=1$, then m may equal -1, 0, or $+1$. It follows that when $n=2$ there are four possible orbitals. These orbitals are said to constitute an *electron shell*. Thus, for example, the electron shell for $n=3$ contains nine orbitals.

Bohr's theory, and Schroedinger's after it, was evolved initially to describe the simplest of atoms—the hydrogen atom. This atom, as is well known, consists merely of a single electron 'orbiting' a nucleus consisting of a single positively charged proton. In the average hydrogen atom the electron will occupy the orbital with the lowest energy level. This is the orbital corresponding to $n=1$. If the atom is excited, however, the electron will be lifted to a higher orbital—either one of those specified when $n=2$, or, higher still, one of those specified when $n=3$. From these dizzy eminences it will, in due course, fall back to its ground level emitting as it does an appropriate quantum of electromagnetic radiation.

Although wave mechanics was concerned at the outset to describe the hydrogen atom it can also be applied, less rigorously, to larger and more complex atoms. These atoms all have two or more electrons. It transpires that these additional electrons cannot all crowd into the lowest electron shell. This fact follows, as we shall see, from a generalisation called Pauli's exclusion principle. Before this principle can be described, however, it is necessary to mention that electrons possess a property called 'spin'.

The suggestion that an electron, which we have for some time now been considering as a wave, might, nonetheless, be spinning on its axis serves only to confirm Heisenberg's scepticism about the feasibility of pictorial analogies. The idea of electron spin has, however, arisen from a close analysis of line spectra—which, it will be remembered, initiated this whole intricate discussion. This analysis reveals detail which cannot be accounted for in terms of the three quantum numbers, n, l and m. A fourth number, s, is required. This quantum number may have the value of $+\frac{1}{2}$, or $-\frac{1}{2}$, but none other. Pictorially this is represented as a clockwise, or anticlockwise spin on the electron.

If values are assigned to the four quantum numbers—n, l, m, and s—an electron is completely described. It has no other quantum properties. Now the Austrian physicist Wolfgang Pauli was able to show that no two electrons in the same atom can share all four quantum numbers. Let us take an example. Referring to Table 2.1 we can see that when $n=1$ only one orbital exists. According to Pauli only two electrons can exist in this orbital. These electrons will be defined by the following quantum numbers: $n=1$, $l=0$, $m=0$, and $s=+\frac{1}{2}$, and $n=1$, $l=0$, $m=0$, and $s=-\frac{1}{2}$. There are no other possibilities. The shell is full. All other electrons are excluded. Hence the title of Pauli's principle—the *exclusion* principle.

Armed with this brief qualitative outline of the principles of wave mechanics we can now go on to review the structure of some of the more complex atoms. We have already seen that the structure of the hydrogen atom determines its properties; we shall find that this insight is confirmed by atoms more complicated than hydrogen.

7

It has already been emphasised that hydrogen is the simplest of all atoms. To paraphrase Voltaire's apophthegm, if the hydrogen atom had not existed it would have been necessary for the scientist to invent it. Now it is found that many other atoms have atomic weights which are roughly simple multiples of that of hydrogen. William Prout, a London physician, noted this fact at the beginning of the nineteenth century. In 1815 he published a paper in *Annals of Philosophy* which suggested that 'all elements are made up of hydrogen as the primary substance'. Indeed he went so far as to identify hydrogen as the primary substance for which the Greeks had searched in antiquity.

Prout's hypothesis occasioned a good deal of research chiefly directed towards an accurate determination of the atomic weights of the elements. The hypothesis, however, soon proved untenable; many atoms, for example chlorine (atomic weight 35·5 times that of hydrogen) were found to have weights which were certainly not integral multiples of that of hydrogen. In spite of this we find that in more recent times a revised and deepened version of Prout's hypothesis has developed. This suggests that hydrogen is indeed the primordial atom (certainly there is far more of it in the Universe than any other element) and that other atoms originated from it by nuclear transformations occurring in the conditions of extreme pressure and temperature existing in the stars. The fact that elements have atomic weight which are not exact multiples of that of hydrogen

61

is explained by the discovery that most elements are mixtures of two or more isotopes. These mixtures are usually very difficult to separate and, in consequence, the listed atomic weight is normally obtained from the isotopic mixture. Nowadays the standard against which these isotopic mixtures are measured is a particular isotope of carbon—^{12}C—defined as having an atomic weight of twelve.

If the modern, deepened, version of Prout's hypothesis is accepted we might have expected the next element above hydrogen to have had an atomic weight of two. We should have been wrong. For the next

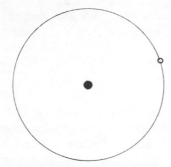

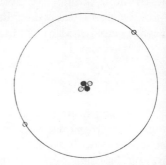

Fig. 2.5 Structure of a hydrogen atom.

The proton is represented by the black spot, the electron by the white circle. The rest of the atom is empty space.

Fig. 2.6 Structure of a helium atom.

The protons are represented by black circles, the neutrons by stippled circles, and the electrons by white circles.

element, helium, turns out to have an atomic weight of four. Nevertheless it can be shown to possess only two electrons. To balance up the negative charges on its two electrons the helium nucleus requires only two protons. Hence in order to make up the observed atomic weight[1] it is necessary to include two other particles in the nucleus. These must have the same weight as the proton, but must carry no electrostatic charge. These particles, accordingly, are called neutrons.

It will have been noticed that whereas the atomic weights of hydrogen and helium are not related in a particularly simple manner the number of electrons in the helium atom is, quite simply, one more than in the hydrogen atom. These relations are shown in figs. 2.5 and

[1] The electrons contribute very little to the mass of an atom. The proton has 1,860 × the mass of an electron.

2.6. The number of electrons possessed by an atom is called its atomic number. It is found that the atomic number increases in a similarly simple fashion throughout the known atoms. Now it can be shown, as we shall see below and in the next chapter, that the electronic structure of an atom determines its chemical properties. In consequence we can omit further description of the atomic nucleus, and concentrate our attention instead on the extra-nuclear electron shells.

The parsimony of Nature sees to it that atoms possess no more energy than is absolutely necessary. But we saw in the previous

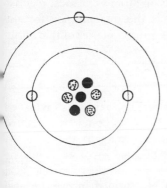

Fig. 2.7 Structure of a lithium atom. Symbolism as in fig. 2.6.

section that the Pauli exclusion principle prevents more than two electrons occupying the lowest energy shell ($n=1$). Thus as soon as we reach the helium atom we find that the first electron shell is complete. The extra electrons of larger atoms are forced to lodge in more distant shells.

The next element in the scale of atomic size and complexity is lithium. It has an atomic number of three. It follows that the third electron is forced to occupy one of the orbitals in the second electron shell ($n=2$). The structure of a lithium atom is schematised in fig. 2.7.

Continuing up the scale we come next to beryllium, and then to boron, carbon, nitrogen, oxygen, fluorine and neon. At each step one electron is added to the second electron shell. Thus by the time we reach neon the outer shell contains eight electrons. Reference to Table 2.1 shows us that eight electrons completely fill the second electron shell. The next atom in the scale is forced to hold one electron in the third electron shell ($n=3$).

It is important to notice at this point in the argument that neon, like helium, is an inert substance. In fact helium and neon are the two simplest members of a group of 'noble' gases. This group of gases which, in addition to helium and neon, includes argon, krypton, xenon and radon, disdains to enter into chemical relations with other atoms.[1] This observation has been of seminal importance in the development of the electronic theory of valency.

The *Penguin English Dictionary* defines valency as 'the combining power of an atom'. It is this power which determines an atom's ability to enter into chemical relations with other atoms. It is this power, in other words, which determines an atom's chemical reactivity. It is, moreover, this power which is the *sine qua non* for the existence of the molecules which form the subject matter of this book.

8

In the later part of the nineteenth century Mendeleyev, a distinguished Russian chemist, had noticed that the elements could be classified into a rather small number of groups according to the types of chemical reaction in which they could become involved. Thus he recognised that the noble gases formed a natural group. He also noticed that lithium, sodium, potassium, etc. formed another natural group. Altogether Mendeleyev recognised eight such groups. Table 2.2 shows the first part of Mendeleyev's classification containing the lightest of the ninety-two naturally occurring elements. As the atomic number increases beyond that of argon the picture becomes more complicated. Restricting our attention to the lightest and simplest atoms enables us to see the essence of Mendeleyev's systematisation.

In Table 2.2 the protons and neutrons are bracketed as, together, they make up the nucleus. For this reason they are sometimes referred to as nucleons. The atomic weight is thus equal to the number of nucleons just as the atomic number is equal to the number of electrons.

Inspection of Table 2.2 shows that the periodicity in chemical properties which was noticed by Mendeleyev is exactly reflected in the electron complement of the outer shells of the various atoms. For

[1] Compounds of xenon have been synthesised in recent years. This, however, does not upset the ideas enshrined in the electronic theory of valency, but in fact confirms them at a deeper level. See Isaac Asimov, *The Noble Gases*, Basic Books Inc, New York, 1966.

ATOMS

TABLE 2.2

The first three periods of Mendeleyev's Table.

Group / Period	I	II	III	IV	V	VI	VII	VIII
1	Hydrogen P1 ⎫ N0 ⎬ E1							Helium P2 ⎫ N2 ⎬ E2
2	Lithium P3 ⎫ N4 ⎬ E3	Beryllium P4 ⎫ N5 ⎬ E4	Boron P5 ⎫ N6 ⎬ E5	Carbon P6 ⎫ N6 ⎬ E6	Nitrogen P7 ⎫ N7 ⎬ E7	Oxygen P8 ⎫ N8 ⎬ E8	Fluorine P9 ⎫ N10 ⎬ E9	Neon P10 ⎫ N10 ⎬ E10
3	Sodium P11 ⎫ N12 ⎬ E11	Magnesium P12 ⎫ N12 ⎬ E12	Aluminium P13 ⎫ N14 ⎬ E13	Silicon P14 ⎫ N14 ⎬ E14	Phosphorus P15 ⎫ N16 ⎬ E15	Sulphur P16 ⎫ N16 ⎬ E16	Chlorine P17 ⎫ N18 ⎬ E17	Argon P18 ⎫ N22 ⎬ E18

P=Proton.　　N=Neutron.　　E=Electron.

example, all the noble gases resemble each other in possessing either two (helium) or eight (neon, argon, etc.) electrons in their outer electron shells. Similarly all the Group I atoms—lithium, sodium, etc.—possess a single electron in the outer shell. On the other hand, all the Group VII atoms possess seven electrons in this shell.

This coincidence cannot be merely accidental. It would seem that the chemical properties of an atom are largely dependent on the electron complement of its outer electron shell. We saw in the previous section that the chemical properties of an atom amounted largely to its ability to combine or not to combine with other atoms. We saw that this combinatorial power was said to constitute the atom's valency. It follows that the atom's outermost electron shell is usually referred to as its *valency shell*.

It will be shown in Chapter 3 that the combination of one atom with another in the formation of a molecule involves the exchange, or sharing, of electrons. These electrons are electrons belonging to the valency shells of the interacting atoms. It will also emerge in the next chapter that this interchange of electrons occurs in such a way that the electronic structure of both atoms comes to resemble that of a noble gas. We have seen that noble gases do not readily form compounds with other atoms. The reason for this is that the valency shells of these gases possess a minimal quantity of energy. In other words they are particularly stable. It follows that in mimicking the structure of noble gases interacting atoms are able to achieve particularly low energy states.

65

It is important to notice that the periodicities displayed in Mendeleyev's table can also be symbolised in the language of wave mechanics. This symbolism is shown in Table 2.3. In this table the atomic orbitals are represented by rectangular boxes, and the direction of spin of the electron(s) by arrows.

TABLE 2.3

Electronic configurations of the first ten elements of Mendeleyev's Table. The arrows indicate the presence and direction of spin of electrons in the orbitals of the first two electron shells

Atom / Quantum numbers	$n=1$ $l=0$ $m=0$	$n=2$ $l=0$ $m=0$	$n=2$ $l=1$ $m=-1$	$n=2$ $l=1$ $m=0$	$n=2$ $l=1$ $m=+1$
H	↓				
He	↓ ↑				
Li	↓ ↑	↓			
Be	↓ ↑	↓ ↑			
B	↓ ↑	↓ ↑	↓		
C	↓ ↑	↓ ↑	↓	↓	
N	↓ ↑	↓ ↑	↓	↓	↓
O	↓ ↑	↓ ↑	↓ ↑	↓	↓
F	↓ ↑	↓ ↑	↓ ↑	↓ ↑	↓
Ne	↓ ↑	↓ ↑	↓ ↑	↓ ↑	↓ ↑

9

In conclusion it is interesting to imagine the impact that our modern understanding of the atom would have had on the minds of Pythagoras and his followers. We have already noticed that these philosophers had achieved the first insights into the mathematical character of the world. They had been profoundly affected by their discovery that the basic intervals in Greek music were based on the ratios 1:2, 3:2, and 4:3. It seemed, to quote Guthrie,[1] that 'kosmos—order and beauty—was imposed on the chaotic range of sound by the first four integers'. Moreover it did not escape the Pythagoreans that these integers—1, 2, 3 and 4—produced, when added together, the 'perfect' number, 10. It was natural that, intoxicated by this discovery, they should have gone on to generalise: 'number is the essence of all things'. How much more intoxicated, we may imagine, would these early thinkers have been had they been privy to the deep-rooted mathematics of Nature revealed by the quantum physicist!

[1] Guthrie, W. K. C., *A History of Greek Philosophy*, Vol. 1, Cambridge University Press, 1962, p. 224.

3

Molecules

1

If we take a grain of, say, glucose we can divide it, and divide it again and so on almost *ad infinitum*. Almost, but not quite. For at a certain point in the series of divisions we should find that we no longer had a particle of glucose with all its familiar properties—sweetness, solubility in water, etc.—but something quite different. We should find, instead, that we had minute quantities of carbon, hydrogen and oxygen whose individual properties are totally dissimilar to those of glucose. Indeed we could say that the properties of glucose are 'emergent' properties: they arise from a certain spatial organisation of six carbon, twelve hydrogen and six oxygen atoms. This emergence of new properties when new levels of material complexity are attained is, as we shall see in the later parts of this book, a striking feature of the architecture of the body. Spatial organisations of atoms forming a higher unity are called molecules. A molecule, to put it another way, is the smallest unit into which a chemical substance, for example glucose, can be divided and still retain its characteristic properties.

The majority of molecules are stable. Their constituent atoms show no tendency to fly apart. Quite the contrary; it is often very difficult to break a molecule into its atomic parts. These facts clearly imply that the atoms in a molecule are in particularly low energy states. In order to disrupt a molecule and extract an atom, energy has to be supplied. It is said that the energy breaks the bonds which hold the atoms in their molecular positions.

One of the most important features of the structure of molecules is thus the nature of the bonds which atoms are capable of forming between themselves. In this chapter we shall review some of the different types of chemical bond which hold atoms together in molecular groupings.

MOLECULES

In order to initiate a discussion of the bonding potentialities of atoms we may recall our observation in Chapter 2 that certain gases are too aristocratic to enter into relations with the commonalty of other atoms. We inferred that the electrons in the valency shells of these so-called noble gases were in a particularly low energy state. That the valency shells of such gases do achieve a minimal energy state or, in other words, a peculiar stability can also be rigorously deduced from the theory of wave mechanics. Now let us remember that all our experience leads us to believe that a body presented with two alternative energy states will, other things being equal, naturally gravitate to the state in which its energy will be least.

Next let us consider what is likely to happen if we bring an atom of sodium and an atom of chlorine together. A glance at Table 2.2 shows us that sodium has one electron in its valency shell whilst chlorine has seven. It is easy to see that if sodium loses an electron its valency shell would come to resemble that of neon, whilst if chlorine should gain an electron its valency shell would come to resemble that of another noble gas—argon. It follows that the outcome of such a donation would be the minimisation of the energy associated with the valency shells of each atom. It follows from our observations in the previous paragraph that if chlorine and sodium come into contact this interaction of valency shell electrons is likely to happen. The reaction is schematised in fig. 3.1.

A further consequence of this electron donation is that chlorine

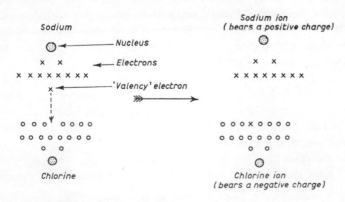

Fig. 3.1 Electron interactions between sodium and chlorine.

possessing an extra electron possesses an additional negative electrostatic charge. Vice versa, sodium, having lost an electron, becomes positively charged. Such charged particles are called ions. It is important to notice that ions, having different electron structures from the atoms from which they are derived, will, in consequence, differ also in their chemical properties. Thus the chloride ion shows few of the properties of the poisonous yellow gas which is chlorine; similarly the sodium ion is radically different from the highly reactive metal which is sodium.

Because the two ions formed by the interaction of sodium and chlorine are oppositely charged they attract each other. In consequence it is found that a crystal of common salt, NaCl, consists of a cluster of sodium and chloride ions held together by electrostatic forces. It would be a great mistake, however, to assume that the ions in the cluster are arranged at random. Indeed the very fact that common salt forms regular crystals in itself suggests that its constituent ions are highly ordered. In fact it is found that each positive sodium ion is surrounded by six negative chloride ions and, vice versa, each chloride ion is surrounded by six sodium ions. Crystallographers have shown that this arrangement is repeated through quite large extents of the sodium chloride crystal thus forming a very regular lattice.

When a crystal of salt is dissolved in water the sodium and chloride ions become surrounded by water molecules which are able, as we shall see later in this chapter, to muffle their electrostatic attraction for each other. In this muffled state the ions are able to drift apart from each other. Indeed the word 'ion', like the word 'planet', stems from a classical root meaning wanderer.

The molecular concept, however, hardly applies to atoms held together by electrovalent bonds. It is unrealistic to single out any two ions in the lattice of a sodium chloride crystal and label them as a 'molecule' of sodium chloride.[1] Furthermore, although ionic solutions are of the very greatest importance in the machinery of life, we find that the molecules of which the body's architecture is fabricated are built according to different principles.

The molecules of which the body is constructed—carbohydrates, lipids, proteins—are held together not by electrovalent linkages but

[1] NaCl molecules do, however, exist in the vapour phase at very high temperatures.

by covalent bonds. Thus in order to gain some insight into the bases of molecular biology it is important to make some effort to understand the nature of this type of chemical bond.

3

In the last section we saw that atoms belonging to Groups I and VII of Mendeleyev's Table could, by the donation and receipt of a valency electron, achieve the stable electron structure of a noble gas. Because the resultant ions are in consequence oppositely charged an electrostatic force develops between them. This electrostatic force is the force of the electrovalent bond. But what sort of force can unite atoms belonging to the central groups of the periodic table? This question is of great importance to the biologist as carbon, oxygen and nitrogen, three of the most important biological atoms, belong to this part of the Table. It is clear that donation and receipt of electrons will not, in general, result in *both* the interacting atoms obtaining the electron structure of a noble gas. In the absence of this possibility it is at first sight rather difficult to see what energy advantage could be conferred on two or more atoms uniting to form a molecule.

There is, however, another possibility. Instead of an electron-rich atom donating its superfluous electron to an electron-poor atom matters may be so arranged that the electrons initially belonging to each atom are shared by both. Let us take a simple and, by now, familiar example—hydrogen. It will be recalled from Chapter 2 that the hydrogen atom consists of a single proton orbited by a single electron. This electron is normally held in the lowest valency shell ($n=1$). The maximum number of electrons that this shell can hold is two (Table 2.1). This number of electrons is to be found in the valency shell of helium, the first of the noble gases. It follows that this electron configuration is particularly stable. On the face of it, therefore, we might predict that if two hydrogen atoms could, in some way, coalesce their valency shells the resulting electronic structure would be such that the low energy state characteristic of helium might be approached.

It will be remembered from Chapter 2 that the lowest valency shell can only contain two electrons if they possess opposite spins. It is possible to show that hydrogen atoms do possess electrons which

71

differ in their direction of spin. It is found that if two such atoms are brought into contact with each other so that their electron shells overlap, then the shells in overlapping coalesce to form a common shell around both nuclei. The shell for $n=1$ contains, it will be remembered, just one orbital. Because this orbital now encloses both nuclei it is called a molecular orbital (MO). The process of forming an MO from two overlapping atomic orbitals (AOs) is shown, very diagrammatically, in fig. 3.2.

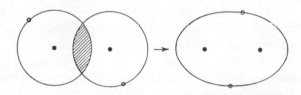

Fig. 3.2 Formation of a molecular orbital around two hydrogen nuclei.

In Chapter 2 it was pointed out that an important alternative way of imagining an electron was to imagine it as a wave, in fact as a probability wave. If we use this alternative 'picture' of an electron it is possible to obtain a more profound insight into the mechanism by which a molecular orbital is formed. It will be recalled that the amplitude of an electron wave is symbolised by Ψ, and that the square of the amplitude—Ψ^2—is proportional to the likelihood of finding an electron at any point in its orbital. Now let us consider how two electron waves might coalesce. Without going into detailed explanations it can be stated that there are in fact only two ways in which atomic orbitals can be combined to form a molecular orbital. Either the electron waves of the atomic orbitals are exactly out of phase, or they are exactly in phase. If the electron waves are exactly out of phase then, as is shown in fig. 3.3(*a*), they will interfere 'destructively'. In other words the peak of one wave will coincide with the trough of the other and hence completely cancel each other out. On the other hand, if the electron waves are exactly in phase then the peak of one wave will coincide with the peak of the other and, similarly, trough will coincide with trough. This is called 'constructive' interference. This second alternative is shown in fig. 3.3(*b*).

Constructive and destructive interference are very well known to students of wave motion, and, in fact, give rise to the diffraction

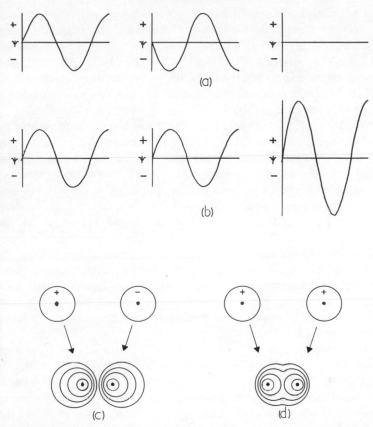

Fig. 3.3 Interaction of atomic orbitals to form a molecular orbital. For explanation see text.

effects we shall be considering in Chapter 6. However, with electron waves we have to bear in mind a very important fact. This is that the amplitude squared is proportional to the probability of finding the electron at any given point. In fig. 3.3(*a*) we see that the amplitude after combination is zero. Clearly the probability of finding an electron at this point in space is also zero. On the other hand in fig. 3.3(*b*) the amplitude after combination is considerably greater than in either of the original atomic orbitals. Hence the probability of finding an electron in this region of space is high.

Now where is this region of space where the electron density may be either zero or quite high? Clearly it is between the two hydrogen nuclei. For as the two hydrogen atoms are brought together prior to forming a molecule the spherical electron shells will first overlap in this position (fig. 3.2). The two conditions shown in fig. 3.3(a) and (b) may thus be redrawn as in fig. 3.3(c) and (d). In fig. 3.3(c) there are no electrons between the two atoms—the electron density is zero; in fig. 3.3(d) the probability of finding an electron in this position is high—the electron density is high.

We are now in a position to perceive the nature of the force holding atoms together in a covalently bonded structure. In fig. 3.3(d) there is a high probability of finding one or more negatively charged electrons between the two positively charged atomic nuclei. We can imagine that these electrons act as a sort of negatively charged cement holding the two positively charged nuclei together. In short the covalent bond reveals itself as just another instance of the ubiquitous electrostatic force. In fig. 3.3(c) we see that the probability of finding an electron between the two nuclei is zero. In consequence there is nothing to cement the two atoms together and, in fact, they immediately drift apart again. Thus the first case represented by fig. 3.3(a) is said to constitute the antibonding condition, and the second case represented by fig. 3.3(b) is said to constitute the bonding condition.

In the simple case of the hydrogen molecule which we have been considering the valency bond is, of course, formed in no particular direction. The orbital in which hydrogen's single electron runs is spherical and in consequence overlapping with the orbital of another hydrogen atom can occur in any position. This, however, is not the case with more complicated atoms. It can be shown that not all the orbitals in the second electron shell are spherical. In fact, those whose azimuthal quantum number (l) is equal to one (see Table 2.1) are disposed at right angles to each other (fig. 3.4). It is clear, therefore, that the overlapping of atomic orbitals on which the formation of a covalent bond depends will be restricted to certain directions.

Let us take an important example—water. A glance at Table 2.2 will remind us that oxygen has six electrons in its valency shell. Hence if matters can be arranged so that it shares an electron with each of two hydrogen atoms then its valency shell will achieve the stability of a neon configuration, while, at the same time, the two hydrogens will come to possess a helium-type valency shell. Clearly the potential energies of the valency shells of all three atoms will be

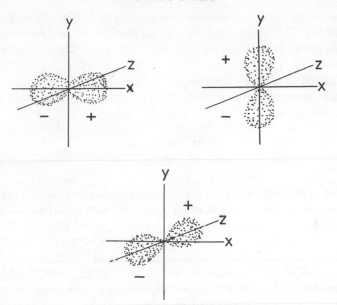

Fig. 3.4 Atomic orbitals for $l=1$ are disposed at right angles to each other in the three dimensions (x, y, z) of space. The algebraic sign refers to the phase of the atomic orbital.

reduced. The overlapping of electron orbitals necessary to bring about this desired result is shown in fig. 3.5.

Fig. 3.5(*c*) shows that the molecular orbitals binding the atoms of the water molecule together are disposed at right angles to each

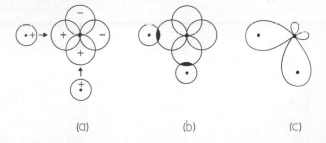

(a)   (b)   (c)

Fig. 3.5 Formation of a molecule of water from one atom of oxygen and two of hydrogen. Reference to Table 2.3 shows that oxygen has two unpaired electrons in its valency shell. The orbitals of these two electrons *only* are shown. The algebraic sign, again, refers to the phase of the orbital.

other. Spectroscopic evidence however, reveals that the true angle is about 105°. The disparity is explained when the repulsion between the two positively charged hydrogen nuclei is taken into account.

Conventionally covalent bonds are represented by straight lines drawn between the interacting atoms. Thus the water molecule is symbolised as:

$$H \diagdown_O \diagup H$$

The symbolisation of covalent bonds by straight lines brings out the fact that they have definite lengths. These lengths may be determined by the techniques of X-ray crystallography (Chapter 6). This technique is able to detect the distance between two atoms held together by covalent linkages. If this distance is measured for a number of atoms it is possible to list a series of 'covalent bond radii'. A number of biologically important covalent bond radii are shown in Table 3.1. The length of the covalent bond between the centres of the carbon and nitrogen atoms is thus, for example, the sum of 0·77 and 0·70 Angstrom units. Similarly the covalent bond distance between the centres of the carbon and oxygen atoms is the sum of 0·77 and 0·66 Angstroms.

TABLE 3.1

Some covalent bond radii (Angstrom units)

Atom \ Type	Single	Double	Triple
C	0·77	0·67	0·60
N	0·74	0·62	0·55
O	0·74	0·62	
H	0·30		
P	1·10		
S	1·04		

MOLECULES

An alternative symbolisation of the covalent bond is sometimes used when it is desired to emphasise the electron sharing basic to this type of bond. Using this second type of symbolism the water molecule may be represented as:

$$\text{H} \quad {}^{\times}_{\bullet}\overset{\bullet\bullet}{\underset{\bullet\bullet}{\text{O}}}{}^{\times}_{\bullet} \quad \text{H}$$

In this representation the dots symbolise electrons originally belonging to oxygen, and the crosses represent those initially belonging to hydrogen.

So far, in our discussion of the covalent bond, it has been implied that the electrons forming the bond are shared equally by all the atoms involved. This is not invariably true. It is sometimes found that some atoms in a molecule have a far greater power of attracting electrons than their neighbours. Such atoms are said to be electronegative. Table 3.2 lists the relative electronegativity of some atoms of importance in biology.

TABLE 3.2

Electronegativity of some atoms of importance in biology

Atom	Electronegativity
O	3·5
N	3·0
Cl	3·0
C	2·5
P	2·1
H	2·1

Electronegativity is probably related to the compactness of the electron cloud around an atom's nucleus. The values in the Table are based on the assignation of an arbitrary value of 2·1 to the hydrogen atom.

Let us take a simple example of a covalently bonded molecule containing a highly electronegative atom: hydrochloric acid. Table 3.2 shows that chlorine is a very much more electronegative atom than hydrogen. Hence in the hydrochloric acid molecule the electron contributed by hydrogen is pulled far over into chlorine's sphere of influence. This feature of the hydrochloric acid molecule is symbolised in fig. 3.6.

77

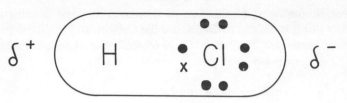

Fig. 3.6 Hydrochloric acid is an example of a polar covalent molecule.

Fig. 3.6 shows that the hydrochloric acid molecule is electrically polarised. The preponderance of electrons at chlorine's end of the molecule results in a small negative charge ($\delta-$); vice versa the lack of electrons at the opposite end results in the development of a small positive charge ($\delta+$). Molecules of this type are in consequence called polar molecules. It is clear that the ionic compounds we considered in the previous section are extreme cases of polar molecules. It follows that the distinction between electrovalently bound and covalently bound molecules is not so sharp and clear cut as it appears at first sight.

4

Our outline up to this point has concentrated on the nature of the *single* covalent bond. The reader will, however, probably be aware that double and even triple covalent bonds are formed in some molecules. This is particularly the case in carbon compounds, and it is carbon compounds which, after all, form the major biological molecules. Carbon, as Tables 2.2 and 2.3 show, has four electrons in its valency shell, and hence, to form a stable octet, requires four more. It is, in short, quadrivalent. One of the simplest carbon compounds known is methane, CH_4. Plainly in this molecule four hydrogens share their lone electrons with a single carbon and, in this way, all five atoms achieve the stability of the appropriate noble gas. An all-important feature of the carbon atom is its ability to combine with other carbon atoms. No other atom possesses this power to the same extent, and it is largely this talent which fits the carbon atom as a basic unit for the construction of biomolecules. Good examples of the long chains of atoms which this proclivity of carbon for combining with itself produces are to be found amongst the close relatives of methane—ethane, propane, butane etc.

$$
\begin{array}{ccc}
\overset{\displaystyle H}{\underset{\displaystyle H}{|}} \overset{\displaystyle H}{\underset{\displaystyle H}{|}} &
\overset{\displaystyle H}{\underset{\displaystyle H}{|}} \overset{\displaystyle H}{\underset{\displaystyle H}{|}} \overset{\displaystyle H}{\underset{\displaystyle H}{|}} &
\overset{\displaystyle H}{\underset{\displaystyle H}{|}} \overset{\displaystyle H}{\underset{\displaystyle H}{|}} \overset{\displaystyle H}{\underset{\displaystyle H}{|}} \overset{\displaystyle H}{\underset{\displaystyle H}{|}}
\end{array}
$$

```
    H   H            H   H   H            H   H   H   H
    |   |            |   |   |            |   |   |   |
 H—C———C—H        H—C———C———C—H        H—C———C———C———C—H
    |   |            |   |   |            |   |   |   |
    H   H            H   H   H            H   H   H   H
   Ethane             Propane                 Butane
```

As we have already mentioned, not only do carbon atoms unite with each other by means of single covalent bonds but also, not infrequently, the union is by means of double or triple bonds. Simple examples of carbon compounds containing such links are ethylene and acetylene:

```
  H           H
    \        /
     C  =  C
    /        \
  H           H
     Ethylene
```

H—C≡C H

Acetylene

What is the electronic reality lying behind these multiple covalent linkages? The triple covalent bond is of little or no importance in the architecture of biomolecules; hence we can concentrate our attention on the double bond as found, for instance, in ethylene.

The carbon atom, we have just seen, possesses four unpaired electrons in its valency shell. In the formation of the ethylene molecule it is easy to see that three of these unsatisfied orbitals are satisfied. This is achieved by overlapping with the atomic orbitals of the two hydrogens and the adjacent carbon. The fourth atomic orbital, as fig. 3.7(a) shows, remains unsatisfied: it contains, in other words, an unpaired electron. Now a very interesting thing happens. As can be seen in fig. 3.7(a) these unsatisfied orbitals overlap. If the electron waves in these two orbitals are in phase then, as we saw in the previous section of this chapter, the conditions are right for the formation of a bond. The phase relations in fig. 3.7(a) are indicated by plus and minus signs. It is clear that, in our diagram, the electron waves are in phase both above and below the main covalent bond. The upshot of this conjunction of orbitals is the formation of two new 'sausage-shaped' orbitals—fig. 3.7(b). The electrons in these new orbitals do not orbit any atomic nucleus, indeed they do not 'belong' to any particular atom but are associated with the molecule

79

as a whole. Such 'delocalised' electrons are called π electrons, and the bond they form is called a π bond.

It is easy to see that a π bond will only form when the appropriate orbitals of the two carbon atoms are in nearly the same plane. In consequence we can immediately see a reason for the well known observation that atoms united by a double covalent bond are not free to rotate about that bond. This fact is of considerable import ance, as we shall see, in the design of protein molecules.

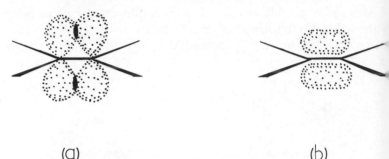

(a)   (b)

Fig. 3.7 A new departure. The double covalent bond of ethylene possesses electrons which orbit neither carbon nucleus. For explanation see text.

We have already noticed that carbon atoms can be united into long chains by single covalent bonds. In several very important bio molecules—for example vitamin A, retinene, the porphyrins, and the carotenoids—we find that long lines of carbon atoms are joined by alternate single and double covalent bonds. Such a chain of carbon atoms is said to be conjugated. The simplest case of a conjugated molecule is butadiene, shown in fig. 3.8.

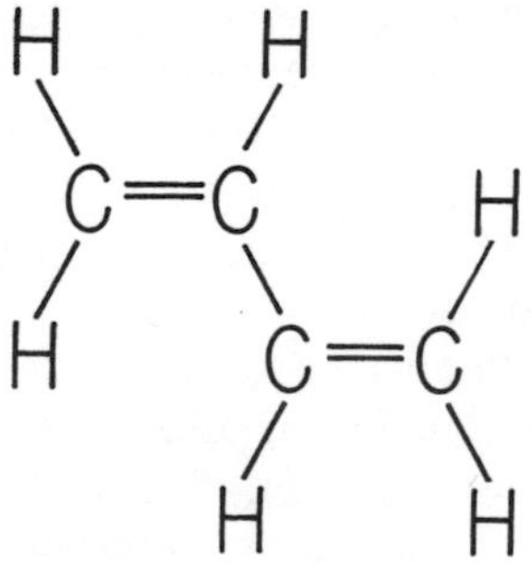

Fig. 3.8 Butadiene is the simplest example of a conjugated molecule.

Another very important case of conjugation is shown by the benzene molecule. This molecule also shows that carbon chains have the ability to bend round and swallow their own tails. The possibility that such a thing might happen was first grasped by Kekulé, dozing, so the story runs, before a flickering fire. In the flames his imagination saw carbon chains bending to form six-membered rings.

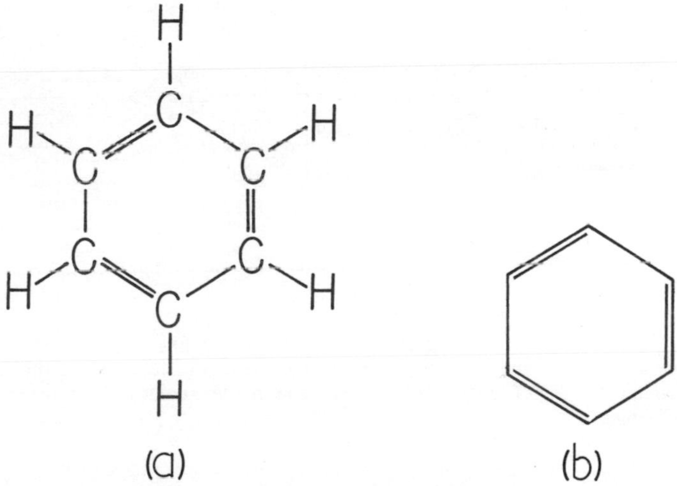

Fig. 3.9 Carbon chains may grasp their own tails. The best known example of this is the six-membered ring of benzene.

(*a*) Shows the full formula of this important molecule.

(*b*) Shows an abbreviated form by which it is often symbolised.

The treatment of conjugated molecules by molecular orbital theory yields an important insight. It can be shown that the incipient electron delocalisation which we encountered in the ethylene molecule is carried further. The conventional drawing of the benzene molecule (fig. 3.9) masks the electronic reality. Instead of a sequence of alternating single and double bonds it transpires that the π electrons are not restricted to the positions indicated by the double bonds but are in fact 'smeared' out over the whole ring system. It follows that there are no distinctions between the carbon-carbon bonds in the benzene molecule. They all have the same character: intermediate between that of a typical single and a typical double covalent bond. For example we noticed in Table 3.1 that double and single covalent bonds differ in length. If the carbon-carbon bond distances in benzene are measured it is found that they all have the same length (1·40A), intermediate between the normal double bond length (1·34A) and the normal single bond length (1·54A). A more 'correct' pictorial representation of the benzene molecule is thus shown in fig. 3.10. In this figure only one of the three delocalised π orbitals is shown.

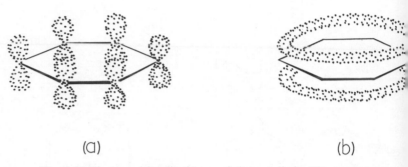

(a)   (b)

Fig. 3.10 Electron delocalisation carried to a limit. The π electrons associated with the double bonds of benzene are in fact spread out all around the ring. The figure shows how one of these delocalised π orbitals is formed.

5

At the beginning of our discussion of chemical bonding we saw that the reason why groups of atoms are held together in a molecular structure is that in this configuration they are able to achieve particularly low energy states. In short, work has to be done to break the structure up. The quantity of energy required to break a bond is defined as equivalent to the energy of that bond.

Some biologically important bond energies are listed in Table 3.3. It will be noted in this Table that single covalent bonds have, in general, energies slightly less than 100 kcal./mole, whereas double covalent bonds have energies slightly in excess of this value. It is worth while referring back to Table 3.1 and comparing the covalent bond energies of Table 3.3 with the corresponding bond lengths. In general it can be seen that the higher the energy the shorter the bond, and vice versa.

Now it is possible to obtain a very approximate idea of the energy

MOLECULES

TABLE 3.3

Some bond energies of importance in biology

Type of Bond	Energy (kcals/mole)
A. *Ionic* (electrovalent)	
Na Cl	118
B. *Covalent*	
(i) *Double*	
C=O	170
C=C	145
(ii) *Single*	
H O	110·6
H—H	104·2
H—C	98·8
H—N	93·4
C—O	84·0
C—C	83·1
C—N	65·0
C. Hydrogen	4
D. Dipole-dipole	5
E. Van der Waals	1
F. Hydrophobic	4

required to completely destroy a molecule by adding up the energy required to rupture each of the molecule's chemical bonds. Putting it the other way round we can obtain, by summing the bond energies of a molecule, a value for the energy liberated when previously isolated atoms come together to form that molecule. This energy is called the energy, or heat, of formation of the molecule.

If the heat of formation is calculated in this way for a conjugated molecule it is found to be rather less than the value observed. If, for

83

TABLE 3.4

Van der Waals radii of some atoms of biological importance

Atom	Radius in A
P	1·90
S	1·85
Cl	1·80
N	1·50
O	1·40
H	1·20
CH_3	2·0

Carbon is never 'bare' in biological situations, hence the radius of the methyl group (CH_3) is tabulated.

Note also that the van der Waals radius is approximately 0·80A to 0·90A greater than the single covalent bond radius.

example, the heat of formation of the benzene molecule is calculated it is found to be some 40 kcal./mole less than the value observed. Our discussion in the previous section gives us a hint as to the reason for this discrepancy. The unexpectedly high value observed for the heat of formation is due to the particularly low energy state achieved by the development of the large π orbital system. It follows that more energy than expected is liberated when the appropriate atoms come together to form the benzene molecule.

The extra energy liberated on the formation of a conjugated molecule like benzene is called 'resonance' energy. This is because the electronic reality, partially represented in fig. 3.10, is more usually symbolised by the forms shown in fig. 3.11.

Fig. 3.11 shows five alternative 'straight-line' representations of the

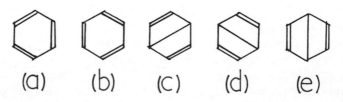

(a) (b) (c) (d) (e)

Fig. 3.11 According to the theory of resonance each benzene molecule is believed to consist of a smudge of all five of the forms shown in the figure.

benzene molecule. Now it has already been emphasised that straight-line representations of the covalent bond are much more matters of pictorial convenience than true reflections of the physical reality. However, if this convenient fiction is accepted then the theory of resonance suggests that a molecule like benzene exists in all five of the configurations shown in fig. 3.11. It is said to 'resonate' between these alternative forms. The more resonance forms there are the greater the resonance energy is said to be and, in consequence, the more stable is the molecule.

It has already been mentioned that there are many important cases of electron delocalisation, or resonance, in biology. In this chapter, where we are principally concerned with the nature of the chemical bonds holding molecules together, it will, nevertheless, be logical to describe one of these instances. This is the case of the so-called 'energy-rich' bond. It will emerge in Chapter 10 that one of the chief ways in which energy is stored in the living cell is in the form of these chemical bonds. The most well-known and important examples of energy-rich bonds are those by which the two terminal phosphate radicals are attached to adenosine in a compound called adenosine triphosphate (ATP).

The structure of ATP is shown in fig. 3.12. It can be seen that it

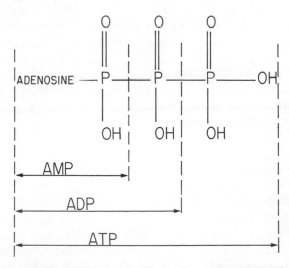

Fig. 3.12 A triplet of adenosine phosphates. Only ATP and ADP, however, possess energy-rich bonds. For further explanation see text.

consists of a string of three phosphate radicals attached to adenosine. The chemical structure of the latter molecule will be described in Chapter 14. Progressive removal of the terminal phosphates yields first adenosine diphosphate (ADP), then adenosine monophosphate (AMP) and finally adenosine (A) itself. It is found that all three of the terminal phosphates can be hydrolysed away from adenosine by appropriate enzymes. The important point to notice, however, is that the energy of hydrolysis varies according to which phosphate is detached. Hydrolysis of either of the two terminal phosphates yields 7 or 8 kcal./mole, whereas hydrolysis of the phosphate nearest adenosine yields only about 4 kcal./mole. In consequence the bonds holding the two terminal phosphates to the rest of the molecule are called 'energy-rich' bonds.

What, then, is the secret of the two terminal bonds? Why should their hydrolysis yield more than the usual amount of energy? It turns out that the most important of a number of reasons for the excessive energy of hydrolysis is that the products (ADP and H_3PO_4) can exist in rather more resonance forms than the reactants (ATP and H_2O). In this way the products can achieve particularly low energy states. Consequently the difference in energy between the reactants and the products is greater than would otherwise be the case. This excessive energy difference appears as an excessive energy of hydrolysis.

The attentive reader will have noticed that the expression 'energy-rich' bond, or, alternatively, 'high-energy' bond, is a little misleading. The term 'energy-rich' refers to the unusually high energy of hydrolysis. It does not indicate that the bond is particularly strong. Indeed it is quite the opposite: it is very readily broken by hydrolysis. Because of its very great importance to the cell's economy biochemists use a special symbol to denote it: $\sim$.

6

Reference back to Table 3.3 will show that covalent bonds are not the only forces involved in the construction of biological molecules. Quite a number of weak forces play, collectively, an important part in determining the complex configuration of, say, a protein. Moreover weak forces are particularly advantageous in many biochemical processes. The transient union of enzyme and substrate (Chapter 7), the coming together and falling apart of nucleic acid strands during DNA replication (Chapter 13) and during protein synthesis (Chapter 14) are all based upon, and all depend upon, the 'selective stickiness' conferred on molecules by weak chemical forces.

One of the strongest of these weak forces is the so-called 'dipole-dipole' interaction. This is a straightforward case of electrostatic attraction similar to, though much weaker than, the electrostatic attraction between ions. We have already noticed (fig. 3.6) that some covalently bound molecules are electrostatically polarised. It is not difficult to see that if a number of these polar molecules come into close proximity with each other they will orientate themselves into a loosely held structure (fig. 3.13).

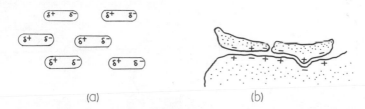

Fig. 3.13 Dipole-dipole interactions. These weak forces may serve to orientate a number of small rod-like molecules (*a*), or serve to locate substrate molecules in the correct position on an enzymic surface (*b*).

Because these forces are so weak (Table 3.3) it is clear that if they are to have an organisational influence (fig. 3.13) then it is important that they should 'mirror-image' each other. Thus we see that complementary surfaces (fig. 3.13(*b*)) may well play a vital rôle in biological structure and function. It is also clear that the concentration of protons (pH) in the immediate environment is critical. For the size and nature of the charge on the molecule can be shown (Chapter 4) to vary in proportion to this concentration.

Dipole-dipole forces are rated at about 5 kcal./mole. Much weaker than these are the van der Waals forces. These forces develop when non-polar molecules are brought very close together. Understanding of their precise nature is still somewhat slender. The most widely accepted explanation is that they are due to a fluctuating dipole-dipole interaction *induced* between molecules or atoms in close proximity to each other. It is found that the van der Waals force is always rather small (Table 3.3) and falls off very rapidly as the interacting atoms or molecules are moved apart.[1] On the other hand the attractive force is replaced by a strong repulsion as the interacting species are brought closer together. This repulsion is due to the electrostatic forces engendered by the interpenetration of the outer electron shells of the two atoms or molecules.[2] The distance of closest

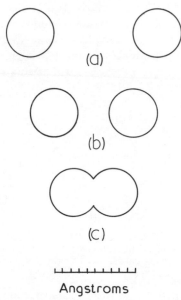

Angstroms

Fig. 3.14 The van der Waals force only becomes effective at distances less than 10A. The figure shows two atoms (a) 10A apart, (b) about 5A apart when the force is strong and (c) with their electron shells interpenetrating when the attractive force is replaced by a strong electrostatic repulsion.

approach is defined as the van der Waals radius. These ideas are shown schematically in fig. 3.14.

A knowledge of van der Waals radii is of great importance to the molecular biologist who wishes to understand the structure of proteins, nucleic acids, and other large biomolecules. It is evident that one of the conditions which must be satisfied by any proposed model is that the atoms of the model possess their normal van der Waals

[1] The van der Waals force in fact varies in proportion to $1/d^6$ where d is the distance between the two atoms.

[2] If an unpaired electron is present in the valency shells of both atoms then the conditions are, of course, appropriate for the formation of a covalent bond. The two atomic nuclei are then able to move even closer together.

radii. The radii of some biologically important atoms are listed in Table 3.4.

Dipole-dipole and van der Waals forces are non-directional. They radiate out in all directions from an atom or molecule. This is not the case with the next type of weak bond to be considered. This is the hydrogen bond. Because the H-bond depends on specific donor and acceptor atoms, and because it has a strong directional character, it forms a considerably more specific link than either of the two types of weak force already discussed. In consequence H-bonds are deeply implicated in the formation of complementary surfaces between enzyme and substrate, and ensuring accurate replication of nucleic acid molecules.

Much intellectual effort has been expended in the attempt to understand the nature of the hydrogen bond, and several books have been written on the subject.[1] It is found that it only forms when hydrogen, covalently bound to one electronegative atom, is brought into the close vicinity of another similarly electronegative atom. Table 3.1 shows that two commonly occurring biological atoms which possess a high electronegativity are oxygen and nitrogen. It follows that if, say, an N-H group is brought into the near neighbourhood of an oxygen atom then the formation of a hydrogen bond is probable (fig. 3.15).

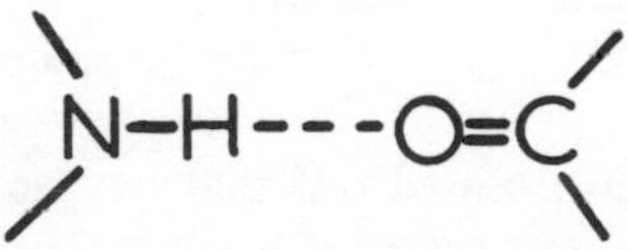

$$\diagup N-H---O=C\diagdown$$

Fig. 3.15 Hydrogen bonds play a very important role in molecular biology. In the figure a bond, represented by the broken line, is formed between the hydrogen covalently bound to nitrogen and a neighbouring oxygen atom.

In fig. 3.15 the hydrogen bond is represented by a dotted line. In spite of the great efforts mentioned above the precise nature of the hydrogen bond remains a little obscure. In general it can be said that the bond is a species of ionic bond. It is believed that the highly electronegative atom to which hydrogen is attached strips the latter

---

[1] For example: Pimental, G. C. and McClellan, A. L., *The Hydrogen Bond*, W. H. Freeman & Co., San Francisco, 1959.

atom of its lone electron. In the example shown in fig. 3.15 we may imagine that hydrogen's electron is pulled far over into nitrogen's sphere of influence. In consequence the small, and intensely charged proton is left comparatively exposed. It is not difficult to see that an electrostatic attraction would develop between it and any strongly electronegative atom in its immediate vicinity. As in the case of covalent bonds the presence of a hydrogen bond reveals itself through the fact that the hydrogen and oxygen atoms which it links approach each other more closely than their van der Waals radii would otherwise allow.

H-bonds, as we have already mentioned, are of considerable importance in many biochemical activities. We shall also see in Chapter 5 that they are of great importance in the structure of protein molecules. In addition they are deeply implicated in the structure of what is perhaps the most important of all biological materials—water.

7

It may come as a surprise to read that water, proverbially the most yielding and transient of materials, nevertheless has a structure. The fact that it has is, however, of the greatest importance for life on this planet. From this fact flow many of the properties which make water unique amongst its chemical relatives.[1] These properties go far, to use L. J. Henderson's phrase,[2] to fit the planet's surface for the emergence of life.

It has already been pointed out that oxygen is a highly electro negative atom. It follows that, in the water molecule, the electrons originally belonging to hydrogen are dragged in towards the oxygen atom. The 'bare' protons which result are, in consequence, favour ably disposed for H-bonding. Now the only electronegative atoms in a mass of pure water are other oxygen atoms. Hence H-bonds develop between the hydrogens of one water molecule and the oxygen of another. Thus water molecules tend to aggregate into loosely bound fraternities or rafts (fig. 3.16).

These rafts have only a very transient existence at room tempera ture and the hydrogen bonds are continually breaking and reforming

[1] See Edsall, J. T. and Wyman, J., *Biophysical Chemistry*, Vol. 1, Academic Press, New York and London, 1958, Chapter 2.
[2] L. J. Henderson, *The Fitness of the Environment*, New York, 1924.

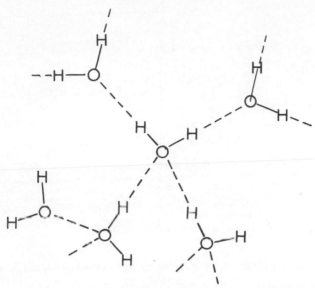

Fig. 3.16 Water has a structure! Flickering arrays of water molecules held together by hydrogen bonds are believed to form and reform at normal temperatures.

As the temperature rises water's quasi-crystalline structure becomes more and more disrupted.

It is extremely important to notice, next, that water molecules are able to form hydrogen bonds with other molecules than water. For example, the imino, or N-H, group, which we mentioned in the previous section, is well able to form H-bonds with water's oxygen. It follows that molecules containing chemical groupings potentially able to form H-bonds readily insert themselves into the transient quasi-crystalline arrays of water molecules. They disperse amongst the crowding water molecules making, breaking and remaking H-bonds. In other words molecules of this sort are soluble in water.

Yet another feature of the water molecule allows it to form those intimate mixtures with other chemical species which we call solutions. This character is its electrical polarity. Fig. 3.17 shows that the oxygen end of the molecule, because it has removed hydrogen's electron, bears a small overall negative charge compared with the hydrogen end.

Because of this electrical polarity water molecules are attracted by

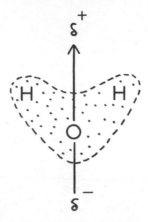

Fig. 3.17 The water molecule is electrically polarised.

other polar molecules (or ions), and tend to cluster around them thus keeping them apart from each other and, consequently, 'afloat'. The extreme cases of polar molecules are, as we saw earlier in this chapter, ionic substances like NaCl, KCl, etc. The polar nature of water molecules thus provides us with an explanation of the very great solubility of salts in water. NaCl, we have seen, tends to split into its constituent Na^+ and Cl^- ions. Both ions quickly attract clouds of water molecules. These clouds effectively separate the two ions. In the absence of these clusters of water molecules the Na^+ and Cl^- ions would quickly attract each other and, aggregating into larger and larger masses, soon 'crystallise' out of solution.

Very important amongst the substances which the polar nature of water molecules brings into solution are the acids and bases. For these, too, are polar molecules. We have already noticed that this is the case for the well-known mineral acid, HCl (fig. 3.6). Just as in the case of NaCl, HCl tends to ionise when mixed with water:

$$HCl \rightleftharpoons H^+ + Cl^-$$

Both H^+ and Cl^- become surrounded by water molecules. This is particularly the case with the hydrogen ion. This ion is, of course, a 'bare' proton and as such has an exceedingly high ratio of charge to radius. Indeed so intensely charged is it that only infinitesimally few $(1/10^{190})$ can exist free in aqueous solutions. To all intents and purposes they all become attached to the negatively charged ends of

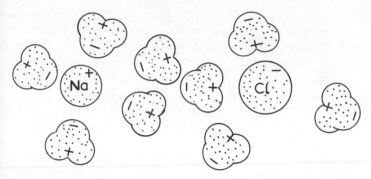

Fig. 3.18 The polar nature of water molecules causes them to cluster around ions such as chloride (Cl^-) and sodium (Na^+) and thus keep them separate from each other. In this way ionic solutions are made possible.

water molecules. Thus, in fact, the phrase 'H^+ ion' is convenient shorthand for the reality of the H_3O^+ ion, or the $H_5O_2^+$ ion.

The quantity of H^+ ion in a solution is of very great importance to many biochemical reactions and structures. A useful scale has been developed to measure this concentration. It is called the pH scale. The pH of a solution is defined by the following expression:

$$pH = \log 1/(H)$$

In the above expression (H) stands for the molar concentration of hydrogen ions. Acids are usually defined as solutions with a pH of less than 7, and bases solutions with a pH of greater than 7. In other words acid solutions contain large numbers of H^+ ions, whereas basic solutions contain rather few H^+ ions. Neutral solutions, of course, have a pH of about 7.

We have so far concentrated the discussion on the means by which water is able to act as a solvent for many different types of molecule. There are, however, many molecules which are neither polar, nor capable of forming H-bonds. In consequence these molecules are insoluble in water and aqueous solutions.

Let us take an example—benzene. The six hydrogen atoms of this molecule are all attached to carbon atoms (fig. 3.8). Reference to Table 3.2 shows us that carbon is not markedly more electronegative than hydrogen itself. It follows that the electrons contributed by each atom to the covalent bond are shared equitably between them. Thus when we mix benzene and water no hydrogen bonds form between the two groups of molecules and, as benzene is not electrically polarised, no clusters of water molecules form around it. In other words benzene is insoluble in water; it is neither able to join in the game of exchanging hydrogen bonds nor is it able to keep itself 'afloat' by attracting clouds of water molecules.

However, benzene, the outsider molecule, is not merely ignored but is actively shunned by the sociable water. Hydrogen bonds, we have seen, have energies in the region of 5 kcal./mole and this, of course, is liberated when they are formed. We have also emphasised in several places that physical systems always seek their state of lowest energy. Clearly the formation of H-bonds will bring the mass of water to an energy value lower than that which it would have in their absence. This spontaneous tendency to form H-bonds is interfered with if molecules incapable of forming H-bonds are present in solution. Hence benzene and similar molecules tend to be 'squeezed' out of aqueous solution. It is observed that first of all droplets of benzene form in the aqueous phase, and later these droplets tend to coalesce so that finally the solution is divided into two distinct phases—an aqueous phase and a benzene phase.

Water's ability to force non-polar molecules out of solution is of considerable importance in the architecture of some large biomolecules and cell organelles. In Chapter 4 we shall find that a number of amino-acids have non-polar, or hydrophobic, side chains. When these amino-acids are strung together with others to form polypeptide chains they will, in general, find themselves in a cytoplasm whose main constituent is water. In consequence the amino-acid chain is caused to twist and turn until the hydrophobic amino-acids are facing inwards away from the hostile aqueous environment. Thus the polypeptide chain is caused to take up a particular and specific conformation. Similar arguments, as we shall see in Chapter 9, go far towards accounting for the organisation of lipid structures like cell membranes.

4

The Primary Structure of Proteins

1

In Chapter 3 we briefly reviewed the principal forces which hold atoms together in the form of molecules. We saw, in particular, that quantum mechanics provided a rigorous explanation of the nature of the covalent bond. In fact this theory can only be applied with full mathematical precision to the covalent bond joining two hydrogen atoms together in the simplest of all molecules—the hydrogen molecule. However, by making various simplifications and approximations the theory of wave mechanics can be extended to cover all the other, more complicated, atoms the chemist studies. Wave mechanics may thus be said to provide a physical explanation for the enormous number of observations made by chemists on the interactions and activities of atoms. W. G. Palmer, for example, writes[1] that 'the focusing of physics in the guise of the new quantum mechanics upon the great empirical structure of chemistry led, not earlier than 1927, to an understanding of the periodic system of classification. . . .'

Is it perhaps possible to discern an analogous process occurring in contemporary biology? We seem to be living through a period in which the science of chemistry is focusing on the similarly great empirical structure of biology. Is it being too fanciful to liken the enlightenment which followed the development of quantum mechanics in the nineteen-twenties to the clarification produced in the present decade by the development of our understanding of proteins and nucleic acids?

J. M. Rudall, writing in the first volume of *Advances in Biophysics* as long ago as 1950, suggested that 'a knowledge of the structure of protein molecules is as important to biology as atomic structure is to physics'. The similarity goes quite deep. The wave-mechanics theory

[1] *A History of the Concept of Valency*, Cambridge University Press, 1965.

of valency, as we saw in Chapters 2 and 3, shows that the chemical properties of atoms arise from their detailed electronic structure. It is the ambition, as yet largely unachieved, of molecular biologists to show that the biological activity of enzymes, hormones, antibodies, genes, etc. emerges from their detailed molecular structure. This ambition is, as we noticed in the Introduction to this book, in line with one of the principal trends in the history of scientific thought: the foundation of function on structure.

2

The body of even the simplest living organism is, of course, a complex of innumerable different molecules and ions. So remarkably well organised and integrated is such a body that for many years men were content to believe that a physico-chemical approach to an understanding of its structure was not feasible. The developing techniques of organic chemistry, however, allowed Wohler, in 1828, to synthesise a simple animal product—urea—and thus to show that a science of biochemistry was possible.

An initial problem for the early biochemists was to classify the bewildering array of complicated chemical substances to be found in a living body. It is thus a considerable tribute to their perspicacity to find that quite early on they had recognised the group of substances we now call proteins, and had guessed at their importance to the body. These substances were grouped together on the grounds that they showed common properties of coagulability by heat, strong acids or alkalis, and that they all contained nitrogen. The name 'protein' was first applied to this large group of compounds by Muldner, acting on a suggestion made in 1838 by the famous chemist Berzelius.[1] The word 'protein' was derived from the Greek root 'proteios' meaning 'of the first rank'. A hundred and thirty years later we have every reason to believe that Berzelius' intuition was correct when he suggested so portentous a name. For it is nowadays known that enzymes, without which 'life-as-we-know-it' could not exist, are proteins; that much of the fabric of the animal body is protein; that muscular movement is based on protein; that oxygen is transported around our bodies attached to protein; that the anti-

[1] Vickery, H. B. (1950), *Yale J. Biol. and Med.*, *22*, 387. (Quoted in Fruton, J. S. and Simmons, S., *General Biochemistry*, John Wiley, 1963).

bodies by which we gain immunity from microbial invasion are proteins—the list could be extended almost indefinitely.

It is evident that an understanding of proteins will lead us far towards an understanding of some of the most important and characteristic phenomena of biology. It was pointed out above that an understanding of the biological activity of proteins depends on a prior understanding of their structure. Now although proteins as a group of chemical substances and something of their biological importance were recognised so long ago, an intimate knowledge of their structure is a relatively recent acquisition. The reason for this tardiness is quite simple. Proteins happen to be very large and very intricately organised molecules. Moreover, this character is not merely contingent but is essential to their biological function.

3

Although an understanding of the intimate details of protein structure has only been achieved very recently, the fact that they were composed of amino-acid units was well known by the last quarter of the nineteenth century. It is not difficult to show that amino-acids are present in solution after a protein has been hydrolysed by acid or alkali. Nowadays about twenty different amino-acids are recognised. They all, however, have important properties in common; in fact they are all variations on a single molecular theme. This fundamental theme is shown in the following formula:

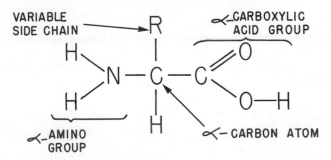

Fig. 4.1 Chemical formula of a typical amino-acid.

In the formula shown in fig. 4.1 'R' is a variable, and symbolises a side chain which may simply be a hydrogen atom, as in glycine, or may be a complicated ring structure, as in tryptophan. It is usual, as in fig. 4.1, to refer to the amino group (NH_2) as the α-amino group, the central carbon atom as the α-carbon atom, and the carboxylic acid group (COOH) as the α-carboxylic acid group. This terminology is to make them distinguishable from similar groups which sometimes occur in the variable side chain—'R'.

Perhaps the most important chemical feature of an amino-acid is that whilst one end of the molecule is basic the other end is acidic. In other words one end of the molecule consists of a group—NH_2—which is able to take up protons whilst at the other end is a group—COOH—which liberates protons.[1] Whether either or both of these processes occurs depends on the hydrogen-ion (proton) concentration of the solution in which the amino-acid finds itself. If the hydrogen-ion concentration is high (low pH) protons are forced on to the amino group converting it into a positively charged NH_3^+ group; vice versa if the hydrogen-ion concentration is low (high pH) then protons can escape from the carboxylic acid group leaving it, in consequence, negatively charged—COO^-. At one particular pH, called the iso-electric point, protons detach themselves from the carboxylic acid group whilst other protons attach themselves to the amino group.

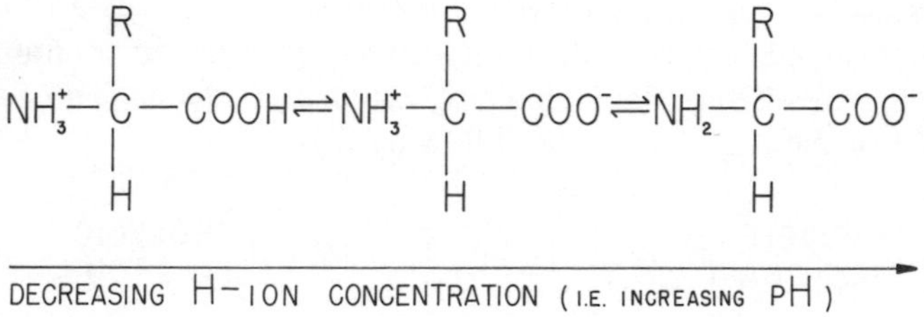

$$NH_3^+ - \underset{\underset{H}{|}}{\overset{\overset{R}{|}}{C}} - COOH \rightleftharpoons NH_3^+ - \underset{\underset{H}{|}}{\overset{\overset{R}{|}}{C}} - COO^- \rightleftharpoons NH_2 - \underset{\underset{H}{|}}{\overset{\overset{R}{|}}{C}} - COO^-$$

DECREASING H−ION CONCENTRATION (I.E. INCREASING pH)

Fig. 4.2 The concentration of hydrogen ions in the immediate vicinity of an amino-acid affects its electrostatic charge.

The resultant doubly charged structure is called a dipolar ion, or zwitterion. The isoelectric point differs from one amino-acid to another. These relationships are summarised in fig. 4.2.

The fact that all amino-acids possess an acidic group at one end and a basic group at the other enables them to join together, end to

[1] This follows from the Bronsted theory of acids and bases which defines the former as proton donors and the latter as proton acceptors.

end, to form long chains. We may picture this process by representing amino-acids as arrow-shaped structures:

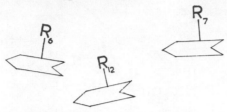

Fig. 4.3 Amino-acids may be represented by arrow-like structures.

Let us imagine that the pointed end represents the acidic, and the recessed end represents the basic, group. It is clear that a number of such units could join together to form a chain.

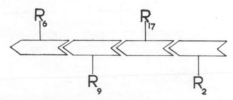

Fig. 4.4 Long chains of amino-acids may form.

Proceeding from the general to the particular, it can be shown that the chemical reaction which underlies this type of chain formation is a species of that very well-known reaction whereby acids and bases form salt and water. This reaction is shown in fig. 4.5.

It can be seen in fig. 4.5 that in the reaction between the carboxylic acid group of one amino-acid and the amino group of another, water is eliminated, and a bond formed between the two amino-acids. This bond unites the nitrogen atom of one amino-acid to a carbon of the other. This very important bond is called a peptide bond. The resulting molecule, consisting of two amino-acid residues,[1] is called a dipeptide.

It will have been noticed that the dipeptide resulting from the reaction depicted in fig. 4.5 resembles its amino-acid precursors in possessing an amino group at one end and a carboxylic acid group at the other. Evidently it is capable of undergoing further condensation reactions either with additional amino-acids, or with other

[1] The term 'residue' is used to denote an amino-acid incorporated into a peptide or protein.

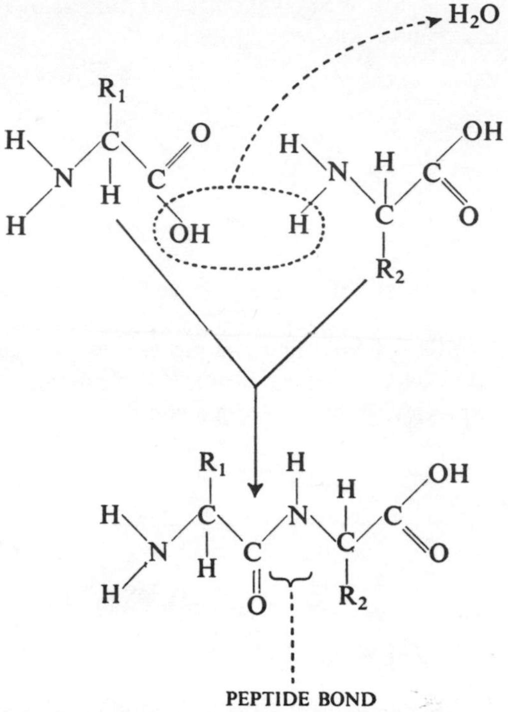

Fig. 4.5 The chemistry of the formation of a peptide bond.

peptides. It is not difficult to see that, in this way, long chains of amino-acids can be built up as was symbolised in fig. 4.4.

It is very much a matter of definition whether we refer to one of these lengthy amino-acid chains as a polypeptide or as a protein. A polypeptide above a certain size is called a protein. This certain size is quite arbitrary. Some authorities define a protein as any amino acid chain having a molecular weight of 5,000 or above; other workers prefer to set the lower limit for a protein's molecular weight a 10,000. If we take a very rough average value for the molecular weight of an amino-acid in a polypeptide, or protein, chain as 100 (in fact, this value is a little on the low side) then it follows that some investigators call an amino-acid chain consisting of 50 or more residues a protein, whereas others regard the smallest proteins as being built of at least 100 residues.

In many cases, for example haemoglobin (Chapter 6), proteins are found to consist of several subunits. In the case of haemoglobin these subunits are called polypeptides even though, as we shall see, they each consist of considerably more than 100 amino-acid residues. Again, when the synthesis of protein by the living cell is being discussed (Chapter 14) it is common practice to refer to the amino-acid chain whilst it is being synthesised as a polypeptide, and to reserve the term 'protein' for the chain when it has finally assumed its definitive three-dimensional structure.

If one thing is clear from this discussion it is that the use of the terms 'protein' and 'polypeptide' are by no means clear defined.

Although, as we have seen, amino-acids have important properties in common, many other important properties depend on the nature of the side chain—R. There are twenty different commonly occurring varieties of R. In other words there are twenty different amino-acids. These are shown in Table 4.1.

Examination of Table 4.1 shows that two amino-acids—arginine and lysine—possess a second amino group and are, in consequence, comparatively basic. Histidine is another important basic amino-acid. Two amino-acids—aspartic acid and glutamic acid—possess a second carboxylic acid group. These two, and also tyrosine, are comparatively acidic amino-acids. Whereas the majority of amino-acids have 'linear' side chains, four—phenylalanine, tyrosine, histidine and tryptophan—are encumbered with bulky ring structures. Two amino-acids—cysteine and methionine—contain sulphur atoms in their side chains; we shall find that the sulphydryl group (SH) of cysteine is particularly important in the formation of covalent links between polypeptide chains.

Another feature of amino-acid side chains which is of the greatest importance in the architecture of protein molecules is their hydrophobicity. We shall see in Chapter 6, as we mentioned at the end of Chapter 3, that one of the principal forces causing an amino-acid chain to assume a particular three-dimensional conformation is the repulsion between hydrophobic residues and their aqueous environment. Hydrophobic and hydrophilic residues are listed in order of strength in fig. 4.6.

Hydrophobic residues   phe $>$ ala $>$ val $>$ gly $>$ leu $>$ cys.

Hydrophilic residues   tyr $>$ ser $>$ asp $>$ glu $>$ asn $>$ gln $>$ arg.

Fig. 4.6 Some amino-acids are more hydrophobic and some more hydrophilic than others.

101

TABLE 4.1 *Amino-acids*

In general amino-acids have the following formula:

$$NH_2-\underset{\underset{H}{\displaystyle|}}{\overset{\overset{R}{\displaystyle|}}{C}}-COOH$$

R, in the formula above, is variable and determines the particular amino-acid:

Name	Abbreviation	R
Glycine	gly	$-H$
Alanine	ala	$-CH_3$
Serine	ser	$-CH_2OH$
Threonine	thr	$-CH\big\langle\substack{OH \\ CH_3}$
Valine	val	$-CH\big\langle\substack{CH_3 \\ CH_3}$
Leucine	leu	$-CH_2-CH\big\langle\substack{CH_3 \\ CH_3}$
Isoleucine	ile	$-\underset{\underset{CH_3}{\displaystyle|}}{CH}-CH_2-CH_3$
Aspartic acid	asp	$-CH_2-COOH$
Asparagine	asn	$-CH_2-CONH_2$
Glutamic acid	glu	$-CH_2-CH_2-COOH$
Glutamine	gln	$-CH_2-CH_2-CONH_2$
Arginine	arg	$-CH_2-CH_2-CH_2-NH-C\big\langle\substack{NH_2 \\ NH}$

TABLE 4.1 (*continued*)

Lysine	lys	$-CH_2-CH_2-CH_2-CH_2-NH_2$
Cysteine	cys	$-CH_2-SH$
Methionine	met	$-CH_2-CH_2-S-CH_3$
Phenylalanine	phe	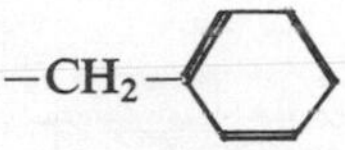 $-CH_2-$ ⬡
Tyrosine	tyr	$-CH_2-$ ⬡$-OH$
Histidine	his	$-CH_2-$ (imidazole ring with N N)
Tryptophan	try	$-CH_2-$ (indole ring, N H)

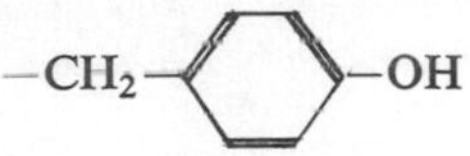

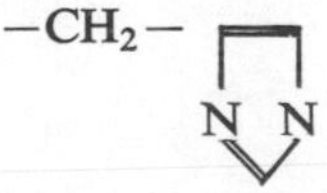

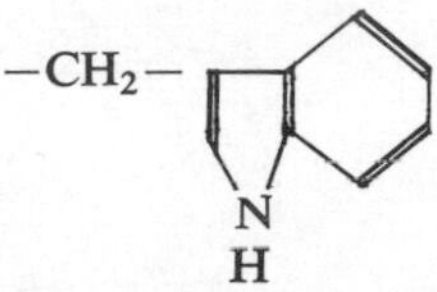

Finally it is necessary to mention that there are two molecules which, because of their common occurrence in protein hydrolysates, are normally listed with the other amino-acids, yet do not share the general formula shown in fig. 4.1. These two are proline and its derivative hydroxyproline.

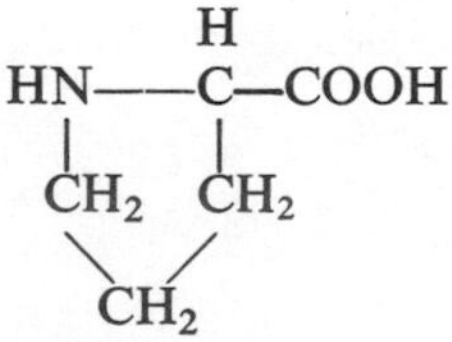

$$
\begin{array}{c}
\overset{\displaystyle H}{} \\
HN\!\!-\!\!-\!\!C\!\!-\!\!COOH \\
|| \\
CH_2 \quad CH_2 \\
\diagdown\diagup \\
CH_2 \\
\end{array}
$$

Proline

If we examine the formula of proline shown above we can see that it is as if a straight chain of three carbon atoms and their attached hydrogens had been bent back on itself and attached to the α-amino group. This connection displaces one of the hydrogens from the amino group. Consequently, although proline is still able to combine with another amino-acid the resulting peptide link differs from those formed between conventional amino-acids by lacking a hydrogen atom attached to nitrogen. This is shown in fig. 4.7.

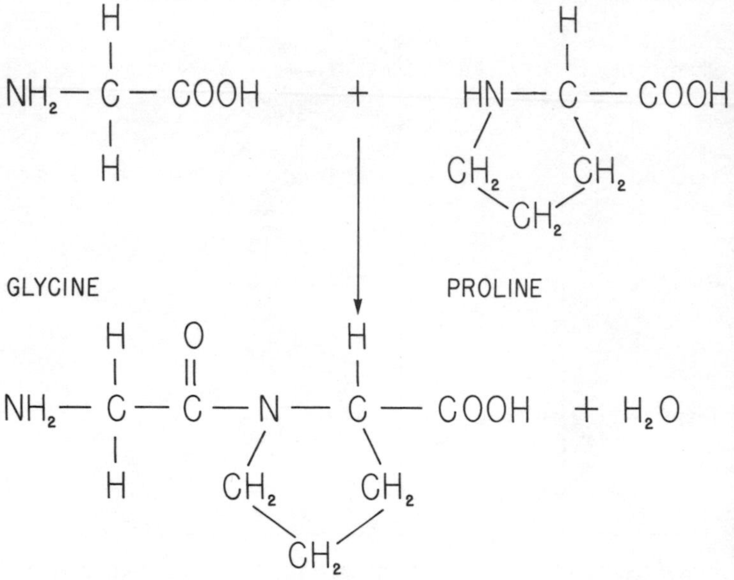

GLYCINE   PROLINE

GLYCYLPROLINE

Fig. 4.7 Glycylproline lacks an NH, or imino, group.

The reader may regard this fact as a mere detail but it will be shown in Chapters 5 and 6 that it has consequences of considerable importance to the three-dimensional structure of proteins.

4

Techniques for determining the quantities and types of amino-acids in a protein have, in recent years, been brought to a fine art. In essence the procedure is first to hydrolyse the protein, then to separate the resulting amino-acids from each other, and then to identify, and determine the quantities, of each amino-acid present. Hydrolysis is brought about by means of acids or alkalis, or by the application of specific enzymes. Separation of the resulting amino-acids is usually achieved by some form of chromatography. This technique also allows the investigator to identify the amino-acids. Finally estimation of the quantity of each amino-acid is usually accomplished by spectrophotometry.

Many different types of chromatography have been developed. Basically the technique depends on the existence of two phases—one fixed in position, or stationary, the other mobile. The mobile phase is caused to flow over or through the stationary phase. The mixture to be chromatographed consists of a variety of molecules which differ amongst themselves in their adherence to the stationary and mobile phases. Thus as the mobile phase flows over the stationary phase the molecules which adhere most strongly to the latter will tend to get left behind. It follows that these molecules will be spatially separated from the molecules adhering less strongly to the stationary phase.

The earliest amino-acid separations were carried out by a type of chromatography known as partition chromatography.[1] A chromatography column (fig. 4.8) filled with starch was used. Before chromatography was commenced the column was washed through with a mixture of butanol and water. The water forms a thin film surrounding the starch grains. The protein hydrolysate, dissolved in the butanol-water solvent system, was placed on top of the column. This solution was washed through the column with further quantities of the solvent system. Now the rate at which the various amino-acids are washed through such a column depends on their relative solubilities in water and butanol. Those amino-acids readily soluble in water tend to dissolve in the water film surrounding the starch particles of the stationary phase. It follows that the passage of these amino-acids through the column is much retarded. On the other hand those amino-acids which are hydrophobic do not experience this retardation and are, in consequence, washed rapidly through the column. By carefully adjusting the conditions it proved possible to arrange matters in such a way that the various amino-acids in the hydrolysate arrived separately, one after the other, at the bottom of the column.

[1] Fisher and others had separated amino-acids by more laborious and less efficient methods in the late nineteenth and early twentieth centuries.

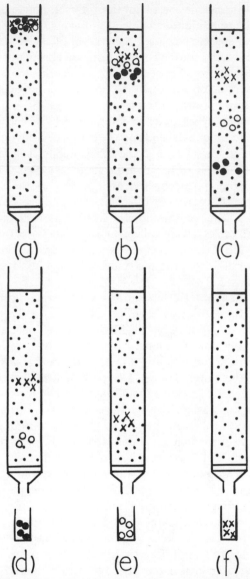

Fig. 4.8 Essential features of column chromatography. Three different species of amino-acids (represented by crosses, open and filled circles) are placed on top of the column (a). As the amino-acids are washed through the column the different species separate from each other. They may thus be collected separately (d), (e) and (f). For further explanation see text.

THE PRIMARY STRUCTURE OF PROTEINS

Nowadays a slightly different technique has tended to supersede partition chromatography on starch columns. Instead of making use of the differential solubility of amino-acids this technique utilises differences in their electrostatic charge. It was emphasised in the previous section that the magnitude and sign of the electrostatic charge borne by an amino-acid both varied from one amino-acid to another, and depended to a large extent on the pH of the surrounding solution. In ion-exchange chromatography, as this more recent method is called, the chromatography column is packed with a resin whose particles can, in effect, be given a positive or a negative charge. By carefully adjusting the pH of the hydrolysate a separation of amino-acids can, once again, be achieved by washing the solution through the column. Very good separations are obtained by continuously altering the pH of the solvent being used to elute the hydrolysate.

An alternative technique which is sometimes used to separate and identify amino-acids also makes use of the fact that these molecules bear different quantities of electrostatic charge. In this technique—called electrophoresis—a voltage is applied across the two ends of a stationary phase and the amino-acids, in solution, are thus caused to migrate towards either the cathode or the anode. The distance they move depends on the size of the charge they carry and this, in turn, depends on the pH of the mobile phase and on the particular amino-acid. If the conditions are skilfully chosen, good and diagnostic separations can be achieved.

In some cases a combination of paper chromatography and electrophoresis has been employed to analyse protein hydrolysates. Chromatography is carried out in one direction and then, after the paper has been dried, electrophoresis is carried out in a direction at right angles to the first. If the conditions are rigorously controlled amino-acids and peptides separate to give a very specific pattern of spots on the paper. These spots can be visualised by spraying with an appropriate chromogenic agent. So diagnostic are the patterns of spots obtained that the technique is called 'finger-printing'.

Having separated the amino-acid mixture into its constituent molecular species, the next task is to estimate how much of each species is present. Fortunately a fairly simple colorimetric method was developed by Moore and Stein in 1948. In this method each amino-acid is mixed with a ninhydrin reagent and the resulting colour measured by a spectrophotometer. If all the quantities are accurately

107

standardised the depth of colour is proportional to the quantity of amino-acid present.

The original chromatographic analyses of protein hydrolysates carried out by Stein and Moore in the late nineteen-forties, although a great improvement on earlier methods, were time-consuming and tedious. It is clear from the above description that the process lends itself to automation. Thus in recent years several firms of scientific instrument manufacturers have marketed fully automatic amino-acid analysers. The protein hydrolysate, which need not contain more than about 3·5 milligrams[1] of protein, is placed on the top of the chromatographic column in a suitable solvent—the machine does the rest. The investigator is presented with a graph showing the amino-acids found in the hydrolysate and their relative quantities. It should be noted, however, that the initial 3·5 milligrams of protein must be a pure sample, and that this condition is by no means always easy to satisfy.

Table 4.2 shows the amino-acid composition of some well-known proteins. A fuller list may be found in the addendum to Chapter 1 of *The Proteins*, Vol. 1, edited by H. Neurath and published by Academic Press.

5

The discussion in the preceding section shows that, provided a pure sample can be obtained, it is not too difficult nowadays to carry out a complete amino-acid analysis. Important though this is, a protein chemist would nevertheless regard it as only the very first step in the trail leading to a complete understanding of a protein's structure. Indeed it has been said that the protein chemist in 1950 was in a position similar to that occupied by his colleague, the organic chemist, a hundred years earlier. In 1850 the organic chemist knew the nature and number of the atoms in a number of organic chemicals, but he had no inkling of the spatial relations of these atoms in the molecule. In other words, he knew the empirical formula of the organic chemical but not its structural formula. Similarly, in 1950, the protein chemist was beginning to know the amino-acid constitution of a number of proteins, but he had yet to discover the spatial relations of these residues to each other in the protein molecule

[1] Light, A. and Smith, E. L., in *The Proteins*, Vol. 1, Academic Press, New York and London, 1965, p. 126.

TABLE 4.2

The amino-acid composition of some proteins

Protein Amino-acid	Insulin (bovine) M/W 5,733	RN-ase (bovine) M/W 12,700	Lysozyme (canine) M/W 15,000	Cyto- chrome C (equine) M/W 12,500	Haemo- globin (human) M/W 68,000
Gly	70·5	35·7	65·3	98·2	60·3
Ala	44·8	82·9	98·3	49·5	114·5
Ser	53·0	105·0	58·2	1·7	52·4
Thr	17·3	72·9	43·0	82·6	51·3
Pro	16·7	34·3	57·6	33·7	43·5
Val	71·0	65·0	61·3	24·5	94·8
Ile	10·0	24·3	35·8	47·4	2·4
Leu	101·0	25·7	58·1	49·8	116·2
Phe	49·8	25·0	20·5	30·8	48·0
Tyr	66·0	40·7	20·1	30·2	24·3
Try	0	0	40·5	8·3	5·9
Cys	52·0	53·6	64·4	16·4	8·6
Met	0	25·7	14·4	15·7	10·7
Asp	53·0	93·5	122·0	65·8	79·7
Glu	115·8	69·3	66·5	101·2	49·0
Amide N	n.d.	85·7	n.d.	64·3	64·3
Arg	16·3	26·4	56·1	17·5	19·7
His	34·5	27·1	6·7	25·5	54·6
Lys	14·5	72·8	53·6	154·1	72·6

n.d.=not determined   RN-ase=ribonuclease

Quantities of amino-acids are given in moles per 100,000 gm. of protein.
Amide N includes *gln* and *asn* residues.

Data from Tristram, G. R. and Smith, R. H. (1963),
Adv. in Prot. Res., 18, 227.

Indeed some influential workers believed that proteins consisted merely of random assemblages of amino-acids, not of unique sequences. Thus we can gain some impression of the magnitude of the break-through made by Sanger and his colleagues when, in 1955,[1] they published the first complete amino-acid sequence of a protein—insulin.

Perhaps the most important result of Sanger's work was the demonstration that proteins, or at least insulin, did indeed consist of a unique sequence of amino-acids. It will be appreciated as this book continues just how vital and far-reaching a discovery this was; if proteins were not built of unique sequences of amino-acids, molecular biology, as we know it today, would hardly have been possible.

The analysis of insulin was very far from being an easy task. Success came only after a decade of intensive and brilliant investigation. Why, we might ask, was insulin chosen to be the object of such an exhaustive study?

First of all, insulin is of great importance in the functioning of the body. Secreted into the blood by the pancreas it plays a major part in controlling the passage of glucose from the blood into the tissue cells. Lack of insulin, as is well known, causes the condition known as diabetes mellitus. The diabetic, his cells deprived of their vital supplies of glucose, is liable to lapse into a coma from which he may never emerge. Today, of course, injection of insulin allows the patient to live a nearly normal life. Insulin, then, is first of all of great physiological and medical importance. It was hoped that a complete understanding of its structure would be of value to the science of medicine.

Second, a considerable amount was already known about the chemistry of insulin. As protein molecules go it is small, having a molecular weight of about 6,000.[2] It was also known that 17 out of the possible 20 amino-acids were present in the molecule (Table 4.2).

A molecular weight of 6,000 indicates that the insulin molecule consists of at least 50 amino-acid residues. Thus the problem which faced Sanger and his colleagues at Cambridge in 1945 was formidable. It was to determine the precise sequence, if any, in which these 50 or so amino-acids were arranged in the molecule.

How, then, did Sanger set about solving this sequence problem?

[1] Ryle, A. P., Sanger, F., Smith, L. F. and Kitai, R. (1955), *Biochem. J.*, *60*, 541.
[2] Insulin tends to aggregate into complexes of six units. Thus early investigators reported inflated molecular weights of 36,000.

THE PRIMARY STRUCTURE OF PROTEINS

First of all, let us recall that proteins and polypeptides normally possess an amino group at one end and a carboxylic acid group at the other end of the molecule. The former end of the chain is conventionally referred to as the N-terminal end, and the other end as the C-terminal end. An important initial innovation of Sanger's was the introduction of a compound which could label the N-terminal end of a protein or peptide. This compound is 2,4-dinitrofluorobenzene, or DNFB for short. DNFB unites so strongly with a protein's free amino groups[1] that even reagents which break peptide bonds do not displace it. The reaction of DNFB with the N-terminal amino group of a protein is shown in fig. 4.9.

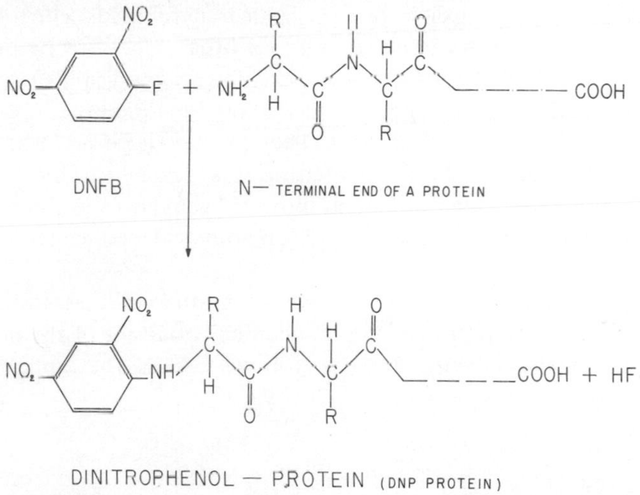

DINITROPHENOL — PROTEIN (DNP PROTEIN)

Fig. 4.9 The figure shows how the N-terminal end of a polypeptide (or protein) chain may be tagged with DNFB.

Not only does DNFB unite extremely firmly with a free amino group but it also colours the resulting compound yellow. It follows that this technique enables the biochemist to identify the N-terminal residue. After reaction with DNFB the amino-acid chain can be hydrolysed by acid or enzyme and the resulting yellow DNP-amino-acid identified by chromatography against standard DNP-amino-acids.

[1] Amino-acids which have free amino groups in their side chains, e.g. lysine and arginine, will, of course, also be labelled.

THE PRIMARY STRUCTURE OF PROTEINS

The C-terminal amino-acid can be identified by making use of a rather different technique. Instead of using a specific label biochemists use a specific enzyme. This enzyme is called carboxypeptidase. It acts only on peptide bonds joining amino-acids which possess a free carboxylic acid group. It is clear that reaction of a protein or peptide with this enzyme will result in one or more[1] amino-acids which can be identified chromatographically.

The ability to identify either the N-terminal or the C-terminal amino-acid or, preferably, both, was an essential prerequisite if Sanger's approach to the problem was to succeed. This approach involved splitting the molecule into a number of peptide fragments which could be identified chromatographically. The hydrolysis was achieved on some occasions by the use of mineral acids which break peptide linkages indiscriminately, and on other occasions by the use of proteolytic enzymes which have the advantage of splitting apart only specifiable amino-acid residues. Having identified the fragments into which the amino-acid chain has been broken (itself no mean task) the crucial stage of the investigation was reached. This was to identify, if possible, overlapping amino-acid sequences in the peptide fragments and thus to deduce an unequivocal sequence for the original chain.

The process, in its final stages, was thus not unlike assembling a jigsaw puzzle. The results of the biochemical analyses of the peptide fragments might be symbolised as follows, where the alphabetical letters stand for amino-acids:

DNP—G—A—R
P—Q—A—S—T

L

M—N—L
A—S—T—R—M—N
A—R—P—Q—A
R—P—Q—A—S
Q—A—S—T
DNP—G

The business of assembling the jigsaw puzzle is thus the business of fitting these fragments together in the correct order. The terminal

[1] If the protein consists of more than one amino-acid chain, or if the amino-acid chain is branched, it is evident that there will be more than one C-terminal amino-acid.

112

amino-acids, G and L, are identified by the methods already described. To establish the sequence in the rest of the chain it is necessary to find overlaps amongst the peptide fragments. It is not difficult to see that the sequences in the diagram above permit only one total chain:

$$G-A-R-P-Q-A-S-T-R-M-N-L$$

An initial finding in the analysis of insulin was that the molecule consisted of two separate polypeptide chains. It was shown, for example, that if the molecule was subjected to oxidation by performic acid its molecular weight was approximately halved. It turned out that the two peptide chains, referred to as the A and B chains, were attached to each other by covalent bonds developed between adjacent cysteine residues. Fig. 4.11 shows that there are two sets of these interchain linkages. Treatment with performic acid results in the formation of sulphonic acid residues and thus allows the two chains to be separated (fig. 4.10).

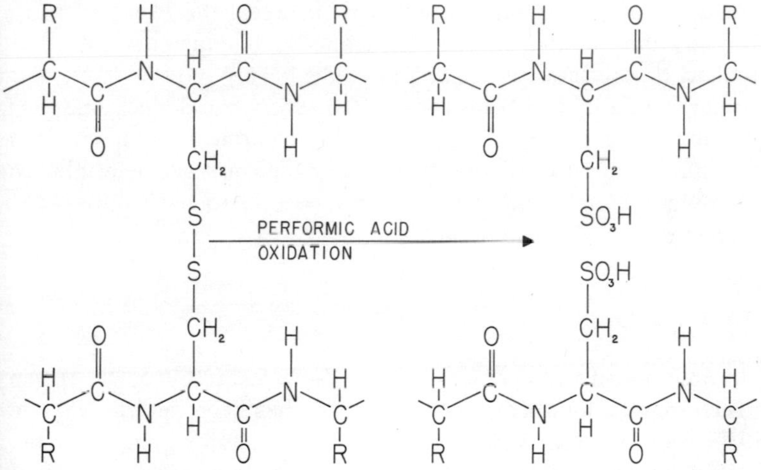

Fig. 4.10 Scission of a disulphide linkage between two polypeptide chains by performic acid oxidation.

The position of these interchain disulphide linkages can be established by subjecting the unoxidised protein to enzymic hydrolysis. Peptides containing the disulphide linkage can then be isolated by chromatography or electrophoresis. Lastly the S—S bonds can be broken by performic acid oxidation, and the amino-acid compositions of the resulting peptides determined.

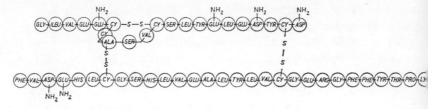

Fig. 4.11 The primary structure of bovine insulin.

Inspection of fig. 4.11 shows that, in addition to the interchain disulphide linkages, another such linkage occurs between some of the amino-acid residues of the A chain. The amino-acids constituting this so-called peptide-disulphide ring are found to vary slightly from one animal to another. Some of these variations are shown in fig. 4.12.

Fig. 4.11 summarises ten years of exacting work by Sanger and his colleagues. It shows insulin to consist of two peptide chains, one consisting of twenty-one amino-acid residues, the other of thirty. For any one animal species the sequence is constant: indeed the method of overlapping sequences could hardly have worked if the primary structure had been variable. In 1955 when Sanger completed his investigations he had developed techniques which could, in principle, be applied to any other protein. In short the determination of insulin's amino-acid sequence may be said to have initiated the modern era of protein chemistry.

6

The amino-acid sequence or, as it has come to be called, the primary structure, of a number of other proteins has been determined since 1955. The methods which Sanger developed for insulin have been refined and sharpened. Particular attention has been paid to the development of agents which cleave the amino-acid chain at restricted and specifiable points. Two proteolytic enzymes—trypsin and chymotrypsin—have proved particularly useful in this respect. Both are crystallisable and, consequently, both can be obtained in a reasonably pure form. Trypsin can be shown to cleave only those peptide bonds whose carbonyl groups are contributed by either lysine or arginine. Its action can be made even more specific if the ε-amino group of lysine is 'masked' by reacting it with DNFB. Trypsin will

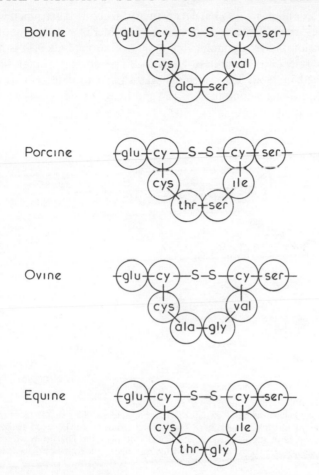

Fig. 4.12 The peptide-disulphide ring of insulin tends to vary from one animal to another.

hen only hydrolyse peptide bonds adjacent to arginine. Chymorypsin is a less specific enzyme. However, its most vigorous attack is made on peptide bonds contributed by amino-acids possessing an aromatic side chain—tyrosine, phenylalanine and tryptophan. In general, a great advantage of enzymatic hydrolysis is that the conditions under which it occurs are milder and more physiological than the conditions prevailing when hydrolysis is brought about by mineral acids. In the latter case fragile amino-acids like tryptophan, glutamine and asparagine may be considerably altered.

115

The second protein to have its primary structure determined was an enzyme—ribonuclease. Although a considerably larger molecule than insulin, having a molecular weight of about 14,000, it is nevertheless one of the smallest enzymes. The complete analysis was published in 1960. The molecule was shown to consist of a single polypeptide chain composed of 124 amino-acid residues. Its structure is shown in fig. 4.13.

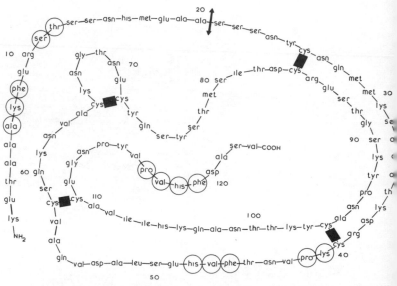

Fig. 4.13 The primary structure of ribonuclease. The black rectangles represent disulphide linkages. The circled residues are believed to be of importance in the enzymatic activity of the protein. The double-headed arrow indicates the bond ruptured by subtilisin to form ribonuclease S.

Ribonuclease has some rather interesting features. It can be shown that in certain circumstances the bacterial enzyme subtilisin cleaves the bond connecting residues twenty and twenty-one. If the two fragments are not separated the result (ribonuclease S) retains its full biological activity. If either fragment is removed the enzymatic activity of the protein is destroyed. This discovery has interesting implications for the activation and control of enzymes.

In addition to insulin and ribonuclease the primary structures of several other proteins have been elucidated in recent years. Amongst these are the protein moiety of tobacco mosaic virus (TMV) (15' residues), egg-white lysozyme (129 residues), myoglobin (15 residues), the α- and β-chains of haemoglobin (141 and 146 residues respectively), cytochrome c (104 residues), and, largest of them all, chymotrypsinogen (246 residues).

The primary structures of several of these proteins have been determined in a number of different species. This has opened up a rich field both for chemists interested in the relation of structure to function, and for biologists interested in evolution at the molecular level.

7

Our discussion so far has dealt with the non-historical aspects of the architecture of atoms, molecules and organisms. Biology itself is, however, a profoundly historical science. Biological phenomena are always seen in the context of evolutionary time. This extra dimension —time—is nowadays penetrating the worlds of biochemistry and beyond. Indeed J. D. Bernal[1] has defined life 'in physical-chemical-evolutionary terms as a form of dynamic realisation of the inherent properties of the quantum states of atoms'.

One of the most interesting of the new fields which have been opened by this development might be called 'comparative molecular anatomy'. We find that the classical biological concern to detect homologies and analogies is nowadays being pursued at the molecular level. We are witnessing the first attempts to establish evolutionary relationships between the multitudes of biological molecules and biochemical reactions.

It has, of course, long been obvious that certain biomolecules are identical across a very wide spectrum of organisms. Some of the small respiratory co-enzymes, for instance FAD and NAD (fig. 10.11), remain the same from one organism to the next; the various intermediates in carbohydrate metabolism—pyruvic acid, oxalo-acetic acid etc.—are also universally distributed in living organisms. On the other hand it has also long been clear that the more complex biomolecules, in particular the proteins, differ markedly from one organism to another. Indeed this fact is one of the major problems which transplantation research seeks to circumvent. For it is virtually impossible to transplant an organ or part of an organ from one adult animal into another because the recipient quickly recognises that the

[1] Bernal, J. D. in *The Origins of Pre-biological Systems*, edited by S. W. Fox, Academic Press, New York and London, 1965, p. 83.

transplant is foreign and hastens to reject it. This foreignness is recognised largely on the basis of the foreignness of the donor's macromolecules.

There are various techniques for estimating the degree of difference between two macromolecules but the most precise method, so far as proteins are concerned, is to determine the degree of difference between their amino-acid sequences. The most thoroughly investigated group of homologous proteins are the important respiratory co-enzymes: the cytochromes c.

Cytochrome c is to be found in the tissues of practically all organisms. It is, as we shall see in Chapter 10, an indispensable prerequisite for cellular respiration. Moreover, the cytochromes c from a great variety of organisms all appear to have nearly identical biochemical characteristics. They are all, for example, oxidised by an enzyme—cytochrome oxidase—which may be extracted from, for instance, mammalian tissues. It looks as though we have a case where Nature, having once hit on a satisfactory molecule, has never had cause to change it.

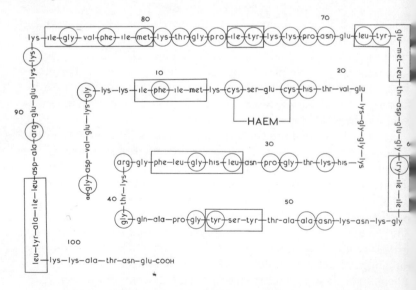

Fig. 4.14 The primary structure of equine cytochrome c. The circled residues are invariant over a wide spectrum of organisms. The amino-acids in rectangles are all hydrophobic and although the individual residues may change they are always replaced by other hydrophobic residues. Hence these hydrophobic segments of the chain are conserved.

118

THE PRIMARY STRUCTURE OF PROTEINS

At the time of writing the structures of more than twenty different cytochromes c, from a wide spectrum of organisms, are known (Table 4.3). The first cytochrome c to have its primary structure successfully elucidated was obtained from horse heart. Margoliash and Smith showed, in 1961, that this co-enzyme consisted of 104 amino-acid residues (fig. 4.14).

Since 1961 cytochrome c molecules from many different organisms have been successfully analysed. Margoliash and Schetjer[1] point out that the work on cytochrome c constitutes 'the most extensive study of any one protein yet undertaken'.

TABLE 4.3

Organisms whose cytochromes c have been completely analysed[1]

Mammals	Birds	Reptiles	Fish	Insects	Miscellaneous
Man	Chicken	Rattlesnake	Tuna	Screw worm	Yeast
Rhesus monkey	Pigeon	Snapping turtle		Saturnid moth	Neurospora
Ox	Peking duck				
Sheep	Penguin				
Pig	Turkey				
Horse					
Dog					
Rabbit					
Whale					
Kangaroo					

[1] Data from Margoliash, E. and Schetjer, A. (1966) *Adv. in Prot. Chem.*, *21*, 113.

The results of this study are of considerable interest to both biologists and chemists. The biologist can gain some insight into the rates of evolutionary change of protein molecules, and the chemist can discern which parts of the cytochrome c molecule are essential to its structure and function.

With one exception—the tuna fish—the cytochromes c of all the vertebrates yet examined consist of 104 amino-acid residues. In contrast it is found that the cytochromes c of the rather small number of invertebrates so far investigated all possess more than 104 residues. How, then, are vertebrate and invertebrate cytochromes to be compared? Are the extra residues of the invertebrates to be interpolated in the middle of the chain, or are they to be added to the

[1] Margoliash, E. and Schetjer, A. (1966), *Adv. in Prot. Res.*, *21*, 173.

beginning or the end or, perhaps, a combination of all three possibilities?

Now it is known that the biological function of the cytochromes is intimately associated with their haem group. This group will be described more fully in Chapter 10. Accordingly it was decided to line up vertebrate and invertebrate cytochromes so that their haem groups coincided.

When this alignment was carried out it became apparent that the amino-acid sequences of all the cytochromes c, whether vertebrate or invertebrate, bore a strong family resemblance. It was found that the extra residues in the invertebrate cytochromes came at the N-terminal end of the sequence.

Certain regions of the chain exhibited complete identity across a wide spectrum of organisms. These regions are circled in fig. 4.14 One such region is involved in binding the all-important haem group to the protein. This region consists of cys (14), cys (17) and his (18) Another region which remains unchanged across the wide range of forms listed in Table 4.3 consists of residues 70 to 80 inclusive. In all 35 amino-acids remain invariant[1] in the cytochromes c of all the organisms so far studied.

Of the residues which vary several different classes can be distinguished. In many cases only 'conservative' substitutions are observed For example, it is found that a basic residue like lysine is replaced by another basic residue, perhaps arginine. Similarly it is found that hydrophobic residues are normally replaced by other hydrophobic residues. In certain parts of the chain distinct clusters of hydrophobic residues are to be found. These clusters, though not always composed of the same amino-acids, are conserved. Such regions are enclosed by rectangular boxes in fig. 4.14. It is not difficult to imagine, from our discussion in Chapter 3, that the conservation of these cluster may have important structural implications.

In other cases 'radical' substitutions occur. In these position amino-acids totally dissimilar in physico-chemical characteristic appear in different cytochromes. In yet other positions both con servative and radical replacements have been observed.

In a few positions a great deal of variation occurs. Position 89, 92 and 103, for instance, are occupied by 7, 6 and 6 different amino-acids respectively. Altogether the presence of more than on

[1] Jukes, T. H., *Molecules and Evolution*, Columbia University Press, New York, 1966.

amino-acid has been observed in 69 different positions along the chain.

It has been shown[1] that the degree of difference between two cytochromes c roughly reflects the closeness of the donor organisms in the evolutionary tree. This can be explained if it is assumed that mutations occurred more or less at random throughout the vast stretches of time which divide two organisms from their common ancestor. We thus see that studies on the primary structures of homologous proteins are beginning to help the taxonomist in his endeavour to perceive the evolutionary relationships of organisms.

The study of molecular evolution is as yet in its infancy. Probably the greatest value, at present, in the study of homologous proteins derived from different organisms lies in the possibility of relating chemical structure to biological function. Darwinian selection will ruthlessly weed out proteins whose structures have been altered to such an extent that their biological function is destroyed. Biological function depends, as we shall see in the next two chapters, on the three-dimensional conformation of a protein and this, in turn, largely depends on the amino-acid sequence of its primary structure. It follows that amino-acids occupying similar positions in the primary structures of proteins derived from diverse sources will, probably, be vital to the structure and thus function of that protein. On the other hand those which vary from one homologous protein to another cannot be of much importance.

8

The possibility of relating chemical structure to biological function has also motivated research on the biologically active polypeptides. Perhaps the most important and well known of these are the peptide hormones. These molecules range in size from the 9 residue chain of oxytocin to the 39 residue chain of ACTH.[2]

The study of polypeptide hormones has benefited greatly from the efforts of organic chemists. It is nowadays possible to synthesise polypeptides with molecular weights of up to 5,000, and to insert

[1] Margoliash, E. and Smith, E. L., in *Evolving Genes and Proteins*. Edited by Bryson, V. and Vogel, H. J., Academic Press, New York and London, 1965, p. 231.

[2] ACTH: the initials stand for adreno-cortico-trophic hormone.

any one of the twenty different amino-acids at any position in the chain.[1] Indeed so rapid has progress been in this field that the 51 amino-acid structure of insulin, which it will be remembered took Sanger and his co-workers a decade to decipher, was, in 1966, synthesised *in vitro* by groups of workers in the United States and China.

$$\text{phe—asp—met—tyr} \text{—gly—tyr—ala—glu—glu—glu—glu—glu—met—tyr—pro—gly—glu}$$

$$\text{SO}_3$$

Fig. 4.15 The structure of gastrin. The residues essential to the hormone's activity are circled. Note that this peptide and peptides in fig. 4.16 are, for convenience, drawn with their C-terminal ends on the left-hand side.

These developments in organic chemistry enable the scientist to synthesise 'strange' hormones with one or more 'foreign' amino-acids inserted at known positions in the chain. It is clear that an investigation of the biological activity of these altered hormones can be most revealing.

One of the most striking of these structure-function studies has been carried out on a peptide hormone called gastrin. Fig. 4.15 shows gastrin to consist of a single chain of 17 amino-acids:

The principal function of this hormone is to initiate the secretion

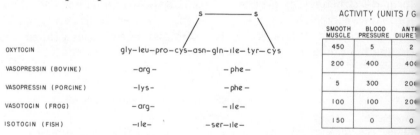

		ACTIVITY (UNITS / G		
		SMOOTH MUSCLE	BLOOD PRESSURE	ANTI DIURE
OXYTOCIN	gly—leu—pro—cys—asn—gln—ile—tyr—cys	450	5	2
VASOPRESSIN (BOVINE)	—arg— —phe—	200	400	40(
VASOPRESSIN (PORCINE)	—lys— —phe—	5	300	20(
VASOTOCIN (FROG)	—arg— —ile—	100	100	20(
ISOTOCIN (FISH)	—ile— —ser—ile—	150	0	0

Fig. 4.16 The structure and activity of oxytocin and vasopressin from several different vertebrates. After H. K. King (1966), *Sci. Progr.*, *54*, 421.

of gastric juice by the walls of the stomach. It is surprising to find that of the 17 residue sequence only the first four (Phe-Asp-Met-Tyr) are essential to the hormone's biological activity. Indeed it can be shown that this tetrapeptide shows all the properties of natural gastrin! In short it seems to constitute the hormone's 'active site'.[2]

Equally interesting structure-function relationships emerge from a

[1] Hofmann, K. and Katsoyannis, P. G., in *The Proteins*, Vol. 1, Second Edition. Edited by Neurath, H., Academic Press, New York and London, 1963, p. 53.
[2] The meaning of this term is discussed and defined in Chapter 7.

study of some of the peptide hormones secreted by the pituitary gland. The posterior lobe of this gland secretes two small peptide hormones called oxytocin and vasopressin. The structures and activities of these two hormones are shown in Fig. 4.16.

Oxytocin and vasopressin can be shown to have three functions:

(a) oxytocic—stimulating the contraction of unstriped muscle.
(b) antidiuretic—stimulating the absorption of water from the urine by the kidney.
(c) vasopressor—increasing the blood pressure.

Fig. 4.16 shows that several interesting experiments have already been performed for the biochemist by the processes of organic evolution. It can be seen that the oxytocic activity of the nonapeptide can be converted to a vasopressor and antidiuretic activity by replacing the leucine in position 2 by a basic amino-acid—preferably arginine. Vasopressor activity is also enhanced if the isoleucine at position 7 is replaced by a phenylalanine residue. This substitution, however, seems to have little effect on the antidiuretic activity of the peptide. In addition to these naturally occurring variations organic chemists have produced about 120 different analogues and derivatives of the nonapeptide. It is clear that by this means many interesting experiments on the relation of hormonal function to molecular structure can be carried out. The outcome of this work on these posterior pituitary hormones is the insight that certain amino-acids, notably the residue at position 8, and the overall shape of the molecule, govern its biological activity.

However, perhaps the most interesting, and certainly the most complex, work on the relation of molecular structure to biological function has concentrated on three hormones produced by the anterior lobe of the pituitary gland. These hormones are ACTH, α-MSH and β-MSH. The most important of the three is ACTH. This has the vital job of controlling the production of steroid hormones by the cortex of the adrenal gland. In addition the hormone also has a slight effect on melanophores. The latter are cells whose cytoplasm contains large quantities of a pigment called melanin. When a melanophore is stimulated melanin migrates from its central position around the nucleus to become evenly distributed throughout the cytoplasm. If a number of melanophores are situated just beneath the epidermis, as is often the case, stimulation results in a darkening in the colour of the skin. Thus ACTH, having a small

123

stimulatory effect on melanophores, is able to cause a slight darkening of pigmented skin. However, the two other hormones mentioned above—α- and β-MSH—have a much more powerful effect. The initials in fact stand for 'melanophore-stimulating hormone'.

A very interesting finding has emerged from the chemical analysis of these three hormones. It has been shown that their amino-acid sequences are remarkably similar.

The structure of ACTH is shown in fig. 4.17. The 39 residue sequence has been elucidated for four different mammals. The only variations occur in positions 25–32. It is interesting to note that in addition to some straightforward substitutions there are also a number of transpositions. An example of both these phenomena occurs in positions 31 and 32. In pig ACTH position 31 is occupied by leucine, in cattle and humans this position is occupied by serine, whilst in sheep ACTH serine and alanine are transposed. These and

Fig. 4.17 The comparative molecular anatomy of α- and β-MSH and of ACTH. Homologous residues of the various molecules are drawn in register so that similarities and differences may be noted. For further explanation see text.

other observations take on an added interest when an attempt is made to relate them to the genetic code—Table 14.1.

The structures of α- and β-MSH are also shown in fig. 4.17. It can be seen that the sequence of α-MSH is identical in all the animals for which it has been determined. In contrast the sequence of amino-acids in β-MSH is found to vary, slightly, from one animal to another. Next, it will be observed that the amino-acid sequence in α-MSH exactly matches the first 13 residues of ACTH. The one point of difference is that the first residue in α-MSH is acetylated. Examination of β-MSH reveals a somewhat similar situation. If the tyrosine occupying position 5 in the β-MSH molecule is aligned with the tyrosine in position 2 of ACTH it can be seen that, with the exception of lysine in position 6 and serine in position 14, the sequence 5–15 of β-MSH matches the sequence 2–12 of ACTH.

In recent years organic chemists have succeeded in synthesising the complete ACTH molecule in the laboratory, and also in preparing many differently sized and differently constituted fragments.[1] Several interesting results have emerged from this chemical work.

First, it can be shown that if the N-terminal serine is acetylated the resultant molecule loses all ACTH activity. It is very suggestive to notice that the N-terminal residue of α-MSH is also acetylated. Second, it has been possible to remove amino-acid residues from the C-terminal end of ACTH so that a 20-unit fragment is obtained which, surprisingly, can be shown to possess practically the same biological activity as the normal 39 residue molecule. If we believe in the parsimony of Nature—that entities are not multiplied unnecessarily—the biological function of the 19 C-terminal residues becomes an interesting speculation.

Still further shortening of the chain has, however, spectacular results. If the two arginine residues occupying positions 17 and 18 are removed the biological activity of the fragment drops by a factor of a thousand. If the chain is reduced to a 13 unit fragment very little ACTH activity can be detected at all. But if the 13 residue peptide shows little ACTH activity it *does* show a very marked MSH action. This, of course, is hardly surprising for the 13 residue fragment quite simply *is* α-MSH (fig. 4.17). It seems possible, therefore, that the 19 C-terminal residues of ACTH in some way inhibit the potential MSH activity of the N-terminal end of the molecule.

Carrying the shortening process still further it is found that the smallest peptide capable of exerting any influence on melanophores is the pentapeptide:

His-Phe-Arg-Try-Gly

[1] Li, H. (1962), *Rec. Progr. Horm. Res.*, *18*, 1.

It will be noticed that this sequence exists in both α-MSH (residues 6–10) and in β-MSH (residues 9–13).

The activity of β-MSH is considerably less than that of α-MSH though much greater than that of the pentapeptide described above. It is puzzling to know why β-MSH should be synthesised at all in animals able to manufacture α-MSH. It may be that it has some, as yet, unsuspected function; or it may be merely an evolutionary relic: a molecular analogue of man's appendix.

9

It was suggested at the beginning of this chapter that it is as important for the molecular biologist to understand the amino-acid sub-structure of proteins as it is for the chemist to understand the electronic sub-structure of atoms. In both cases, it was suggested, function depends on structure.

The studies we have briefly reviewed above support this idea. The combined work of organic chemists, biochemists and endocrinologists are beginning to relate the functions of polypeptide hormones to their amino-acid structure.

We have also seen that the amino-acid structure of a protein is very constant within a single species. Indeed an analogy may be drawn between the amino-acid sequence of a protein and the sequence of letters and spaces which form a sentence. For just as the order of letters and spaces defines the meaning of a sentence so the order of amino-acids in a protein defines its biological significance. Similarly just as the structure of a sentence may be altered slightly by different stylists without impairing its basic meaning, so the order of amino-acids in a protein may vary in different organisms without destroying its biological activity.

The biological activity of a protein depends, as we shall see in the next chapters, on its three-dimensional structure, and this, as we have already hinted, emerges from its amino-acid sequence. If the amino-acid sequence is given, the protein's higher structure largely looks after itself. It is, however, to a consideration of this higher structure, which is often exceedingly intricate, that the next two chapters are devoted.

5

The Three-dimensional Structure of Fibrous Proteins

1

Linderstrøm-Lang, in 1952,[1] proposed that the structure of protein molecules could be treated at three levels. The lowest level is represented by the amino-acid sequence. This level was discussed in Chapter 4. It is said to constitute the *primary* structure of the protein. Next it is found that the amino-acid chain is frequently twisted into one of several helical configurations. The nature of these helices will be discussed in this chapter. This level is said to constitute the *secondary* structure of the protein. Finally the helical amino-acid chain may be twisted and turned into a yet more intricate geometrical configuration. This third level of structural complexity constitutes the *tertiary* structure of the protein. It will be considered in Chapter 6.

Another way of looking at these successive levels of structural complexity is to regard primary structure as being built with the strong cement of covalent bonds—principally peptide bonds; secondary structure as held together by the weaker forces of hydrogen bonds, and tertiary structure to emerge from the action of the still weaker van der Waals and hydrophobic forces.

It was stressed at the end of Chapter 4 that the biological function of a protein usually depends on the integrity of its three-dimensional structure. It will be evident from the preceding paragraph that this structure is a very fragile thing held together only by a multitude of weak forces. It follows that if a protein is exposed to harsh physical or chemical conditions it usually loses its biological activity. It is said to be denatured.

In certain cases it can be shown that denaturation is reversible. These cases are of great interest to the molecular biologist as it is one of the important premises of his branch of science that the

[1] Linderstrøm-Lang, K. *Proteins and Enzymes: Lane Lectures 6*, Stanford University Press, California, 1952, p. 93.

three-dimensional structure of a protein is in some way implied by its primary structure. To put it another way, it is believed that the particular 'set' of an amino-acid chain represents its thermodynamically most stable position.

A widely quoted experiment on the renaturation of a protein was performed by Anfinson on the enzyme ribonuclease. Reference to fig. 4.13 will remind us that the 124 residue chain is held together by four intra-chain disulphide linkages. The precise run of the polypeptide chain has recently been elucidated. It is twisted into an intricate three-dimensional pattern which will be discussed further in Chapter 7. The enzymatic activity of the protein depends on the integrity of this higher structure. If, for example, it is disrupted by exposure to 8-molar urea then the enzyme's ability to hydrolyse ribonucleic acid is utterly destroyed. 8M urea, in addition to destroying the weak forces on which higher structure depends, also breaks the disulphide linkages. Thus we can imagine that after exposure to 8M urea ribonuclease exists simply as a flexible polypeptide chain of no particular shape (fig. 5.1(b)).

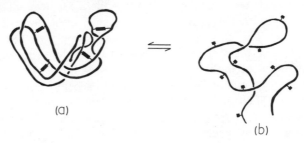

(a)

(b)

Fig. 5.1 Denaturation and renaturation of ribonuclease.

Now it is possible by a chemical technique to rejoin the separated sulphydryl (—SH) groups. In the denatured ribonuclease molecule there will, of course, be eight of these groups (fig. 5.1 (b)). Simple mathematics shows that there are 105 different ways of rejoining these eight groups. Clearly only one of these ways results in the correct three-dimensional structure. It follows that if the sulphydryl groups rejoined merely on a chance basis the prospects for obtaining a biologically active enzyme would be far from bright. In fact, however, it is found that if the ribonuclease is put back into its normal physiological environment and the sulphydryl groups rejoined the enzyme displays nearly 100 per cent of its original activity. It is concluded that in its normal, physiological, environment the enzyme naturally assumes its usual configuration. The correct sulphydryl groups are thus correctly aligned, ready to be rejoined.

Similar experiments giving similar results have been performed on several other enzymes. Amongst these has been lysozyme which, in its natural state, also possesses four intra-chain disulphide linkages (fig. 7.4).

Some of the forces which cause an amino-acid chain to twist itself into a particular configuration were outlined in Chapter 3. Molecular biologists have, however, still very far to go before they can begin to predict the three-dimensional structure of a protein from its primary structure. Investigators are still at the 'stamp-collecting' stage—amassing knowledge of amino-acid sequences and of the three-dimensional structures which they form.

2

We shall see more fully in Chapter 6 that the only really satisfactory method for determining the details of the three-dimensional structure of proteins is the method of X-ray diffraction. Basically this technique consists in carefully examining the reflections produced when a beam of X-rays interacts with a protein fibre or crystal. In certain cases it is possible to deduce from these reflections the arrangement of atoms in the crystal or fibre.

In this chapter it is proposed to describe the structures which X-rays have revealed in protein fibres. In Chapter 6 we shall consider the configuration of globular proteins.

3

The X-ray diffraction pictures obtainable from protein fibres are much less clear than those derived from globular proteins (Plate I). The spots are few in number and, instead of being precisely localised, are rather 'smeared' out. In consequence the techniques necessary to interpret these so-called fibre diagrams are rather specialised. Crick and Kendrew[1] describe them in the following terms: 'The method of attack is to try to deduce the symmetry of the

[1] Crick, F. H. C. and Kendrew, J. C. (1957), *Adv. in Prot. Res.*, *12*, 133–214.

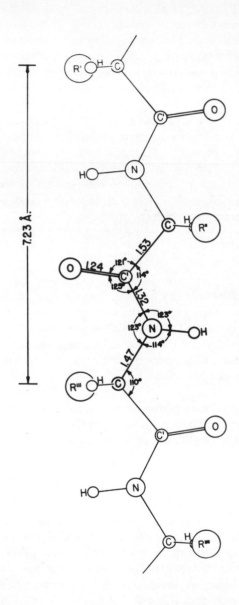

Fig. 5.2 Accurate dimensions of a normal polypeptide chain. From R. B. Corey and L. Pauling (1953), *Proc. Roy. Soc. B.*, *141*, 10.

THE STRUCTURE OF FIBROUS PROTEINS

fibre molecule from the X-ray picture; then to build scale models having this symmetry; and finally to show that only one of these models fits the available data, X-ray and other.'

It is clear, therefore, that an essential item of the technique is the building of scale models. These are in fact used as a species of analogue computer. Their structure is progressively altered until the X-ray picture they would give if they were the reality, instead of a model of the reality, coincides with the X-ray picture observed. When this is achieved there is good reason to believe that the model is a true representation of the molecular reality.

In order to carry out this technique it is obviously essential that the various atomic parameters should all be accurately to scale. The van der Waals radii of the atoms, for example, the covalent bond distances, the bond angles, etc. must all be known accurately, and must all be built into the atomic models from which the molecular model is constructed. These all-important measurements were made by Pauling, Corey and their group at the California Institute of Technology in the late nineteen-forties. By subjecting amino-acids and small peptides to X-ray crystallography these workers were able to determine the parameters mentioned above to an accuracy of ± 0.02A and $\pm 2°$. The results of the Caltech work are shown in fig. 5.2.

One of the most important results of the Californian crystallography was the demonstration that the bond lengths in the peptide linkage differed from the lengths of similar bonds in other molecules (Table 3.1). Fig. 5.3 shows the bond lengths observed, with the usual lengths in brackets.

It will be recalled from Chapter 3 that such an observation indicates that resonance is occurring between the double and single bonds. This has, as we also saw in Chapter 3, an important consequence. It implies that the atoms of the peptide group all lie in one plane. Moreover, it also follows that rotation about the peptide bond is impossible.

Rotation of the α-carbon atoms is of course possible, as these are connected by single covalent bonds to their neighbours. The fact that rotation is forbidden about the peptide link, however, drastically reduces the number of configurations a polypeptide chain can assume.

The Caltech group proposed two further features which, they said, would be expected in polypeptide chains. First, a maximum number

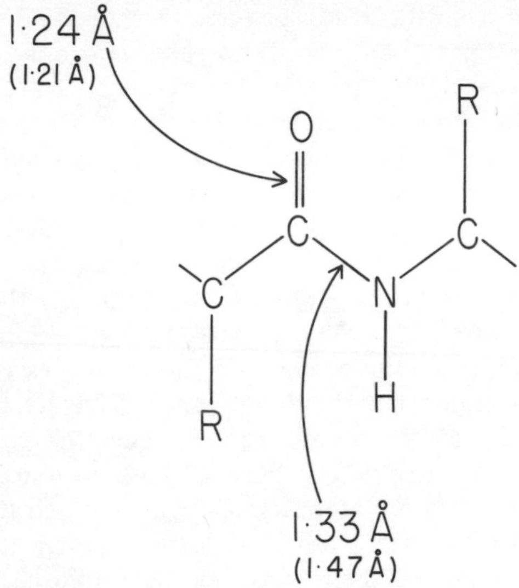

Fig. 5.3 The lengths of the bonds forming the peptide group show that resonance is occurring. The usual lengths of these bonds in non-resonating structures are shown in brackets.

of hydrogen bonds would be expected to form between the imino-groups (NH) and carbonyl-groups (CO) of the amino-acid residues. Second, it would be expected that each amino-acid residue would be placed in an exactly similar position to any other. In other words the residues would all be disposed symmetrically with respect to each other.

In a fibre consisting of naturally occurring amino-acids[1] it is possible to show that the only way of arranging the residues symmetrically with respect to each other is in some form of 'screw-axis'

4

Screw symmetry consists of a simultaneous translation and rotation around the axis of translation. Fig. 5.4 shows, schematically, some possible screw symmetries. A screw-axis along which there are '*n*

[1] The vast majority of naturally occurring amino-acids are *l*-amino-acids. This optical asymmetry prevents other symmetrical dispositions—mirror and glide planes—being possible.

equivalent units of matter (for example, amino-acids) per complete turn is said to have an 'n-fold' screw-axis. Fig. 5.4 shows screws in which $n=1$, 2, 3 and 4. It will be appreciated that the case where $n=1$ is very special. It is normally, and more simply, regarded as straightforward translational symmetry.

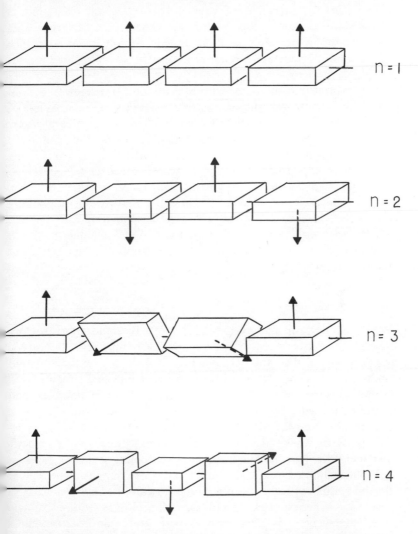

Fig. 5.4 Screws axes for $n=1$, 2, 3 and 4. In the case of fibrous proteins the boxes may be taken to represent amino-acids.

133

The screw-axes quoted in the previous paragraph are all cases in which 'n' is an integer. In fact crystallographers have known for many years that 'n' must be an integer restricted to 2, 3, 4 or 6 *if the screw is to pack into a regular and extended crystal structure.* It can be shown that if 'n' does not have one of the values quoted above then the principle of equivalence, by which each unit is disposed in the same environment as any other, is controverted. This crystallographic principle made it difficult for physicists to realise that the most important biological fibre structure of all had a non-integral screw axis.

It turns out that the possession of a non-integral screw axis need not, in fact, controvert the fundamental crystallographic principle of equivalence. For it is possible for any unit in a non-integral screw axis to be orientated in an equivalent manner to any other unit *in the same fibre.* In other words although fibres with a non-integral screw axis cannot pack to form a regular and extended crystal in which each unit is equivalent to any other throughout the entire structure, they can, nevertheless, so arrange themselves that the position of any unit is equivalent to that of any other in the same fibre.

After this very brief outline of the topic of fibre symmetry we can now proceed to a consideration of the structures of some important biological fibres.

5

W. T. Astbury, for many years Professor of Biomolecular Structure at the University of Leeds, pioneered the field of fibre crystallography. Astbury was fired by the belief that concealed beneath the apparent multifariousness of biological fibres were certain great regularities. Although some of Astbury's speculations were premature, and although the vital break-through came in the end from California and not the West Riding, his intuition has proved remarkably penetrating. Much work remains to be done, but the outlines of Astbury's vision of order lying behind disorder are becoming steadily clearer.

Biological fibres seem to be built to but three designs. Where great flexibility and suppleness are required a twofold screw symmetry is employed. Where strength in addition to flexibility is required a single non-integral helix is developed. Where great tensile strength is required three threefold screw axes are twisted together to form an unstretchable rope.

The simplest of the three designs consists of an amino-acid chain exhibiting twofold screw symmetry. Each amino-acid is related to its neighbour by a translation of 3·6A and a rotation of 180°. Such a fibre is believed to form the basis of the silk obtained from the silkworm *Bombyx mori*. The structure of this material has, in fact, been studied by X-ray crystallographers since the early nineteen-twenties. The X-ray picture obtained shows that the material posseses a highly regular molecular structure. The molecular structure appears to repeat itself every 7A. It would seem, therefore, that the amino-acid chain is in an extended form (fig. 5.2), although the 7·0A repeat distance is rather less than the 7·2A predicted by Pauling and Corey.

The variety of amino-acids found in silk is rather restricted. Greatly preponderating are amino-acids with small side chains—glycine, alanine, and serine. This finding makes it less difficult to propose a structure. Marsh *et al.* suggested a configuration in 1955 and this has come to be generally accepted. Marsh's proposal is shown in fig. 5.5. It is known, technically, as an anti-parallel pleated sheet.

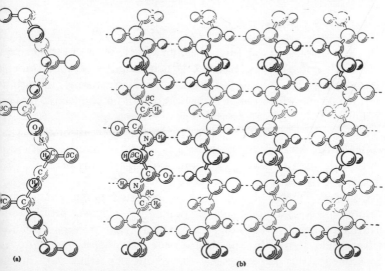

Fig. 5.5 Anti-parallel pleated sheet of amino-acids. The sheet is seen edge-on in (*a*) and from above in (*b*). This compact structure is believed to form the molecular basis of silk. From R. E. Marsh, R. B. Corey and L. Pauling (1955), *Biochim. et Biophys. Acta 16*, 1.

If the sheet is looked at edge-on it can be seen that the α-carbon atoms are not co-planar. This slight zigzag above and below the mid-line of the sheet decreases the longitudinal distance between one α-carbon atom and the next. This is believed to account for the fact that the structure repeats every 7·0A instead of the theoretical 7·2A.

Fig. 5.5 shows that if two of the amino-acid chains are laid side by side (running in opposite directions) their respective carbonyl and imino groups come into alignment so that hydrogen bonding can occur. The amino-acid chains are thus held together to form a 'pleated sheet'.

The side chains project alternately above and below the sheet. Now silk fibroin, as we have already mentioned, contains a high proportion of simple amino-acids, particularly glycine. In fact it seems quite possible that every other residue is glycine. It will be remembered that the side chain of glycine consists of a single hydrogen atom. It follows that it is quite possible that all the side chains projecting from one side of the sheet are simply hydrogen atoms. In consequence two such sheets could pack together very closely 'back to back'. It is believed that this close packing forms the molecular basis of *Bombyx mori* silk.

7

The next simplest of our three structures possesses a threefold screw axis. Each amino-acid is related to its neighbour by a translation and a rotation of 120°. It turns out that collagen, the extremely important fibrous protein which confers tensile strength on connective tissues is built of fibres possessing this type of symmetry.

Collagen is a ubiquitous protein being found throughout the animal kingdom from the coelenterates up to the mammals. It looks as though Nature, having once hit upon this means of conferring tensile strength, has never been able to better it.

Collagen, like silk fibroin, has a rather restricted amino-acid constitution. Three amino-acids preponderate—glycine, proline and hydroxyproline. When collagen is hydrolysed a very common tetrapeptide found in the hydrolysate is: *gly-pro-hypro-gly*. In consequence this sequence has played an important part in the structures proposed by crystallographers.

X-ray analysis shows that collagen has the very small repeat distance of 2·86A. This presented something of a challenge to crystallographers. A great deal of work was carried out and a number of false trails pursued before a satisfactory solution was achieved.

Because collagen possesses an amino-acid constitution consisting mainly of glycine and proline it is clear that one fruitful line of approach to its structure lay in the study of the synthetic poly-peptides—polyglycine and polyproline. Now we have already noticed that silk fibroin consists largely of glycine. It is not surprising, therefore, to find that one form of polyglycine (polyglycine 1) assumes the anti-parallel pleated sheet structure of silk. However, it turns out that it is possible to precipitate polyglycine from solution in a quite different form. This form is called polyglycine 2 and gives a diffraction pattern totally different from that given by polyglycine 1.

Several groups of investigators arrived independently at a structure which accounted very well for the observed X-ray picture of poly-glycine 2. It was proposed, firstly, that the polyglycine chain possessed a threefold screw axis. Secondly, it was suggested that the density of the fibre could only be accounted for by assuming that each polyglycine chain was surrounded by six others to each of which it was bound by hydrogen bonds. The resulting fibre, shown end-on in fig. 5.6, utilises all the hydrogen-bonding potentialities of polyglycine and, consequently, results in a strong and compact fibre.

A similar structure has been proposed, and generally accepted, for synthetic fibres of polyproline. Moreover, the threefold screw of polyproline can be shown, of necessity, to be left-handed.

It would seem likely that collagen, being largely composed of glycine and proline residues, might well be built to a similar design. However collagen's repeat distance militated against such a com-paratively straightforward solution. Both polyproline and poly-glycine showed a repeat distance of 3·1A in contrast to collagen's 2·86A.

In order to account for collagen's unusually short repeat distance it was suggested that the parallel helices of fig. 5.7(a) were, in colla-gen, twisted around each other as in fig. 5.7(b). The degree of twisting could be arranged so that the residues followed each other every 2·86A instead of every 3·1A.

In order to fit the X-ray diffraction and other data more accurately a third amino-acid chain is added either behind or in front of the original two chains of fig. 5.7(a). The three chains are then twisted around each other in the same way as the two chains in fig. 5.7(b).

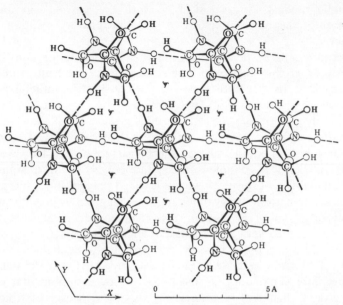

Fig. 5.6 Polyglycine 2 viewed end-on. Each chain is surrounded by six others running parallel to it as is the centre chain in the figure. Broken lines represent hydrogen bonds. From F. H. C. Crick and A. Rich (1955), *Nature*, *176*, 780

The three-stranded rope which is generated in this way is called collagen 1 when the third chain is added behind the first two, and collagen 2 when it is added in front of the other two.

It is found that when sequences like *gly-pro-hypro-gly* are inserted into the structure in place of a monotonous chain of glycines or prolines, collagen 2 proves to be a much more satisfactory structure than collagen 1.

Collagen 2 is a remarkably compact and tightly bound structure. It is easy to see that it is admirably suited to the biological function of collagen in connective tissues. The organisation of these triple helices into the collagen fibre visible under the microscope will be considered in Chapter 8.

8

The last, but very far from least, architectural principle underlying protein fibres is the non-integral screw axis. This configuration forms the structural basis of an important group of fibrous proteins called by Astbury the *k.m.e.f.* series. The initials stand for keratin, myosin, epidermin and fibrin. Non-integral screw axes are not, however, restricted to these fibrous proteins. They are also to be found, as we shall see in the next chapter, in many globular proteins.

Astbury initially grouped the *k.m.e.f.* proteins together because they all gave a rather similar X-ray diffraction picture. Moreover, he noticed that this diffraction picture changed when the proteins were stretched. Astbury named the diffraction pattern obtained from the natural, unstretched, fibres the α-pattern, and that obtained from the fibres after stretching the β-pattern.

Astbury was perhaps unlucky in that having discovered these diffraction patterns in fibrous proteins he found himself unable to

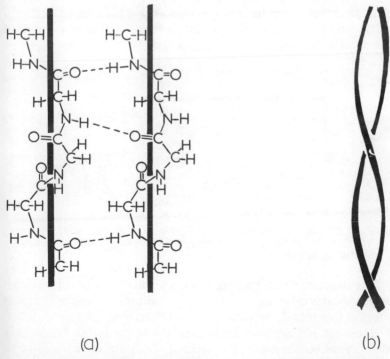

(a)   (b)

Fig. 5.7 Two polyglycine chains each with a three-fold screw axis are shown running parallel to each other in (*a*). The broken lines represent hydrogen bonds. In (*b*) the axes of the two screws are twisted around each other as is believed to be the case in collagen.

THE STRUCTURE OF FIBROUS PROTEINS

formulate a satisfactory model of their molecular structure. The insight denied Astbury was achieved by the Caltech group under Pauling.

Pauling and his co-workers approached the problem by means of a programme of careful model-building.[1] Accurate values for bond angles and lengths, for van der Waals radii, etc. were incorporated in the models. Infra-red spectroscopy had shown that practically all the hydrogen-bonding potentialities of the polypeptide chain were satisfied. Moreover, these hydrogen bonds could be shown to run parallel to the fibre axis. These facts were all made use of in the building of feasible models.

Fig. 5.8 shows some of the hydrogen-bonding potentialities of a portion of polypeptide chain. By building a series of models the Caltech group investigated which of these potentialities resulted in the most satisfactory helix. They determined which system of hydrogen bonds best fitted the known bond angles and lengths, etc. of a polypeptide chain. It turned out that a thirteen-atom ring provided the most satisfactory structure (fig. 5.8).

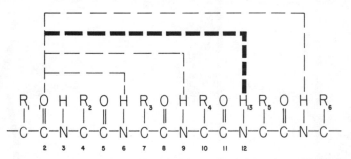

Fig. 5.8 Some hydrogen bond possibilities in a twisted polypeptide chain. The thick broken line represents the possibility deemed most satisfactory by Pauling and his colleagues.

The structure which Pauling and Corey finally proposed is shown in fig. 5.9. It is called the α-helix. Edsall has called it 'one of the great creative triumphs in the field of protein chemistry'.[2]

There are 3·67 amino-acids in each turn of the spiral. The helix is thus, as has been stressed, non-integral. The pitch of the helix is, as

[1] Pauling, L., Corey, R. B. and Branson, H. R. (1951), *Proc. Nat. Acad. Sci.* **37**, 105.
[2] Quoted by Crick, F. H. C. (1954) in *Sci. Progr.*, **42**, 219.

fig. 5.9 shows, 5·44A. It follows that as there are 3·67 residues in each spiral the 'rise' per residue is $5·44/3·67 \approx 1·5$A. X-ray techniques have, subsequent to Pauling's work, shown this repeat distance to exist. The radius of the helix is 2·3A and the side chains of the amino-acid residues project outwards, away from the mid-line of the helix.

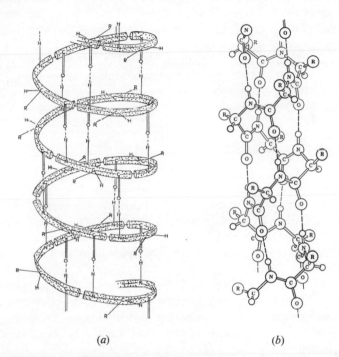

(a)   (b)

Fig. 5.9 (a) Very diagrammatic representation of an α-helix. The stippled cylinders represent amino-acids. The coils of the 'spring' are held together by hydrogen bonds. This is a left-handed helix.

(b) Accurate representation of an α-helix. This is a right-handed helix: the type normally found in proteins.

The fact that the amino-acid side chains project away from the helix's mid-line implies that there need be no restriction as to their type. Amino-acids with bulky or reactive side chains are just as easily accommodated as their simpler or less reactive relatives.

It will be recalled from Chapter 4 that of the twenty commonly occurring amino-acids one—proline—possesses no imino group when incorporated into a polypeptide chain (p. 104). It follows that

141

the presence of this amino-acid will disrupt the regular hydrogen-bonded structure of the α-helix. This has indeed been found to be the case in proteins possessing a high α-helical content such as, for example, haemoglobin and myoglobin.

Finally the structure of the α-helix allows us to see why the X-ray diffraction picture changes when the fibre is stretched. Tensile stress pulls apart the hydrogen bonds which hold the coils of the 'spring' together. The polypeptide chain is straightened out so that its dimensions come to resemble those shown in fig. 5.2. The chain will then give the β-pattern as Astbury observed. It should be noted, however, that the energy released when hydrogen bonds are formed (Chapter 3) ensures that the helical configuration is the most stable, and hence natural, form.

9

The fibrous proteins are principally used by the body as structural proteins. They form the material of tendons and ligaments, of hair, wool and feather. In carrying out these important structural functions it is found that the molecules which we have considered in this chapter are organised into higher and more complex designs. These will be considered in Chapter 8.

In the next chapter we shall discuss the structure of globular proteins. These have many important functions in the body acting as enzymes, oxygen carriers, antibodies and in many other ways. We shall find that their structure is yet more intricately organised than that of the fibrous proteins of this chapter. But like the proteins of the present chapter, the function of globular proteins is very intimately related to their structure. Once again we shall see how function emerges from, and is determined by, structure.

6

The Three-dimensional Structure of Globular Proteins

1

'A protein molecule', writes Perutz,[1] 'may be compared to an animal in having a three-dimensional anatomy laid out to a definite plan, rigid in some parts and flexible in others, with perhaps some minor variations in different individuals of the same species. The nature of this anatomy constitutes the central problem of protein chemistry.'

Unfortunately it is not as easy to dissect the anatomy of a protein as it is to dissect the body of an animal. The normal techniques of biochemical analysis are powerless when it is required to understand the intimate weave of a protein's amino-acid chain. The intricate structure is also beyond the limits of resolution of modern electron microscopes. In short, there is at present only one technique capable of probing the three-dimensional architecture of macromolecules, and this is the technique of X-ray diffraction.

2

X-rays are, of course, a form of electromagnetic radiation. Their wave-lengths vary, according to the source, from about $0.1A$ to $150A$. Evidently they have a very much shorter wave-length than electromagnetic radiation in that part of the spectrum visible to us.[2] The value of this very short wave-length will become apparent later.

That electromagnetic radiation, in common with other forms of wave motion, could be diffracted has been known since the time of Huyghens in the seventeenth century. It was not, however, until

[1] Perutz, M. F., *Proteins and Nucleic Acids*, Elsevier, Amsterdam, London and New York, 1962, p. 15.
[2] See Chapter 10, p. 255, footnote.

the beginning of the twentieth century that von Laue suggested that a crystal would diffract X-rays. Shortly afterwards the two Braggs, father and son, made use of von Laue's idea to determine the structure of a crystal.

What, then, is diffraction? The dictionary defines the word as meaning 'breaking up' an oncoming wave-front. The continuous wave-front is fragmented into a large number of small wavelets which then interfere with each other. Everyone who has watched a regular wave system rebounding from a sea-wall to form a choppy and broken surface will have witnessed a form of diffraction.

In the same way that all sea-walls diffract water waves, so all matter diffracts X-rays. The regular oncoming beam is broken up into a confused and irregular motion. However, in certain cases regularity rather than confusion can be discerned in the diffracted waves. These are cases where the matter on which the X-rays impinge has a regular, repetitive structure.

By definition, matter possessing a regularly repeating structure is said to be crystalline. The repeating units are called 'unit cells'. The unit cell may contain one molecule or it may contain a number of molecules. Let us now consider how a crystal interacts with an X-ray beam.

X-rays are partially reflected by the electron shells of atoms. In a crystal, as fig. 6.1 indicates, atoms and their electron shells are arranged in a regular manner. They will, in fact, be arranged in a number of planes. Each plane will be separated from the next by a distance, 'd'.

The number of different planes in a crystal is large. A well-known simile likens the atoms in a crystal to the trees in a regularly planted orchard. As the traveller observes these trees from a swiftly moving train, he will notice how many different planes they could be said to be arranged in. However, in our example, fig. 6.1, we will concentrate our attention on just one of these planes.

In fig. 6.1 we consider what happens when a beam of X-rays impinges on the crystal at an angle θ. When X-rays meet the electron shells of the crystal's atoms they will be reflected. It will, moreover, be remembered from elementary physics, that the angle of reflection equals the angle of incidence (θ).

Fig. 6.1 shows that some of the X-rays will be reflected from the 'top' row of atoms, and other X-rays will pass through the top row and be reflected by the next row, and so on. The X-rays reflected

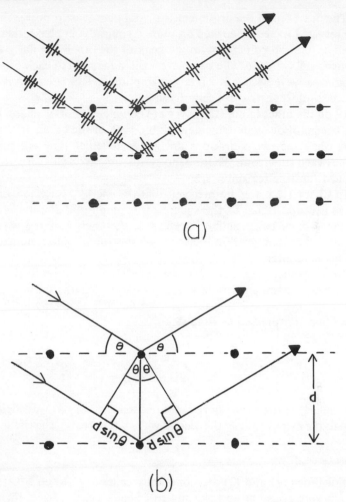

(a)

(b)

Fig. 6.1 Diffraction of X-rays by a crystal. In (*a*) two parallel beams of X-rays impinge on a crystal. The first beam is reflected by the top row of atoms, the second beam by the row immediately beneath. When they emerge the beams are out of phase. The path difference between the two rays is shown in (*b*) to be a function of '*d*' and '*θ*'. For further explanation see text.

rom the second (and deeper) rows of atoms will have further to travel han those reflected from the topmost row. This distance, as fig. 6.1 hows, is a function of *d* and *θ*. It is, in fact, equal to 2*d* sin *θ*.

The next step in the argument is a vital one. It is to notice that if the reflected waves are in step or, more technically, in phase, then the peak of one will coincide with the peak of the other. Similarly their troughs will coincide. The two waves will in fact add to each other to produce a wave with a much larger amplitude. This situation is said to constitute 'constructive' interference.

If, on the other hand, the waves are completely out of phase, then the trough of one will coincide with the peak of the other. It follows that when the two vibrations are added together they completely cancel each other out. There is no resultant wave. This situation is termed 'destructive' interference.

In Chapter 2 it was pointed out that the energy associated with a wave is proportional to the square of its amplitude. It follows that in the case of constructive interference the energy of the wave is greatly increased, and in the case of destructive interference the energy is reduced to zero.

Now whether or not constructive interference is to occur depends on whether or not a whole number of wave-lengths occurs in the extra distance wave 2 (fig. 6.1(b)) has to travel. Mathematically this condition is expressed as follows:

$$n\lambda = 2d \sin \theta \qquad \ldots \ldots (1)$$

where n is an integer

Similarly destructive interference occurs when $(n+\frac{1}{2})$ wave-lengths equals the extra distance the second wave has to travel, that is:

$$(n+\tfrac{1}{2})\lambda = 2d \sin \theta \qquad \ldots \ldots (2)$$

Equations (1) and (2) are commonly called the Bragg equations. If λ is kept constant and the angle of incidence, θ, varied, then, by observing exactly which values of θ result in constructive and which in destructive interference, it is possible to calculate 'd', the distance between the lines of atoms. It is an easy matter to detect constructive and destructive interference if the X-ray beam is allowed to impinge on a photographic plate. The plate will record regions where constructive interference is occurring, but not those where destructive interference is taking place.

The Bragg equations are thus the fundamental equations of X-ray analysis. Nevertheless, the remainder of the theory which allow

146

crystallographers to deduce the structure of a crystal from its diffraction picture is mathematically quite fierce. Thus all we shall attempt here is a brief non-mathematical outline designed to illuminate the nature of what is called 'the phase problem'. It is this problem which has proved the main stumbling-block for the protein crystallographer and has prevented the sharp tool of X-ray analysis being applied to numerous interesting proteins.

3

If a small protein crystal is mounted in the path of a beam of monochromatic[1] X-rays the resulting diffraction pattern should resemble that shown in Plate I(d). The symmetry of this pattern is related to the symmetry of the crystal from which it was obtained. It is the task of the crystallographer, knowing θ and λ, to deduce from this pattern the arrangement of the atoms in the crystal.

4

First let us remember that it is the electron shells which reflect X-rays. Then let us recall from Chapter 3 the fact that valency electrons occupy molecular orbitals. Reference back to fig. 3.3(d) will remind

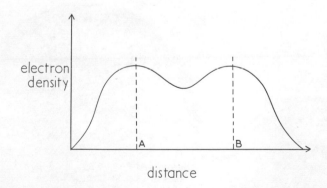

Fig. 6.2 Electron density profile of a hydrogen molecule.

[1] Monochromatic merely means that the wave-lengths of the X-rays used are all nearly the same.

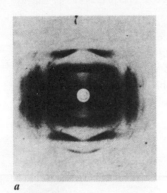

a

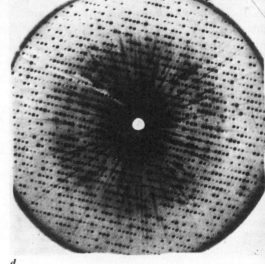

d

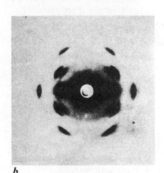

b

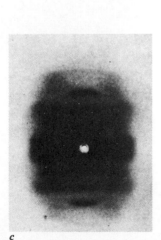

c

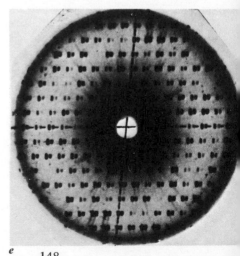

e

148

us that it is usual to speak of 'electron density' and to represent this by a number of density contour lines. Fig. 3.3(d) shows the electron density distribution in a very simple molecule—the hydrogen molecule. The density distribution will be correspondingly more complex in more complicated molecules.

If we cut a longitudinal section through the hydrogen molecule of fig. 3.3(d) we should obtain a profile resembling that drawn in fig. 6.2.

We can thus regard the electron density distribution within the hydrogen molecule as varying in a sinusoidal manner. By analogy a similar sinusoidal wave, though enormously more complicated, would represent the electron density distribution within larger and more complex molecules.

Now wave motion is, as we saw in Chapter 2, a very basic physical notion. Many brilliant minds have investigated it. Not the least brilliant was that of Fourier. Fourier showed that a complicated wave form can be regarded as constructed of a number of simple sinusoidal elements. In other words, if the scientist is provided with a number of simple sinusoidal waves he can add them together in such a way that any complex wave forms can be generated.

The process of discovering the simple elements out of which a given irregular wave is composed is called Fourier analysis. The reverse process—building a complex wave given simple sinusoidal elements—is called Fourier synthesis.

e I X-ray diffraction pictures of some proteins and polypeptides.

(a) diffraction picture of the unstretched or alpha-form of synthetic poly-*l*-alanine.

(b) diffraction picture of the same synthetic polypeptide after it has been stretched into the beta-configuration.

(c) diffraction picture of collagen. Note the great difference in sharpness between a natural fibre such as collagen and a regularly repeating artificial polypeptide such as poly-*l*-alanine.

(d) diffraction picture of myoglobin—a globular protein.

(e) diffraction picture of egg-white lysozyme. In this picture two photographs are in fact superimposed on each other and slightly displaced with respect to each other. One diffraction picture is of pure egg-white lysozyme while the other is of lysozyme containing heavy atom substituents. Note the difference in intensity of the spots.

(a), (b) *and* (c) *courtesy of F. H. C. Crick and J. C. Kendrew* (*1957*), Advances in Protein Research, *XII, 133;* (d) *courtesy of J. C. Kendrew:* Nobel Lectures: Chemistry (1942–1962), *Elsevier Publishing Company, 1964;* (e) *courtesy of R. E. Dickerson:* The Proteins, vol. 2, *edited by H. Neurath, Academic Press, New York and London, 1964.*

In order to carry out a Fourier synthesis we must have complete knowledge of the characteristics of our unit waves. This means that we must know three things about them. We must know

(a) their frequencies
(b) their amplitudes
(c) their phases.

We noticed above that the electron density in a molecule may be regarded as a complicated three-dimensional wave form. Such a wave form, like any other, is amenable to Fourier analysis.

Now we come to the crucial point. For crystallographers have shown that the act of diffraction is an act of Fourier analysis.[1] The X-ray diffraction picture (Plate I(d)) may be regarded as a Fourier analysis of the three-dimensional electron density wave within the crystal.

Each spot on the diffraction picture corresponds to one of the unit waves of a Fourier analysis. If all these waves could be observed and incorporated in a Fourier synthesis the original wave form could be reconstructed. It is thus the crystallographers' endeavour to carry out this Fourier synthesis and thus reproduce the electron density distribution of the crystal.

The position of each spot on the picture gives the frequency (and also the direction) of a unit wave. The darkness, or density, of each spot corresponds to the amplitude of the unit wave. Unfortunately the third piece of vital information, the phase of the unit wave, is lacking. The diffraction picture has nothing to say on this subject.

Without a knowledge of the phases of the unit waves the Fourier synthesis cannot be carried out. Fig. 6.3 shows that waves with identical amplitudes and frequencies, but differing in phase, sum to give quite different wave forms.

A number of stratagems have been developed by crystallographers to circumvent this difficulty. Informed guesswork always plays a part. This, according to Crick and Kendrew,[2] makes crystallography something of an art. 'The pursuit of a structure', they write, 'is rather like hunting: it requires some skill, a knowledge of the victim's habits and a certain amount of low cunning.'

The most important and fruitful of the methods developed to solve

[1] Crick, F. H. C. and Kendrew, J. C. (1957), *Adv. in Prot. Chem.*, *12*, 133.
[2] *Loc. cit.*, p. 139.

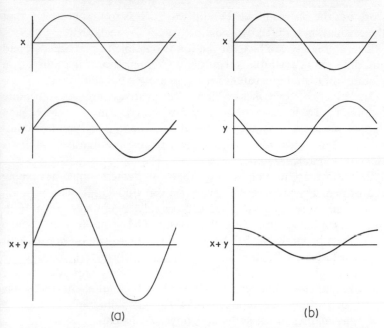

Fig. 6.3 The 'elementary' waves in (*a*) and (*b*) have identical frequencies and amplitudes. Because, however, they differ in phase they sum to give quite different waves.

the phase problem in proteins is the method of multiple isomorphous replacement. This technique has been used to solve all the proteins so far successfully analysed.

In essence, the method involves the introduction of a heavy atom, frequently mercury, into the unit cell of a crystalline protein. The substituted protein is then subjected to X-ray analysis. If the diffraction picture so obtained is carefully compared with a similar picture obtained from an unsubstituted protein, certain differences can be observed. The spots in the two pictures are found to differ somewhat in intensity. This is well shown in Plate I(*e*). In this plate the two diffraction pictures are superimposed on each other but moved slightly out of true so that the intensities of the two sets of spots may be compared.

The heavy atom should ideally displace and substitute a 'light' group, often a water molecule. It has to occupy the same position in each unit cell and this position has to be known. If these conditions are all satisfied it is possible, from the observed intensity changes, to work out the phases of all the unit waves. It is found, however, that the calculation leads to two possible values for each phase.

This ambiguity can be removed if it is possible to prepare a second and different heavy atom substituent. Comparison of the diffraction pictures allows unique values for the phases to be established.

In practice, two heavy atom derivatives are an absolute minimum. To be sure of a structure three, four or more such derivatives are, if possible, prepared and their X-ray pictures compared. Hence we see the significance of the phrase: *multiple isomorphous replacement*.

The above account emphasises that the greatest difficulties facing the protein crystallographer are chemical difficulties. The protein, first of all, must be crystallisable. Secondly, it must be possible to introduce a heavy atom into the crystal. The position of the heavy atom must be known and it must be in a similar position in each unit cell. The heavy atom, moreover, must not greatly distort the structure of the crystal. Finally, not just one of these heavy atom derivatives must be prepared, but several. Only when this initial chemistry has been successfully accomplished can the crystallographer begin to exert his mathematical skills and physical insight.

5

The first rough X-ray diffraction pictures of protein crystals were obtained in the early nineteen-thirties. Various proteins were examined including pepsin, insulin and haemoglobin. The phase problem, however, seemed at that time to be an insurmountable obstacle to progress. Nonetheless Perutz began in 1937 the studies on haemoglobin which were to lead, in 1962, to the Nobel Prize.

Perutz describes how the X-ray pictures of haemoglobin which he obtained at that time fired the imagination of Sir Lawrence Bragg, the then newly-appointed Cavendish professor of physics. Sir Lawrence Bragg, as we saw earlier in this chapter, had been, with his father, one of the founders of X-ray crystallography. His support proved invaluable[1] in the twenty-five years needed to develop the X-ray technique to the level at which structures as intricate as haemoglobin and lysozyme could be solved.

[1] Perutz, M. F., in *Nobel Lectures: Chemistry 1942–1962*, Elsevier, Amsterdam, London and New York, 1964, p. 653.

THE STRUCTURE OF GLOBULAR PROTEINS

Perutz was joined by Kendrew in 1946 and the latter chose to apply the techniques of crystallography to the related but smaller protein—myoglobin.

6

Myoglobin, largely because of its smaller size, was solved before haemoglobin. Myoglobin has a molecular weight of about 17,000 and consists of a single polypeptide chain of 151 amino-acid residues.

The function of myoglobin in the body is to act as an oxygen store in the muscles. This ability is largely conferred on the molecule by its possession of a haem group. This group is also, of course, to be found in haemoglobin and, as we saw in Chapter 4, is, in addition, an important constituent of cytochrome c. Its ubiquity suggests that it has rather unique properties. Its structure will be discussed in Chapter 10.

The first task for Kendrew and his co-workers was to find a suitable source of myoglobin. The fact that the molecule acts as an oxygen storage compound in muscles suggests that it might be found, in high concentration, in the muscles of diving mammals. Thus it is not surprising to learn that Kendrew obtained myoglobin from the muscles of the sperm whale and that other workers have examined myoglobin from the seal.

Having prepared a series of isomorphous replacements, Kendrew first calculated the electron density distribution in the molecule at a resolution of 6A. The technique adopted for plotting this density distribution was to draw contour maps of the electron density at different levels in the molecule. These maps were drawn on perspex sheets which were then stacked one above the other to give the correct spacing. The resulting model gives the impression that the molecule has been sliced with a miniature bacon slicer (Plate II(d)).

At a resolution of 6A it is possible to see that about 75 per cent of the polypeptide chain is in the form of an α-helix. As this high α-helical content can be confirmed by other methods, this result helped to establish the validity of the crystallographic technique applied to proteins.

In order to investigate atomic groupings and thus begin to identify the side chains of specific amino-acids, a resolution of better than 6A is necessary. However, in order to increase the resolution it is necessary to take into account spots further and further away from the

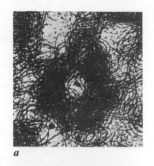

a

d

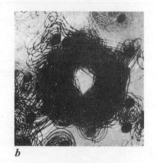

b

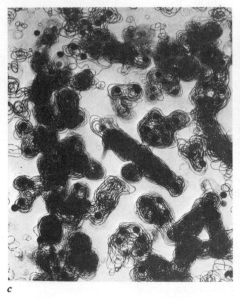

c

e

centre of the picture. The number of spots increases as the cube of the distance from the centre,[1] whereas the resolution increases only as the first power of this distance. Hence increasing the resolution rapidly involves the crystallographer in more and more computation.

In order to calculate a 6A model Kendrew took 400 spots into account. In order to increase the resolution to 2A, 9,600 spots had to be included in the calculation. To increase the resolution to an ultimate 1·4A, over 25,000 reflections were utilised. The task would have been impossible without the use of a high-speed computer. In order to calculate the 2A synthesis, 5×10^9 figures had to be added and subtracted.[2]

At a resolution of 2A it is still impossible to pick out individual atoms, but it is possible to make out the general run of the polypeptide chain and the shape of the majority of the side chains (Plate II(e)).

To the uninstructed eye it would seem impossible to recognise individual side chains in the tangle of density contours shown in Plate II(e). The expert, however, is able to recognise the signatures of many different amino-acids in these contours.[3] Indeed, by carefully

---

[1] This follows from the fact that the X-ray diffraction 'picture' is in reality a sphere. Plate I(d) is merely one plane through this sphere.

[2] Perutz, M. F., *loc. cit.*, p. 662.

[3] Perutz, M. F., *Proteins and Nucleic Acids*, Elsevier, Amsterdam, London and New York, 1963, p. 25.

e II Electron density diagrams of some proteins.

(a) and (b) are electron density contours of an alpha-helix seen end-on. In (a) the resolution is 2A, in (b) 1·5A. It is clear that the higher the resolution the more precise is the location of the atoms.

(c) part of a 1·4A map of myoglobin. In this map the haem group can be seen edge-on in the centre of the plate. Several amino-acid residues may be recognised by the practised eye.

(d) a representation in three dimensions of the electron density in the myoglobin molecule at a resolution of 6A. It can be seen that the model consists of a series of plates fixed one above the other. On each plate lines are drawn representing the electron density of the molecule at that level. Putting them all together gives an indication of the three-dimensional electron density of the molecule. Close inspection shows that a high-density 'vapour trail' winds through the model. This 'vapour trail' represents the position of the polypeptide chain.

(e) three-dimensional representation of myoglobin at a resolution of 2A. The haem group may be observed edge-on.

(a), (b), (c) and (e) *courtesy of J. C. Kendrew:* Nobel Lectures: Chemistry (1942–1962), *Elsevier Publishing Company, 1964;* (d) *courtesy of J. C. Kendrew (1959),* Reviews of Modern Physics, 31, *94.*

exploring their 2A electron density maps, Kendrew and his colleagues were able to identify 78 out of the 151 amino-acid residues. While this work was proceeding, Edmundson and Hirs undertook the analysis of the amino-acid sequence by the chemical techniques described in Chapter 4. This work both confirmed the sequence determined by the X-ray method and ultimately completely resolved the 151 residue primary sequence.

The results of the combined chemical and physical approaches are embodied in the model shown in Plate III(a). Myoglobin is revealed as a roughly triangular prism with dimensions of about 25A×35A×45A. About 118 of the total 151 amino-acid residues are twisted into an α-helical configuration. Practically all the polar amino-acid residues are disposed on the surface of the molecule, while the non-polar residues are tucked away inside. The repulsion between hydrophobic residues and the aqueous environment and, vice versa, the van der Waals attractions between hydrophobic side chains in the interior of the molecule are probably the main forces holding the molecule in its complex configuration. Also of importance in this context is the haem group. In Chapter 10 it will be seen that this group has a non-polar end and a polar end. The haem group fits into an 'oily' crevice in the myoglobin molecule by its non-polar end. In addition to its physiological significance it is also of importance in stabilising the whole molecule.

The above account of the analysis of myoglobin gives some impression of the labour involved in determining the tertiary structure of even a small protein. It is not difficult to sympathise with Kendrew when he writes that he 'would not care to have to undertake such a task a second time'.[1]

7

It has already begun to emerge in this book that the problem of what forces cause a particular amino-acid chain to assume a particular configuration is a problem of central importance in molecular biology. The physico-chemical situation is very complex. A large number of 'weak' chemical forces is probably involved. The task of assessing the relative importance of these multifarious repulsions and attractions is formidable.

[1] Kendrew, J. C., *Nobel Lectures: Chemistry 1942–1962*, Elsevier, Amsterdam London and New York, 1964, p. 681.

THE STRUCTURE OF GLOBULAR PROTEINS

One avenue of approach to the problem lies in the study of proteins possessing a similar three-dimensional structure but a dissimilar primary structure. We have already mentioned this approach when we discussed the heterogeneity of primary structure among the cytochromes c (Chapter 4). This line of attack may allow us to sort out which parts of a primary structure are essential to a particular three-dimensional conformation and which parts have little influence.

In 1960 the long-continued work of Perutz on the three-dimensional structure of haemoglobin finally bore fruit. The structure revealed proved even more interesting than expected. For it transpired that each of the four subunits of which haemoglobin is composed bears a remarkable structural resemblance to a single myoglobin molecule. Yet the primary structures of the haemoglobin subunits vary markedly from the primary structure of myoglobin.[1]

8

Haemoglobin is a molecule approximately four times the size of myoglobin. It consists of four polypeptide chains and has a molecular weight of about 67,000. The molecule has, of course, great physiological importance, for it is responsible for the carriage of oxygen from the lungs to the tissues. In vertebrate animals it is confined to red blood cells, but in several types of invertebrate it is to be found freely suspended in the plasma.

Because of its great physiological and medical importance, and because of the ease with which large quantities can be obtained from slaughter-houses, haemoglobin has been much studied by chemists. Haemoglobins from a number of species throughout the animal kingdom have been examined and in each case the molecule has been shown to consist of a protein—globin—attached to a porphyrin group—haem. The haem is identical to that found in myoglobin and in cytochrome c. The globin, however, varies considerably in physicochemical character and amino-acid constitution from one animal species to the next. Indeed, different globins have been identified in the blood of single individuals.

With the exception of the lamprey[2]—a primitive Agnathan fish—all the globins so far examined have been shown to consist

[1] See discussion at the end of this chapter.
[2] The globin of the lamprey, a representative of the most primitive vertebrate group, consists of a single polypeptide chain.

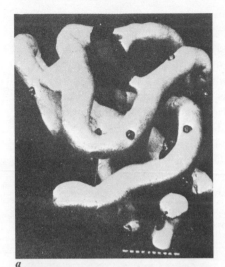

a

b

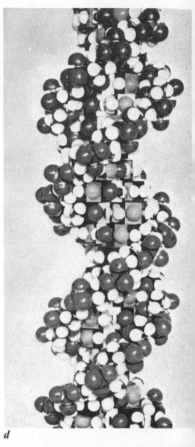

d

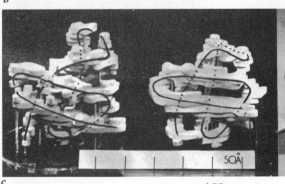

50Å

c

of four polypeptide chains. The primary sequences of a small number of these polypeptide chains have now been determined, and with the advent of sophisticated automatic amino-acid analysers the number of complete analyses should quickly grow. These investigations are of considerable interest, not only because of the light they can and do throw on the relation of primary to higher structure but also because of their implications for molecular genetics and the evolutionary relationships of vertebrates. We shall return to these topics later in this chapter.

To begin with, however, let us concentrate our attention on the three-dimensional structure which emerged from the crystallography of Perutz and his co-workers. The general procedure adopted was, of course identical with that adopted for myoglobin. A number of heavy atom derivatives were prepared, and their diffraction patterns compared with each other and with the parent compound. An electron density distribution model was calculated, first of all, at a resolution of 5·5A.

This initial 5·5A resolution was sufficient to show the main run of the polypeptide chain. In order to construct a model showing the form of the molecule, the electron density was first calculated along sixteen parallel sections through the model. These sections were taken at intervals of 2A. The density contours thus obtained were inscribed on to sixteen sheets of thermosetting plastic. Next a convenient contour line was selected—in fact, the line corresponding to a density of 0·54 electron A³—and the plastic cut off along this line. The sixteen plastic shapes were then assembled in their correct order and the whole model baked to set it permanently. The result is shown in Plate III(b).

III Some molecular models.

(a) model of a myoglobin molecule. The model shows the run of the polypeptide chain. The black disc represents the haem group. The scale is in Angstrom units.

(b) model of a haemoglobin molecule. The haem groups are represented by grey discs. It can be seen that they are set into 'pockets' in the sides of the molecule.

(c) comparison between the total myoglobin molecule and the alpha- and beta-subunits of haemoglobin. The model on the left is of myoglobin, and the models on the right are of the alpha- and beta-chains of haemoglobin.

(d) model of a DNA molecule. The double helical structure is well shown.

(a) *courtesy of J. C. Kendrew (1959)*, Reviews of Modern Physics, 31, *94;* (b) *and* (c) *courtesy of M. F. Perutz (1961)*, Nature, 185, *416;* (d) *courtesy of Griffin & George, Ltd.*

The molecule (Plate III(b)) is spheroidal in shape, the dimensions being approximately 64A × 55A × 50A. Four separate trails of high electron density wind their way through the molecule. These correspond to the four polypeptide chains identified chemically. Plate III(b) shows that two of these chains have been coloured black and two white. The two black chains are identical, as are the two white chains. Although the pair of black chains bears some resemblance to the pair of white chains, there are considerable differences. Biochemists had previously named the two pairs of polypeptide chains the α- and β-chains. It turns out that the two white chains of Perutz's model correspond to the biochemists' α-chains.

Plate III(c) compares the α- and β-chains of haemoglobin with the single chain of the myoglobin molecule. The strong resemblance is unmistakable. In assembling the haemoglobin molecule the two α-chains (white) are inverted and placed on top of the two β-chains (black). Extensive van der Waals contacts are made between the α- and β-chains.

In Plate III(b) the haem groups are represented by grey discs. The points of attachment of oxygen molecules are labelled. It can be seen that each haem is inserted into a deep cleft in the α- or β-polypeptide chain. This arrangement is highly reminiscent of the situation in myoglobin. Also reminiscent of myoglobin is the manner in which the hydrophobic amino-acid residues are tucked away inside the molecule. Projecting from the surface of the globular molecule are the polar or hydrophilic amino-acid side chains. Globular proteins can thus, with some justice, be regarded as oily droplets solubilised in their aqueous surroundings by a coat of polar amino-acid residues.

9

The physiological importance of haemoglobin has already been mentioned. The molecule has many properties which admirably fit it for its job of transporting oxygen from the lungs (or gills) to the tissues. Not the least important of these properties are its oxygen dissociation curve and the sensitivity of this curve to the concentration of CO_2 in the immediate vicinity (fig. 6.4). Presumably these characteristics of the molecule have their basis in its particular structure.

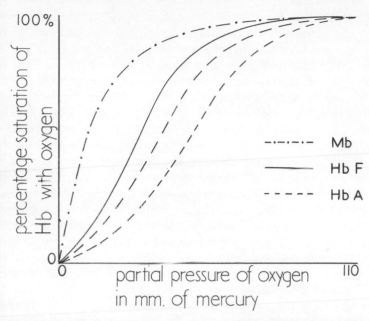

Fig. 6.4 Oxygen dissociation curves of HbA, HbF and Mb. The position of the HbA curve is affected by the quantity of CO_2 in the blood. As this quantity increases the curve shifts to the right as shown in the figure. The sigmoid shape of the haemoglobin curves is believed to be due to a subtle alteration in the protein's three-dimensional structure when oxygen is taken up or liberated. See text.

Fig. 6.4 shows the dissociation curves of both haemoglobin (Hb) and myoglobin (Mb). It will be noticed that whereas haemoglobin's dissociation curve is sigmoid, that of myoglobin resembles a simple hyperbola. The physiological significance of these two curves does not need emphasising. The steepest part of haemoglobin's sigmoid curve lies in the physiologically important region. In other words, the haemoglobin molecule rapidly unloads its oxygen as the concentration of oxygen in its environment decreases, and the most rapid unloading occurs when the environmental oxygen concentration is approximately equal to that usually found in the tissues. The figure also shows that the position of the curve is sensitive to the quantity of CO_2 in the environment. The greater the quantity of CO_2 the more readily haemoglobin unloads its oxygen. The physiological significance of this character is also obvious.

If the four haem groups of the haemoglobin molecule are assumed

161

to interact, then the sigmoid dissociation curve can be explained in physico-chemical terms. The crystallographic data, however, show that the four haem groups occupy widely separated sites on the molecule (Plate III(b)). The question which immediately poses itself is: how can such distant chemical groupings influence each other?

The answer to this question is not yet fully known. However, some very interesting work by Perutz[1] and others indicates that the haemoglobin molecule undergoes a configurational change when it is oxygenated or deoxygenated. It appears that when the molecule is oxygenated the distance between the iron atoms in the centres of the haem groups of the β-chains decreases by 6·5A. At the same time the distance between the iron atoms within the haems of the β-chains increases by 1A. This structural alteration changes the molecule's affinity for oxygen. It is believed, therefore, that when one of the haem groups takes up a molecule of oxygen a configurational change occurs in the polypeptide chain with which it is associated, leading to a change in the oxygen affinity of the other three haems. In short, the sigmoid dissociation curve of haemoglobin is a property which emerges from the detailed molecular architecture of the protein. We shall see, in Chapter 8, that the sensitivity of the dissociation curve to CO_2, usually called after its discoverer, the Bohr[2] phenomenon, is also a property of haemoglobin's higher structure.

The demonstration that a small molecule—oxygen—can alter the three-dimensional structure of a protein is of considerable general interest. In Chapter 7 we shall see that a major focus of interest in present-day molecular biology is the means by which the activity of enzymes may be controlled. Such control is obviously necessary if the highly organised economy of the cell is not to suffer from the stops and goes which are so common in the unmanaged economies of nation states. In Chapter 7 we shall see that there is evidence that the activities of some enzymes are controlled by smallish molecules called allosteric effectors. Allosteric effectors are believed to alter the conformation of an enzyme molecule so that it is no longer able to carry out a specific function. So far haemoglobin is the only molecule where such a conformational change consequent upon the binding of a small molecule has actually been shown to occur.

[1] Perutz, M. F. (1967), *Endeavour*, *26*, 3.
[2] It is interesting in the context of this book to note that Niels Bohr (Chapter 2) is the son of the eponymous discoverer of the Bohr phenomenon.

We have already mentioned that the primary structure of the globin moiety of haemoglobin varies considerably from one animal species to another. The closeness of two animals in the evolutionary tree is to some extent reflected by the similarity in the amino-acid sequences of their haemoglobins.[1] However, not only do globins vary from one animal species to another but they also vary between individuals belonging to the same species.

When we examine haemoglobins from a range of vertebrates we are sampling a time-scale of many hundred million years. It is not surprising that randomisation of amino-acids along the polypeptide chain should have occurred if their presence is not essential to the structure and/or function of the molecule. When we study the haemoglobin of individuals of a large population we are sampling along another dimension. Instead of looking at the variation which has arisen over thousands of millions of generations we are sampling thousands of millions of individuals. Again, if amino-acid substitutions can occur they would be expected to occur somewhere in a vast population.

A population of these dimensions is, of course, nowadays provided by *Homo sapiens*. Amino-acid substitutions in human haemoglobins will not, however, normally come to light unless the individual is in some way affected by them. Hence most of the abnormal human haemoglobins known are pathological.

The first abnormal haemoglobin to be analysed at the molecular level was haemoglobin-S or, more shortly, HbS. This haemoglobin is responsible for the condition known as sickle cell anaemia. That HbS differed chemically from normal Hb was initially demonstrated by Pauling in 1949.

HbS is common among the inhabitants of West Africa. It is inherited in a Mendelian fashion (Chapter 13). Individuals homozygous for HbS do not normally survive childhood; adults possessing HbS are thus heterozygous for this character and are said to exhibit sickle cell trait.[2]

The condition received the name 'sickle cell anaemia' or 'sickle cell trait' because the red blood cells of individuals suffering from it

[1] Zuckerkandl, E. and Pauling, L., in *Evolving Genes and Proteins*, Academic Press, New York and London, 1965, p. 145.
[2] If the genetical phraseology used in this paragraph is unfamiliar the reader will find it explained in Chapter 13.

tend to collapse into sickle-like shapes. The red blood cells of individuals suffering from sickle cell trait do not show this collapse except when deprived of oxygen. This deprivation can and does occur when a sample of the blood is placed on a slide beneath a cover glass to be examined microscopically.

The fact that the homozygous condition results in early mortality would seem to put the gene specifying HbS under a considerable selective disadvantage. Over many thousands of generations one would expect, other things being equal, such a lethal gene to be selected out of the population. However, it seems that other things are *not* quite equal. It seems that individuals suffering from sickle cell trait possess some degree of resistance to malaria. It will be remembered that the malarial parasite—*Plasmodium*—parasitises red blood cells. A change in the nature of the contents of the red blood cells may well make them uncongenial to *Plasmodium*. Whatever the explanation of the resistance, the fact that it exists explains the persistence of genes specifying HbS; and, in particular, their persistence in areas of the world where malaria is endemic.

The suggestion that sickle cell anaemia was a molecular disease was first made, as already mentioned, by Pauling in 1949. It was not however, until 1957 that its exact nature was established. Ingram was then able to show that the glutamic acid at position 6 on both β-chains was replaced by valine. The shorthand which has been adopted to describe abnormal haemoglobins symbolises this substitution by $glu_6^\beta \rightarrow val$.

Why the substitution of valine for glutamic acid should produce so catastrophic a change in the physico-chemical properties of red blood cells is not yet known. With certain other pathological haemoglobins the physico-chemical reasons for the abnormality are clearer. This is particularly the case with the haemoglobins M. The blood of individuals possessing haemoglobin M does not easily take up oxygen. In consequence sufferers from this disease exhibit a condition known as cyanosis, the most obvious symptom of which is excessive blueness of the skin.

It has been found that haemoglobins M result from at least three different substitutions. Using the symbolism introduced in the paragraph above, the molecular alterations responsible for these haemoglobins may be written:

$$his_{58}^\alpha \rightarrow tyr; \; his_{63}^\beta \rightarrow tyr; \; val_{67}^\beta \rightarrow glu.$$

It is interesting to find that all these substitutions are of residues in close proximity to the haem group. It is thought that the phenolic or carboxylic acid groups of the substituents (see Table 4.1) are in a good position to interfere with the oxygen-combining ability of the central iron atom. Hence we can discern a molecular reason for the sufferer's symptoms.

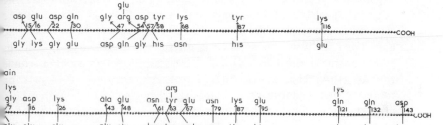

Fig. 6.5 Abnormal haemoglobins A. Each amino-acid in the chain is represented by a spot. Where an alteration is known to have occurred the normal amino-acid is shown below the chain and the abnormal above it. In some cases, as the figure shows, more than one alteration has occurred.

Quite a number of other abnormal haemoglobins have been analysed. In some cases the same amino-acid residue has been substituted more than once. These findings are schematised in fig. 6.5. As is implied in this figure, substitutions always occur in *both* α-chains, or *both* β-chains. There are no known cases of a substitution in one α-chain, or one β-chain, and not the other.

11

It was mentioned earlier in this chapter that although the α- and β-chains of haemoglobin are reasonably alike in their tertiary structure, their primary structure is rather dissimilar. The α-chain consists of 141 amino-acid residues and the β-chain consists of 146. If the two chains are aligned with each other so that a maximal correspondence between their amino-acid sequences is obtained, it is found that only 65 of the 141 amino-acids are in identical positions in each chain. The amino-acids occupying the other 76 sites do not correspond with each other.

The haemoglobin we have been considering so far in this chapter is known as haemoglobin-A. The various abnormal haemoglobins discussed in the previous section are all modifications of this type of haemoglobin. It has been found, however, that other haemoglobins are present in the blood of normal individuals. In the early foetus a haemoglobin is synthesised in which the β-chains are replaced by other chains known as ε-chains. Long before birth the ε-chains are themselves replaced by γ-chains and these persist throughout embryological life, and are only replaced by β-chains after parturition. Foetal haemoglobin (HbF), therefore, consists of two α-chains associated with two γ-chains. It is interesting to note (fig. 6.4) that foetal haemoglobin has a different oxygen dissociation curve from that of HbA. This enables it to absorb oxygen evolved from the maternal haemoglobin—an ability which is clearly of considerable importance to the foetus. Finally a small fraction of adult haemoglobin is, again, found to differ from the $\alpha_2\beta_2$ type we have described. Once again the β-chains are replaced by a different polypeptide. These substitute chains are called δ-chains. This type of haemoglobin —$\alpha_2\delta_2$—is called HbA$_2$.

Thus the β-chains of haemoglobin may be replaced by at least three different polypeptides—ε, γ and δ. All these chains resemble the β-chain in being 146 units long.

The amino-acid sequences of the four chains are slightly different. Thus the γ-chain differs from the β-chain by 37 amino-acid residues; the δ-chain differs from the β-chain by 10. The amino-acid sequence of the ε-chain is not yet known. Now in Chapter 4 it was suggested that the distance apart of two organisms in the evolutionary tree was reflected in the degree of similarity of the amino-acid sequences of their cytochromes. A somewhat similar assumption has been proposed[1] for these different types of haemoglobin. Here, however, the molecular evolution is regarded as having occurred during the evolutionary development of a single organism.

Thus the story starts by suggesting that the archetypal haemoglobin was a considerably simpler molecule than the one we know today. It is suggested, in fact, that instead of consisting of four subunits it consisted of only one. It is thus interesting to find that the haemoglobin of the most primitive surviving vertebrate—the lamprey —does indeed consist of just one myoglobin-like unit. The theory next suggests that gene duplication occurred. One of the products of this duplication governed the production of a protein which has

[1] Ingram, V. M. (1961), *Nature*, *189*, 704.

developed into myoglobin, and the other controlled the synthesis of the α-chains of haemoglobin. We may imagine that this second gene developed in such a way that eventually the α-chains became capable of dimerisation. The formation of dimers, if it allows a haem-haem interaction to occur, will greatly improve the physiological characteristics of the molecule. Hence this evolutionary step is unlikely to be lost.

The next part of the story suggests that duplication of the α-chain gene occurred once again. One of the duplicates would continue to produce α-chains and, because of the complementary surfaces required for dimerisation, would be incapable of much further mutation. This restriction does not apply to the other duplicate, however, and this, it is suggested, evolved further until it produced a second dimer capable of interacting with the α-chains to form the familiar quadruple structure. This second dimer is regarded as consisting of archetypal γ-chains.

Once again, duplication is postulated: this time, that of the γ-chain gene. One duplicate continues to control the production of γ-chains; the other initiates, after suitable evolutionary development, the production of β-chains.

Finally, the most recent duplication of all has been the division of the β-chain gene. One of the results of this division continues to programme the manufacture of β-chains, the other is responsible for the production of δ-chains.

Now in Chapter 14 it will be shown that the amino-acids in an organism's proteins are determined by certain sequences of nucleotides in its DNA. In fact each amino-acid is believed to be specified by one or more nucleotide triplets (Table 14.1). Evidence will be presented in Chapter 14 to show that the molecular basis of many mutations is an alteration of one or more of the nucleotides in a triplet. This has the effect of transforming a triplet specifying one amino-acid into a triplet specifying another. Clearly it is not difficult to calculate the minimum number of alterations necessary to convert a triplet coding for one amino-acid into a triplet coding for another. This number has been called the *mutation value* of the change. If the mutation values of all the dissimilar amino-acids in two homologous proteins are added together the result is said to define the *mutation distance*[1] between the two proteins.

These calculations have been made use of in fig. 6.6 where the

[1] Fitch, W. M. and Margoliash, E. (1967), *Science*, *155*, 279.

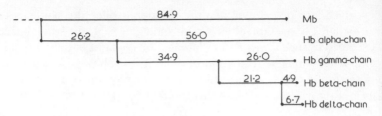

Fig. 6.6 Putative evolution of the haemoglobin molecule. The major events are believed to have been gene duplications (see text). These are represented by branch points in the figure. The numbers appended to the diagram are mutation distances (see text). After Ingram (1961) and Fitch and Margoliash (1967).

probable evolutionary relationships of the various subunits of the haemoglobin molecule are schematised. The figures on the legs of the diagram indicate the mutation distances between the different polypeptides.

If, and when, a mutation *rate* is established for the genes controlling the synthesis of haemoglobin, and if it is assumed that this rate has remained constant over the great stretches of evolutionary time, then it will be possible to assign dates to the various stages depicted in fig. 6.6.

It will have been noticed that not only does fig. 6.6 show the probable evolutionary relationships between the different constituents of human haemoglobin-A, but it also shows their relation to myoglobin. It was mentioned earlier in this chapter that the subunits of haemoglobin show remarkable similarities in tertiary structure to the single myoglobin molecule. It was also pointed out that the primary structure of myoglobin is very different from that of either the α- or β-chains of haemoglobin. Whale myoglobin consists of 153 amino-acids and the best alignment possible gives only 37 sites in which the resident amino-acid corresponds to that present in the haemoglobin α- or β-chain.

It is necessary to end this brief account of the evolution of a protein by emphasising that it is still both tentative and speculative. In the course of time, when the primary structures of many more proteins become known, it will be possible to arrive at firmer conclusions. These conclusions should carry with them insights both into the evolutionary history of living organisms and into the physiological and biochemical mechanisms of that evolution.

7

Enzymes

1

That function emerges from structure has more than once been emphasised in this book. Probably by far the most important function of globular proteins is their function as enzymes. In this chapter it is proposed to consider just what it is about globular proteins which fits them for this function.

Enzymes are of quite central importance to those processes which we are accustomed to call 'living'. It is nowadays a truism to say that a living organism is a vortex of chemical activity. None of the myriad chemical reactions transgresses the laws of thermodynamics. Yet few of them proceed in the absence of appropriate enzymes and still less will they proceed in an organised harmonious fashion.

First of all, then, we have to ask: how does an enzyme set about accomplishing its vital task?

2

Straight away it must be admitted that *au fond* we still do not have the answer to this question. There are, however, many pointers, many hints, many suggestive facts.

An enzyme, as was pointed out above, merely helps a chemical reaction to occur: it oils the machinery. The direction of chemical change is governed solely by the laws of thermodynamics. A chemical system consisting of two species, A and B, and their compound, AB, will change in such a way that energy is minimised and entropy maximised. All that an enzyme does (like any other catalyst) is to alter the rate at which the system attains its equilibrium state.

Let us become more specific. Let us symbolise our reaction system:

$$A + B \rightleftharpoons AB \qquad \ldots \ldots (1)$$

169

In the above system the reaction will occur towards the right if the product, AB, possesses less energy than the reactants A and B. This, it will be remembered, was the case in our example in Chapter 3 where the reactants were hydrogen atoms and the product the hydrogen molecule (p. 71).

The energy difference between reactants and products is usually symbolised as ΔG. Other things being equal, the greater ΔG the more completely A and B react to form AB. In other words, the more complete is the reaction.

However, other things are not always equal. Certain snags may prevent the reaction occurring. A crude example would be the case where the reactants A and B are physically separated from each other by an impermeable membrane. More interesting are the cases where the reactants, though free to mix, are in normal circumstances unreactive.

An important example of this second case is provided by a mixture of hydrogen and oxygen molecules. At normal conditions of temperature and pressure the two molecular species can coexist in the gas phase indefinitely. In certain circumstances, however, the two molecules are able to react together, yielding a small quantity of water and a large quantity of heat, light and noise. An explosive reaction occurs, for example, if a spark is passed through the mixture.

Evidently the reactants—hydrogen and oxygen—possess together considerably more energy than the product—water. The energy difference escapes in the form of the explosion when the reaction occurs. But what prevents the reaction occurring in normal circumstances? Why is it necessary to trigger it by a spark?

It will be remembered that the hydrogen atoms in the hydrogen molecule are held together in a stable system by a covalent bond. A similar bond holds oxygen atoms together in the oxygen molecule. If hydrogen and oxygen atoms are to react together to form water these covalent bonds must first be broken. This is the function of the electric spark. The thermal energy imparted by the spark tears hydrogen from hydrogen and oxygen from oxygen. The separated atoms then fall together to form the lower energy system—H_2O.

These ideas are represented graphically in fig. 7.1. It can be seen from this figure that a mixture of hydrogen and oxygen molecules in normal conditions forms a stable system. If energy is supplied—represented in fig. 7.1 by ΔG^*—then, and only then, can the mole-

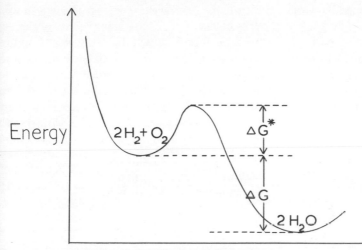

Fig. 7.1 It is necessary to supply energy (ΔG^*) if H_2 and O_2 are to react to form water.

cules react to form a yet more stable system—H_2O. ΔG^* is called the *activation energy* of the system.

Activation energy in our example was supplied in the form of heat. This, in addition to increasing the translational velocity of the reactant molecules, also increases the 'bending' and 'stretching' of the covalent bonds. The links holding the reactant molecules together are effectively loosened. However, heat, such as is provided by an electric spark, would be highly detrimental to the delicate organisation of biological systems. Some other means of providing activation energy must be developed.

Thus we find that living organisms have developed enzymes. The precise mechanism by which an enzyme is able to provide activation energy is not yet fully known. However, although the exact physico-chemical mechanism remains undiscovered, the general principles seem reasonably clear. The most important of these is that the initial step in an enzyme-catalysed reaction involves a close union between enzyme and reactant(s).

Biochemists are accustomed to call the reactant(s) the 'substrate' of the enzyme. Hence the initial complex is called the 'enzyme-substrate complex'. The reality of this union has been proved in several cases by following the course of the reaction with a spectrophotometer.

It is supposed, and this is still speculative, that once the enzyme has

171

combined with its substrate the latter's electronic structure is in some way affected. Perhaps the covalent bonds are subjected to mechanica strain; perhaps electrostatic forces caused by strategically located groups in the enzyme molecule redistribute the electron cloud in the substrate molecule. In one way or another the substrate is subjected to stress, so that it may be said to be activated. In this state the probability of a reaction occurring is, as we saw, greatly increased. If and when a reaction occurs the products escape, or are released, from the complex. These ideas may be symbolised in the following expressions

$$
\begin{array}{c}
\text{Enzyme} \\
+ \\
\text{Substrate}
\end{array}
\rightleftharpoons
\begin{array}{c}
\text{Enzyme-Substrate} \\
\text{complex}
\end{array}
\begin{array}{c}
\text{Enzyme} \\
\text{activated} \\
\rightleftharpoons \text{substrate} \rightleftharpoons \\
\text{complex}
\end{array}
\begin{array}{c}
\text{Products} \\
+ \\
\text{Enzyme}
\end{array}
$$

$$E+S \;\rightleftharpoons\; ES \;\rightleftharpoons\; ES^* \;\rightleftharpoons\; E+P$$

Thus we have answered, in very general terms, the question we se out with. We have seen, in outline, how an enzyme affects the rate o a chemical reaction.

We must now go further. We stated at the beginning of this chapte that enzymes were a sub-class of the class of globular proteins. Wha is it that makes globular proteins particularly suitable to act a enzymes?

3

The answer to this question lies in the fact that their structure parti cularly fits them for the functions outlined in the previous section These functions are, at root, two; the formation of an enzyme-sub strate complex, and the easy release of the products once a reactio has taken place.

The formation of an enzyme-substrate complex implies a clos union between enzyme and substrate surface. There is, moreover much evidence to suggest that this union is very specific. In genera an enzyme catalyses only one, or at the most a few closely similar reaction(s).

Good examples of enzyme specificity are to be found among the proteolytic enzymes we mentioned in Chapter 4. It will be remem bered, for instance, that carboxypeptidase only attacks peptide bond adjacent to a free α-carboxylic acid group, while trypsin affects only those contributed by lysine or arginine residues. Perhaps even mor remarkable is the finding that several enzymes are able to catalys reactions between naturally occurring amino-acids but are incapable of affecting their mirror-images.[1]

Another line of evidence which supports the idea of a close complementarity between enzyme and substrate surfaces comes from studies on inhibitors. Certain types of enzyme inhibitors are called competitive inhibitors. Competitive inhibitors are believed to compete with the substrate for the enzyme's attentions. While the enzyme is occupied by the competitor the genuine substrate will be neglected, and the reaction rate will be much slowed down, or altogether cease, in consequence.

Now it is found that molecules acting as competitive inhibitors all bear a marked structural resemblance to the genuine substrate. A well-known example is the inhibition of the enzyme succinic-dehydrogenase by malonic acid. Succinic-dehydrogenase normally catalyses the conversion of succinic acid to fumaric acid:

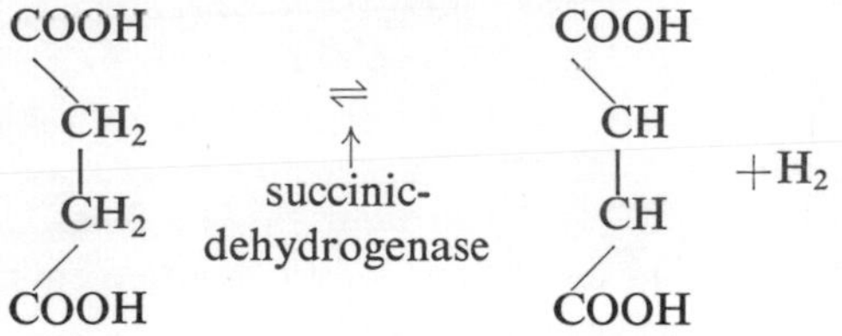

$$\begin{array}{ccc}
\text{COOH} & & \text{COOH} \\
\diagdown & & \diagdown \\
\text{CH}_2 & \rightleftharpoons & \text{CH} \\
| & \uparrow & | \\
\text{CH}_2 & \text{succinic-} & \text{CH} \quad +\text{H}_2 \\
\diagup & \text{dehydrogenase} & \diagup \\
\text{COOH} & & \text{COOH} \\
\text{succinic} & & \text{fumaric} \\
\text{acid} & & \text{acid}
\end{array}$$

Fig. 7.2 The enzymic activity of succinic-dehydrogenase.

In the presence of malonic acid this reaction is inhibited. If we examine the structure of malonic acid we find it to be remarkably similar to succinic acid:

$$\begin{array}{c}
\text{COOH} \\
\diagdown \\
\text{CH}_2 \\
\diagup \\
\text{COOH}
\end{array}$$

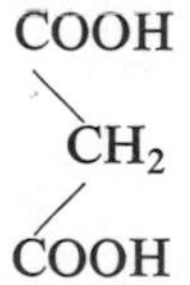

malonic acid

Malonic acid is obviously structurally similar to succinic acid but,

[1] Natural amino-acids are all structurally related to *l*-glyceraldehyde which rotates the plane of polarised light in a left-hand sense. These amino-acids are called *l*-amino-acids. *D*-amino-acids are related to *d*-glyceraldehyde which rotates the plane of polarised light to the right. It follows that *d*-amino-acids are the mirror-images of the corresponding *l*-amino-acids.

at the same time, sufficiently dissimilar to make it impossible for the enzyme to carry out its usual dehydrogenation.

If appreciable quantities of malonic acid are present, succinic-dehydrogenase will be occupied for a considerable proportion of its time in the hopeless task of attempting to dehydrogenate it. The time left over for its proper business of dehydrogenating succinic acid is correspondingly reduced. The enzyme appears to be inhibited.

The important point has already been emphasised. It is that the structure of competitive inhibitors is invariably closely similar to that of the substrate molecule. The enzyme appears to 'mistake' the inhibitor for its accustomed substrate.

'Mistake' is, of course, an anthropomorphism. It is convenient shorthand for the physico-chemical reality. This is that a population of enzyme, substrate and inhibitor molecules coexists in the confined space of a cell or a test-tube. Thermal movements will bring all three together in varying and transient combinations.

Enzyme, however, will not stick to enzyme, nor substrate to substrate. On the other hand, enzyme *will* stick to substrate, and enzyme will also stick to inhibitor. The reason for this is, as we have hinted, that enzyme, substrate and inhibitor possess complementary surfaces. This is shown diagrammatically in fig. 7.3.

Bearing in mind that enzymes are proteins while substrates are

Fig. 7.3 The active site of an enzyme is a small region of its surface precisely fashioned to fit a particular substrate (S).

usually smaller molecules, we are led to the conclusion that the complementary surface is only a small region of the enzyme's total surface (stippled in fig. 7.3). This small region is said to constitute the enzyme's *active site*.

We are now able to see one reason why all known enzymes are proteins. Proteins are unique among molecules in their structural complexity. It is difficult to think of any other type of molecule with the same potentiality for forming specific matching surfaces for the multitude of metabolic molecules.

Because the active site is confined to a small area of the enzyme's surface it does not follow that it is restricted to a few consecutive amino-acids in the primary sequence. Because of the intricate and tortuous twisting of the polypeptide chain, amino-acids widely separated in the primary sequence may be brought into proximity to form the special chemical environment of this region. Nor does it follow that the rest of the protein outside the active site has no biological function. Various functions, as we shall see later, have been assigned to it.

We have briefly rehearsed the evidence for the existence of a template-like active site on the surface of an enzyme molecule. We have, however, not yet made clear what we mean by 'sticky'. This concept may be translated into chemical terms by suggesting that it is the outcome of all the weak short-range forces discussed in Chapter 3. In this context it is probable that hydrogen bonds and van der Waals forces are the most important. If these forces are to be influential they must be numerous and there must be close contact between enzyme and substrate. Hence we see, once more, the necessity for a very accurate fit between active site and substrate.

A further consequence of enzyme and substrate being held together by weak forces is that the products of reaction are easily able to escape. If covalent bonds unified the enzyme-substrate complex the latter would not have so transient an existence. The enzyme could not rapidly become freed of the products of the reaction and hence its ability to act on fresh substrate molecules would be hindered.

In sum, we see that the active site must be closely tailored to fit a particular substrate and that the substrate is held in position, transiently, by the influence of a large number of accurately sited weak forces. It is not difficult to see that globular proteins are ideally suited to meet these specifications. Indeed, it is difficult to imagine any other type of molecule quite so suitable.

The reader will have noticed that the evidence for the existence of an active site, though very strong, is indirect. It is clear that an understanding of the precise structure of this region would be of considerable interest to the molecular biologist. He might then be able to explain the exact way in which an enzyme works.

4

The successful completion of the first X-ray analyses of enzymes has thus been of the very greatest interest.

So far the structures of only two enzymes have been elucidated. Lysozyme was solved to a resolution of 2A in 1965, and this was followed, in 1967, by the solution, at a similar resolution, of ribonuclease.[1]

Ribonuclease turns out to be a kidney-shaped molecule having the dimensions $38A \times 28A \times 22A$. The polypeptide chain assumes a complex configuration which results in the molecule having a deep depression in the middle of one side. The active site is believed to be on the edge of this depression, and is constituted of residues from many different parts of the primary sequence. Referring back to fig. 4.13 it is believed that the residues forming the active site are 6,7,8; 11,12; 41,42; 46,47,48; 117,118,119,120.

The X-ray analysis of ribonuclease is still being continued by groups of workers in both the UK and the USA. The structure of lysozyme, solved in 1965, is at present considerably better established. Hence the structure of this enzyme will be considered in some detail in the next section.

5

Lysozyme was discovered by Alexander Fleming in 1922. The discovery was made in essentially the same way as his much better known discovery of penicillin. Fleming placed a drop of nasal mucus on a dish containing some microbes and a few days later noticed that the microbes nearest the mucus had been liquidated. This phenomenon was attributed to an enzyme present in the nasal

[1] Kartha, G., Bello, J. and Harker, D. (1967), *Nature*, *213*, 862.

secretion and Fleming proposed the name *lysozyme*. Later a similar activity, and hence a similar enzyme, was shown to be present in many animal secretions—tears, saliva, milk, etc. It is also present, in high concentration, in the whites of hens' eggs. It is from this source that the lysozyme used for X-ray analysis has been crystallised.

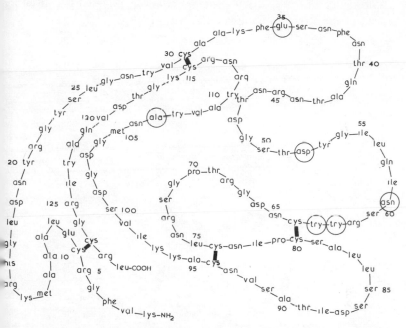

Fig. 7.4 Primary structure of lysozyme. The black rectangles represent disulphide linkages. The circled residues are believed to play an important role in the active site of the enzyme.

Lysozyme is a protein with a molecular weight of about 14,600. Its primary structure was determined in 1963[1] and shown to consist of a single polypeptide chain of 129 amino-acid residues (fig. 7.4). It is interesting to compare this primary sequence with the 124–residue sequence of bovine ribonuclease (fig. 4.13). In both cases the protein consists of a single polypeptide chain and in both cases four intra-chain disulphide linkages are formed.

The X-ray analysis was carried out by a group at the Royal Institution in London, the director of which at that time was Sir Lawrence Bragg. By 1965 the group led by Dr D. C. Phillips, had

---

[1] Caulfield, R. E. (1963), *J. Biol. Chem.*, **238**, 2698.

carried the analysis to a resolution of 2A.[1] This resolution, as we saw in Chapter 6, allows chemical groups to be distinguished. Once again, as in the case of myoglobin and haemoglobin, close investigation of the electron density maps allowed the majority of the amino-acid residues to be identified. This, combined with a knowledge of the primary structure, allowed the position of 95 per cent of the atoms to be located to within 0·3A.

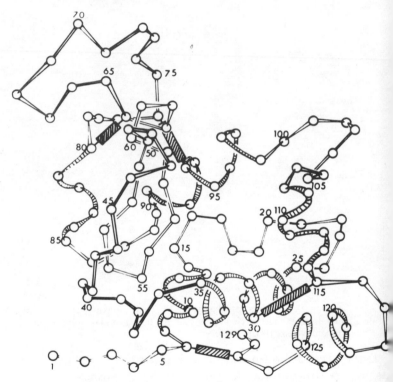

Fig. *7.5* Three-dimensional structure of lysozyme as revealed by X-ray diffraction. See text for further explanation. Courtesy of Sir Lawrence Bragg and Professor D. C. Phillips, and the editors of *Science Progress*.

Fig. 7.5 is a diagram of lysozyme's structure drawn by Sir Lawrence Bragg. The positions of the α-carbon atoms are indicated by circles. To simplify matters the side-groups of the amino-acid residues have been omitted. Every fifth residue has been numbered so that

[1] Blake, C. C. F., Koenig, D. F., Mair, G. A., North, A. C. T., Phillips, D. C. and Sarma, V. R. (1965), *Nature, 206*, 757.

comparison may be made with the chemically-deduced primary structure of fig. 7.4. The disulphide linkages are represented by cross-hatched rectangles.

Fig. 7.5 shows that lysozyme has a compact globular conformation. In contrast with myoglobin and haemoglobin, only very short lengths of the polypeptide chain have an α-helical structure. In this respect it is believed that lysozyme is a more typical globular protein than either of the haem proteins. On the other hand, certain stretches of the chain assume a slightly different helical configuration in which ten instead of thirteen atoms are incorporated into the hydrogen-bonded ring. Also, in a non-helical part of the chain—residues 45 to 60—the sequence is turned back on itself so that the amino-acids run alongside each other. In this region hydrogen-bonding is believed to occur between adjacent sequences to give an anti-parallel pleated sheet type of structure. The parts of the chain not held in position by disulphide linkages or by hydrogen bonds are believed to be moulded by a variety of weaker, non-directional bonds, chief among which are hydrophobic forces.

In spite of the fact that side chains are not represented in fig. 7.5 the complexity is nevertheless so great that it is difficult to appreciate the overall conformation of the molecule. This conformation is better shown by the model prepared at a resolution of 6A (fig. 7.6). This model shows that a deep cleft separates lysozyme into two

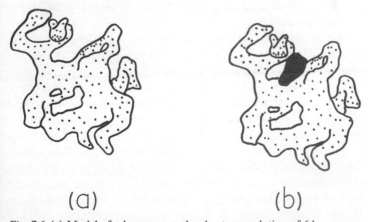

(a)   (b)

Fig. 7.6 (a) Model of a lysozyme molecule at a resolution of 6A.
(b) Model of a similar molecule plus the competitive inhibitor n-acetyl glucosamine. Redrawn from Johnson, L. N. (1966), *Sci. Progr.*, 54, p. 383.

179

'wings'. It is of considerable interest to find that there is good evidence to show that this cleft forms the active site of the enzyme.

First of all let us remember that the action of lysozyme is to dissolve, or lyse, bacteria. The enzyme is able to do this by disrupting certain polysaccharide molecules which commonly occur in bacterial walls. These polysaccharides consist of a regularly repeating sequence of *n*-acetyl glucosamine (NAG) and *n*-acetyl muramic acid (NAM) units. Lysozyme is able to cleave the bond holding NAM to NAG. The polysaccharide consequently disintegrates into dimers consisting of pairs of NAM and NAG units and the bacterial wall soon falls apart. It is clear that a long thread-like polysaccharide might very well fit into lysozyme's cleft and, as a first rough picture, we can see that it might be cleaved at intervals by the chemical forces acting in that groove.

What evidence is there for these ideas? It is clear that to be unambiguously sure of the position of lysozyme's active site it is necessary to mark it in some way so that it reveals itself in the X-ray diffraction pictures. An obvious way to do this would be to react the enzyme with its substrate and to subject the enzyme-substrate complex to X-ray crystallography. Unfortunately, however, the enzyme-substrate complex of lysozyme, as with other enzymes, is so transient that it has so far proved impossible to crystallise it. But there is another approach. It will be remembered from our discussion earlier in this chapter that competitive inhibitors also bind on to the active site. The resulting enzyme-inhibitor complex is, as we saw, much more permanent.

Several competitive inhibitors of lysozyme are known. The first to be used was *n*-acetyl glucosamine. X-ray analysis of the resultant enzyme inhibitor complex showed the inhibitor was indeed located in the cleft between the two 'wings' of the molecule (fig. 7.6(*b*)). The analysis of the complex has not so far been taken beyond the 6A level. Hence details of the interaction between enzyme and inhibitor at the atomic level are not yet available. Nonetheless, this first sighting of an enzyme's active site gives body to the many indirect lines of evidence biochemists have formerly used to support its existence.

The active site of lysozyme like the, as yet more hypothetical, active site of ribonuclease consists of amino-acid residues situated in many different parts of the primary sequence. In particular residues 35, 52, 59, 62, 63 and 107 (see fig. 7.4) seem to be of great importance. Ribonuclease and lysozyme also resemble each other in the fact that in both cases the active site is a groove or cleft in the globular body of the enzyme. In this respect, too, the active site resembles the clefts in which the haem moieties of haem proteins sit. This analogy gains force if we follow Monod's lead and allow haemoglobin and myoglobin the status of honorary enzymes with the haem groups representing their active sites.

Now why should the active sites of all these enzymes be found in depressions in their surfaces? Perutz has put forward an interesting suggestion.[1] It has long been clear that the substrates which enzymes attack can also be disrupted *in vitro* if the physico-chemical conditions are made harsh and 'unphysiological'. The wonder has always been that enzymes are able to tease these same substrates apart, gently, in unextreme conditions. Now it was emphasised in Chapter 6 that the interiors of globular proteins consist almost entirely of non-polar residues. It is also a fact that non-polar media have very low dielectric constants compared with polar solvents such as water. It follows that the electric force developed between two charged particles is very greatly increased.[2] Perutz suggests that when a substrate is drawn into a cleft or groove on the surface of an enzyme molecule it is drawn deeply into this non-polar environment. In consequence strong electrical interactions may be set up between it and polar groups in the walls of the active site. That lysozyme's active site possesses such groups is well established. For example, two strongly polar residues—glu(35) and asp(52)—are disposed opposite each other on each wall of the cleft.

It will be fascinating to see whether future research confirms these first rough insights into enzyme mechanics. Indeed it may not be too speculative to suggest that in the foreseeable future human ingenuity may improve on Nature's trial and error methods and enable the scientist to fashion enzymes to catalyse reactions as desired. In the context of this book, however, it is important, in ending this section, to notice that the properties of an enzyme's active site depend not only on amino-acids widely distributed in the

[1] Perutz, M. F. (1967), *Proc. Roy. Soc. B.*, *167*, 448.

[2] It will be recalled from elementary physics that the dielectric constant (D) is related to the force (F) between two electrostatically charged bodies (q_1 and q_2) by the following formula:

$$F = \frac{q_1 \times q_2}{D \times r^2}$$

where 'r' is the distance between q_1 and q_2. It is clear that if q_1, q_2 and r are held constant then as D decreases F increases.

primary sequence, but also on the particular weave of the enzyme's three-dimensional structure. For this weave, this characteristic twist of the polypeptide chain, ensures that these salient amino-acids are brought to bear on the vital groove. In short, the existence and properties of an active site are dependent on a particular tertiary structure. Destroy this structure and the enzyme inevitably loses its biological function.

6

In the cell enzymes seldom work alone. They are associated with co-factors and organised into systems. Sometimes enzymes and co-factors are believed to be built into solid state assemblies. This, for instance, seems likely in the case of the enzymes catalysing electron transport in mitochondria. In other cases it seems that enzymes and co-factors are freely dissolved in the cytoplasm. This is probably the case with enzymes responsible for general metabolic reactions—for example, the Krebs tricarboxylic acid cycle.

The co-factors which are associated with enzymes and are essential to their activity are of two types. First, it is found that many enzymes are ineffective in the absence of certain metallic ions, for example, K^+, Ca^{2+}, Mg^{2+}. The ions are said to 'activate' the enzyme and are in consequence called 'activators'. Secondly, it is found that many enzymes are unable to exert their influence if certain smallish organic molecules are absent. This second type of co-factor frequently plays an important part in the catalysed reaction. This type of co-factor is called a *co-enzyme*.

One of the most important functions of the co-enzyme is to link enzymes together into systems. Frequently in the cell atoms, like hydrogen, or groups, like phosphate, are transferred from one biochemical substance to another. The way in which this is achieved is shown in fig. 7.7.

$$E_1$$
$$\downarrow$$
$$A\text{-}H_2 + C \rightleftharpoons A + C\text{-}H_2 \qquad \dots\dots (1)$$
$$C\text{-}H_2 + B \rightleftharpoons B\text{-}H_2 + C \qquad \dots\dots (2)$$
$$\uparrow$$
$$E_2$$

Fig. 7.7 The role of a co-enzyme. See text for further explanation.

Fig. 7.7 shows how hydrogen may be transferred from A to B by way of the intermediate C. We have already met, in this chapter, an example of a dehydrogenation reaction. Reference back to fig. 7.2 will remind us that succinic-dehydrogenase is able to remove hydrogen from succinic acid. In fig. 7.2 hydrogen was symbolised as 'free' on the right-hand side of the equation. In fact this seldom happens in the cell. Hydrogen is usually transferred to an intermediate such as C in fig. 7.7.

As the reader will have guessed, co-enzymes play the part of intermediates like C in fig. 7.7. It will be noticed that C is regenerated in reaction (2) and hence can recycle and take up more hydrogen from another AH_2 molecule. It will also be noticed that the transference of hydrogen from A on to C and its further transference from C on to B is enzymically catalysed. Two enzymes are involved— E_1 and E_2. These two enzymes are thus coupled together into a simple multi-enzyme system by the co-enzyme C.

A useful symbolism which emphasised this coupling is shown in fig. 7.8.

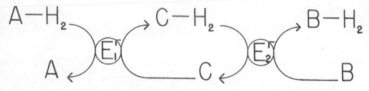

Fig. 7.8 A symbolism for enzyme catalysed reactions.

This symbolism will be made use of in Chapter 10 where the organisation of respiratory co-enzymes is considered.

It is not difficult to see that if additional appropriate co-enzymes and enzymes were present hydrogen could be removed from B and handed on to X, Y and Z. It follows that it is possible for long chains of enzymes and co-enzymes to be organised into an intricate system.

7

We can conclude this chapter by returning it to its beginning. There we saw that in addition to altering the rate at which a biochemical reaction proceeds, enzymes also have an important function in ensuring that the multifarious chemical activities of the cell proceed

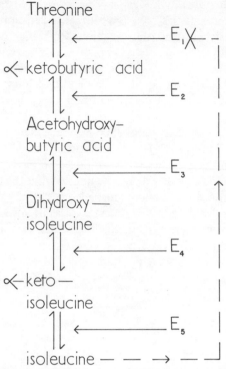

Fig. 7.9 An example of feed-back inhibition. See text for further explanation.

in a harmonious fashion. As we noted in Chapter 6, the cell does not normally suffer from the gluts and shortages which plague industrial economies. The quantities of metabolites present in the cell are normally nicely regulated to its requirements.

In an organism as complicated as a mammal, this regulation is carried out at many different levels: nervous, endocrine, cardiovascular, etc. Restricting ourselves to the molecular level, we still find that regulatory mechanisms exist. Some of these are of a fair degree of complexity and involve DNA and RNA as well as proteins. These mechanisms will be briefly discussed in Chapter 15. Here we will confine ourselves to considering a regulatory mechanism called 'feed-back inhibition'.

This mechanism was first demonstrated in micro-organisms such as the bacterium *Escherichia coli*. It was shown that an essential metabolite—the amino-acid isoleucine—was normally synthesised by a series of steps from threonine. The synthetic pathway is shown in fig. 7.9. It was found that if *E. coli* was placed in a medium containing an excess of isoleucine the bacterium, very sensibly, ceased synthesising the amino-acid for itself. It is clear that this move is of considerable benefit to *E. coli* as its energy can now be channelled into other, in the circumstances more useful, syntheses. But how is the trick worked?

The answer seems to be that an excess of isoleucine inhibits the enzyme which normally catalyses the first step in the transformation of threonine into isoleucine. This is shown by the cross in fig. 7.9. We can thus see the significance of the term 'feed-back inhibition'. We can also appreciate how well the bacterium has solved the problem of regulating the quantity of isoleucine in its cell.

But we must inquire further. How does isoleucine manage to block enzyme 1? Earlier in this chapter we discussed the phenomenon of competitive inhibition. We noticed that competitive inhibitors were always very similar in structure to the genuine substrate molecules. Reference to Table 4.1 will, however, remind us that isoleucine is not very similar to threonine. The inhibition cannot, therefore, be competitive. Isoleucine, in other words, cannot bind on to the active site of enzyme 1 and thus block it for threonine.

Instead the idea of allosteric inhibition has been proposed.[1] It is suggested that, in our example, isoleucine binds to some part of enzyme 1 other than its active site. It is suggested that this attachment alters the three-dimensional configuration of the enzyme so that its active site is no longer active.

It is believed that the allosteric inhibitor binds to a specific site, different from the active site, on the protein. This idea arises from the fact that allosteric inhibition is quite specific. Enzyme 1 is inhibited by isoleucine and no other molecule. Thus we see that the active site of an enzyme may not be the only biologically important region of its surface.

It will have been noticed that in the above account care has been taken to use words like 'suggest', 'propose' and 'idea'. For although the evidence for the existence of allosteric inhibition is reasonably well documented and acceptable to most workers, concrete evidence for configurational changes in protein molecules is, with one important exception, still lacking.

The important exception is, of course, haemoglobin. It will be

[1] Monod, J., Changeux, J. P. and Jacob, F. (1963), *J. Mol. Biol.*, 6, 306.

remembered from Chapter 6 that there is good evidence from X-ray crystallography that the conformation of oxygenated and deoxygenated haemoglobin differs. In other words, the binding of a small molecule like oxygen is sufficient to produce a considerable alteration in the tertiary structure of the globin.

In conclusion, it is fair to say that it is hardly surprising that evidence for configurational change on the binding of an allosteric inhibitor is not more concrete. After all, only four proteins have so far been successfully analysed by X-ray methods. The labour involved in this analysis has already been described; it is no wonder that the labour of studying an allosteric enzyme in its different configurations has not yet been attempted.

8

Protein Assemblies

1

S o far in this book we have considered two levels of organisation: the atomic and the molecular. In particular we have concentrated attention on the functional architecture of protein molecules. In this chapter we ascend to the next level of structure and discuss the assemblage of protein molecules into larger units.

The aggregation of proteins to form more complex structures seems to be an important feature in the architecture of the living body. Assemblies of both globular and of fibrous proteins are of considerable importance. Perhaps of even greater significance are assemblies of protein with other types of molecule. Lipids and proteins, as we shall see in Chapter 9, aggregate together to form the all-important biomembranes. Assemblies of nucleic acids and proteins form the fascinating structures of the viruses. They also form the molecular bases of the ribosomes and of the chromosomes of higher organisms.

In this chapter, however, it is intended to focus on assemblies formed entirely of proteins. Fibrous proteins form many important assemblies which are of both structural (for example, collagen) and functional (for example, actomyosin) significance. Globular proteins also tend to aggregate into assemblies. Klotz[1] has published a Table showing 53 assemblies of globular proteins, many of them of considerable functional importance. All the assemblies listed in Klotz's Table, though not all the assemblies of fibrous proteins, are held together by non-covalent linkages. It follows that a macromolecular assembly is frequently a very fragile thing.

In this chapter it is planned to discuss first the assemblies formed from globular proteins, and then to consider those formed from fibrous elements.

[1] Klotz, I. M. (1967), *Science*, *155*, 697.

2

The larger design which results from the assembly of a number of globular subunits is said to constitute a protein's quaternary structure. There seem to be two main reasons for the assembly of globular proteins into larger units. First, it provides a solution to some of the cell's manufacturing problems. Caspar[1] has shown that the chances of the cell's protein manufactory making a mistake in the synthesis of ten proteins of, say, a hundred amino-acids each, is far less than the chance of its making a mistake in the synthesis of one protein of a thousand amino-acids. It seems, therefore, that the cell's synthetic machinery produces a number of units, or monomers, and in the correct physico-chemical conditions these units come together to form, quite automatically, a higher structure.

Second, it is probable that new and important functional characteristics emerge from a labile quaternary structure. Some examples of this phenomenon will be outlined in the next section. It may be mentioned here, however, that, according to Reed and Cox,[2] it is probable that the constituent enzymes of many multi-enzyme systems (Chapter 7) may be organised into assemblies. Such an organisation, these workers suggest, may well improve the overall efficiency of the system. Only a rather small number of such complexes are known today; it may be anticipated, however, that improved separation methods may soon bring to light many more instances of such assemblies.

3

Let us begin this outline of the quaternary structure of some globular proteins by considering the structure of a few blood pigments. We have already seen (Chapter 6) that haemoglobin is composed of four subunits and that these are held together by weak, non-covalent, forces. It is thus very easy to disrupt haemoglobin's quaternary structure. Indeed it is sufficient merely to arrange that the pH of the surrounding solvent is outside the normal physiological range. If the pH is raised above 11, or reduced below 5, the four subunits are found to 'unstick' and drift apart. If the pH is returned to its normal value (pH 7) the four subunits reassociate.

[1] Caspar, D. L. D. (1963), *Adv. in Prot. Res.*, *18*, 37.
[2] Reed, L. J. and Cox, D. J. (1966), *Ann. Rev. Biochem.*, *35*, 57.

In general, the reconstituted haemoglobin molecules consist, as usual, of two α- and two β-chains. However, the reassociation process can be interfered with and interesting hybridisation experiments have been carried out. If, for example, haemoglobins from two reasonably closely related species are mixed, say horse and dog, then it is possible, on reassociation, to obtain hybrid molecules $\alpha_2^{horse} \beta_2^{dog}$, or, vice versa, $\alpha_2^{dog} \beta_2^{horse}$. Furthermore, using haemoglobins derived from a single species, it is possible to form a molecule consisting entirely of β-chains—β_4-haemoglobin. These molecules resemble the naturally occurring haemoglobin—haemoglobin H. These latter molecules, although of considerable interest to the protein chemist, are of little use to the animal which owns them. For it is found that such molecules do not exhibit a Bohr effect (Chapter 6), and their oxygen affinity is some ten times greater than normal.

Haemoglobin is very far from being the only blood pigment to be found in the animal kingdom. In many invertebrates blood pigments are to be found free in the plasma. Quite a number of these pigments are based on a haem porphyrin. They differ from haemoglobin only in the globin moiety of the molecule. The globin is in all known cases very much larger than that of vertebrate haemoglobin. In consequence these invertebrate haemoglobins are usually distinguished by giving them a different name—erythrocruorins. The reason for the very large size of erythrocruorin molecules is probably connected to the fact that the pigment is free in the plasma, not confined, as in the vertebrates, to red blood cells. It is believed that their large size prevents their diffusing through the walls of the blood vessels and thus becoming lost to the circulation.

Many erythrocruorin molecules approach in molecular weight the very large copper-containing pigments found in the bloods of arthropods and molluscs. These pigments—the haemocyanins[1]—give the blood of these animals a bluish tinge. Elegant electron micrographs of these large proteins have been obtained by van Bruggen and Wiebenga.[2] The haemocyanin molecule of the common snail was, for instance, shown by these workers to have a roughly cylindrical shape. The length of the cylindrical molecule is about 335A and the diameter is about 300A. There is clear evidence in the electron micrographs of an intricate and regular substructure. The molecule, moreover, can be shown to dissociate into smaller units

[1] The molecular weights of haemocyanins range up to six million.
[2] *J. Mol. Biol.* (1962), *4*, 1–7 and 8–9.

as the pH is increased. It seems very likely that the large pigment molecules of other invertebrate bloods are also built of smaller protein subunits.

We noticed when we discussed the haemoglobin molecule in Chapter 6 that the physiological function of this protein emerges from its quaternary structure. Neither a sigmoid oxygen dissociation curve nor a Bohr effect are shown by isolated α- or β-chains. It thus seems probable that the physiological characteristics of invertebrate blood pigments may also arise from particular arrangements of their subunits.

It is very interesting to find that a similar relation between quaternary structure and biological function is exhibited by some enzymes. In 1957[1] it was shown that a commonly occurring enzyme—lactate dehydrogenase—could be separated by electrophoresis into several different fractions. Subsequently it was shown that several other enzymes could also be separated into multiple fractions. It thus appears that an enzyme catalysing a certain reaction may exist in a slightly different form in different tissues. A group of enzymes, catalysing the same reaction but differing slightly in structure, is called a group of *isoenzymes*.

Lactic dehydrogenase has been shown to consist of four subunits. These subunits fall into two different classes. It is clear, as fig. 8.1 shows, that it is possible to arrange four such subunits to form five different quaternary structures. It is these five different molecules which can be distinguished by electrophoresis.

All five different lactic dehydrogenases are frequently found in mammalian tissues. Furthermore, although all are capable of catalysing the metabolically-important oxidation of lactate to pyruvate, the two extremes ((*a*) and (*e*) of fig. 8.1) differ in some respects. One of the extremes, for example, is inhibited by pyruvic

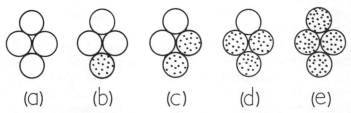

(a)   (b)   (c)   (d)   (e)

Fig. 8.1 Lactic dehydrogenases: an example of a group of isoenzymes.

[1] Vesell, E. S. and Bearn, A. J. (1957), *Proc. Soc. Exp. Biol. N.Y.*, *94*, 96.

acid whilst the other is not; the former is found typically in heart muscle, whereas the latter exists predominantly in skeletal muscle.

An even more striking indication of the dependence of enzymatic function on quaternary structure is provided by glutamic dehydrogenase. This enzyme has a very high molecular weight—about one million. In the presence of NADH, however, its molecular weight is reduced by a factor of four. It looks as though the normal enzyme is composed of four very large subunits. It is very interesting to find that these subunits have a quite different enzymatic activity from that of glutamic dehydrogenase. Instead of catalysing the dehydrogenation of glutamate, the subunits bring about the oxidative deamination of alanine. This is indeed a most striking transformation.

In Chapter 7 the phenomenon of allosteric inhibition was briefly discussed. We saw that the probable action of an allosteric effector was to alter the higher structure of an enzymic protein. The examples we have reviewed above confirm that an alteration in quaternary structure can have a very marked effect on enzymic activity.

At the end of this book, in Chapter 15, we shall discuss the important work which has been done on enzyme induction and enzyme repression. We shall see that in these two mechanisms repressor molecules—probably proteins—are involved. The action of these repressors can be influenced by small molecules in the environment. It seems probable that here again an alteration in higher, possibly quaternary, structure occurs.

In short, it looks as though the quaternary structure of globular proteins may well prove to have important physiological and biochemical functions.

4

The ability to form macromolecular assemblies is not the sole prerogative of globular proteins. Far from it. Fibrous proteins also form some very interesting and very important assemblies. In Chapter 6 we noticed how polypeptide chains composed of aminoacids with, on the whole, small side chains, are able to form extensive sheets or membranes. In silk fibroin, for example, we saw that polypeptide chains were H-bonded to each other to form a two-dimensional lattice. A number of such lattices were piled one on top of the other to form a fibre of silk. The forces in the third dimension are van der Waals forces and electrostatic interactions.

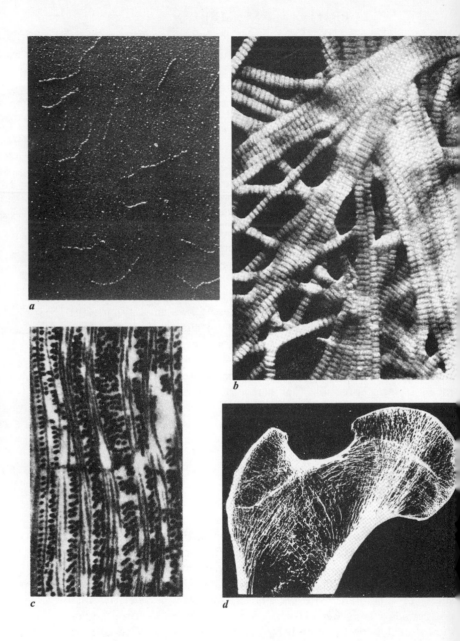

Hence the forces holding the fibre together in the third dimension are similar to the forces holding together the quaternary structure of a globular protein.

However, much more interesting than silk fibroin, from the point of view of higher structure, are collagen and the *k.m.e.f.* group of proteins. Accordingly it is to these two groups of proteins that the rest of this chapter is devoted.

5

The primary and secondary structure of collagen was discussed in Chapter 6. We saw that it was composed of three amino-acid helices wound into a 'super-helix'. Each helix was H-bonded to its neighbours so that the resulting fibre was remarkably compact and possessed a high tensile strength. This structure is well adapted to the function of collagen in the body. From the coelentcrates all the way up to man we find that connective tissues are strengthened by collagenous white fibres. In the vertebrates it is found that these fibres are particularly numerous where tensile strength is required. They are, for example, particularly well developed in the tendons which join muscle to bone, and in the ligaments which join bone to bone.

Now if we examine a small piece of connective tissue in the microscope we see that the collagenous white fibres are thickish unbranched threads. They run through the ground substance, or matrix, in all directions (fig. 8.2(*a*)). Both the matrix, which is

e IV Some features of collagen and of the structures in which it is implicated.

(*a*) electron micrograph of tropocollagen molecules derived from a fish bladder. This micrograph was obtained by shadowing the molecules with metal atoms. Each molecule is about 2800A long and 15A in diameter.

(*b*) tropocollagen molecules join together (see text) to form collagen fibres with characteristic cross striations. This electron micrograph is magnified 17,000×.

(*c*) this electron micrograph (magnification 30,000×) shows an instance where collagen fibres are organised in a very precise fashion. This interesting higher structure is found in the cornea of a tadpole.

(*d*) this photograph is of a section of the head of a human femur. The pattern of bony spicules, or trabeculae, reflects the stresses to which the bone is subjected during life.

(a) *courtesy of C. E. Hall;* (b) *and* (c) *courtesy of J. Gross;* (d) *after Schafer, from a photograph by Professor A. Robinson. Courtesy of the Syndics of the University Press, Cambridge.*

PROTEIN ASSEMBLIES

Fig. 8.2 The structure of collagen.

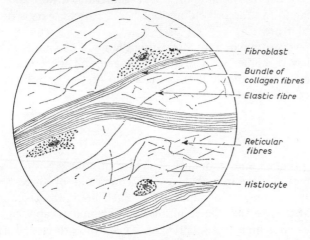

Fibroblast

Bundle of
collagen fibres

Elastic fibre

Reticular
fibres

Histiocyte

(Magnified about 200 diameters)

(*a*) If we take a specimen of connective tissue (for example, from the dermis of the skin), spread it on a slide, and look at it through a microscope, we can make out the structure shown in the diagram.

The major part of the tissue is composed of 'ground substance' consisting chiefly of muco-polysaccharides. Running through the ground substance in all directions are fibres. The collagen fibres run in bundles. Embedded in the ground substance are several different types of cell. The fibroblasts, which—with the exception of the nucleus—are often rather indistinct, are responsible for producing all the fibres of the tissue.

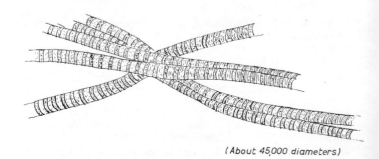

(About 45,000 diameters)

(*b*) If we examine individual collagen fibres with the electron-microscope (see plate IV(*b*)) we are able to see that they have a characteristically cross-banded appearance.

194

PROTEIN ASSEMBLIES

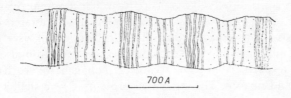

700 A

(c) The bands are about 700 Ångström units apart. If we examine a short segment of a single collagen fibre we find that it has quite an intricate fine structure.

This fine structure is due to the arrangement of the units of collagen: the so-called *tropocollagen* molecules. These are shown in the next diagram.

(d) Each tropocollagen molecule is about 2,800 Ångström units long, and about 14 Ångström units in diameter. They seem to have distinct 'heads' and 'tails' which enable them to join together end-to-end. Along the length of the molecule are irregular bumps due, probably, to the side chains of their constituent amino-acids.

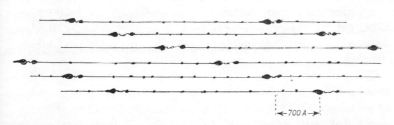

←700 A→

(e) Many tropocollagen molecules line up head-to-tail to form very lengthy chains. A typical collagen fibre consists of a great number of these chains running parallel to each other. The diagram shows that the molecules line up in a staggered array so that each overlaps its neighbour by about a quarter of its length. A quarter of 2,800 Ångströms is 700 Ångströms. Thus it seems that the cross-banded appearance of a collagen fibre (see diagrams (b) and (c) and plate IV(b) is due to the regular positioning of the head-and-tail bumps of its constituent tropocollagen molecules.

195

largely formed of jelly-like mucopolysaccharides, and the fibres are believed to be produced by a small number of scattered cells: the fibroblasts. It is believed that the fibroblast synthesises complete collagen molecules and then extrudes them into the ground substance. In this respect, as in several others, collagen differs from both keratin and myosin. The latter two proteins, as we shall see below, are laid down and remain within cells.

If, next, we examine collagen fibres in the electron microscope we see that they are traversed by a regular pattern of bands (fig. 8.2(b) and Plate IV(b)). The bands are spaced at intervals of about 700A. If the magnification is increased still further it can be seen that each of the bands has an intricate fine structure (fig. 8.2(c)). This, then, is the problem presented by collagen to the molecular biologist. How does the intricate and regular pattern of bands relate, if at all, to the three-stranded collagen molecule we described in Chapter 5?

In order to solve this problem a preliminary question has to be settled. Is the collagen fibre, like silk fibroin, a continuous molecular structure, or is it composed of a number of subunits? If the latter possibility proves to be correct an explanation of the prominent cross striations may well be to hand: they may arise from the alignment of the subunits.

Now if collagen is dissolved in dilute acid the resulting solution can be shown to contain elongated structures of molecular dimensions. Studies with the ultracentrifuge, and measurements of the viscosity of the solution, show that these molecules are about 2,800A long, and about 14A in diameter. These dimensions have been confirmed by electron microscopy. Because, as we shall see, the familar collagen fibres can be reassembled from these molecular elements, the latter have been called *tropocollagen* molecules from 'tropos' meaning 'turning into'.

The problem of the structure of collagen fibres thus comes down to the problem of deriving a 700A repeat distance from an assemblage of subunits each 2,800A in length. By studying the different forms in which collagen fibres could be precipitated from tropocollagen solutions, Schmitt and his colleagues[1] were able to show that the 700A periodicity observed in natural collagen was due to the overlapping of its constituent subunits.

Electron microscopy shows that these constituent subunits—the

[1] See Schmitt, F. O. in *Biophysical Science: A Study Programme*, John Wiley, 1959, p. 349.

tropocollagen molecules—possess a pattern of bumps and bulges along their lengths. This feature is schematised in fig. 8.2(*d*). It is believed that these protuberances are due to the presence of bulky amino-acid side chains. Consequently it is supposed that the fine structure shown in fig. 8.2(*c*) is due to the interaction of these side chains when the tropocollagen molecules are lined up side by side. In addition tropocollagen molecules are also believed to be joined together end to end. This junction is both bulky and dense. Now if we suppose that the molecules overlap each other by a quarter of their length—fig. 8.2(*e*)—then it is clear that we have an explanation for the strong 700A periodicity. For, as fig. 8.2(*e*) shows, the bulky junctional regions of the tropocollagen molecules succeed each other at 700A intervals.

The overlapping of tropocollagen molecules and the interaction of their side chains are probably designed to ensure that the fibre has the greatest possible tensile strength.

The amino-acids basic to tropocollagen are strung together and twisted into a three-stranded 'rope' within the cytoplasm of a fibroblast. The fibroblast is believed to extrude the molecule into the surrounding intercellular ground substance. This is shown diagrammatically in fig. 8.3.

In some not yet clearly understood way the molecules are caused to line up head to tail in the fashion discussed above. It may be that the intercellular (mucopolysaccharide) ground substance plays some part in bringing about this organisation.

Not only are the tropocollagen molecules lined up in a fairly precise manner, but the collagen fibres which they constitute are often themselves organised into larger designs. In the cornea of the eye, for example, the fibres can be shown to be arranged with great regularity in alternating layers at right angles to each other (Plate V(*c*)). It is probable that the transparency of the cornea depends on this precise organisation.

Equally interesting large-scale organisations of collagen fibres are to be found forming the basis of many animal skeletons. In these positions it is common to find collagen fibres orientated along the lines of stress experienced by the structure. Indeed the entire skeleton can with justice be regarded, as D'Arcy Thompson was accustomed to regard it, as a diagram of the forces to which it had, in its life, been exposed. D'Arcy Thompson writes as follows:

'The skeleton as we see it in a museum is a poor and even

197

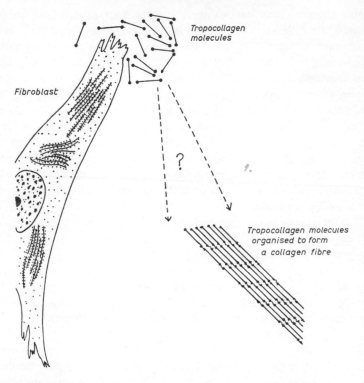

Fig. 8.3 The formation of collagen fibres within connective tissue.

misleading picture of mechanical efficiency. From an engineer's point of view, it is a diagram shewing all the compression lines, but by no means all the tension lines of the construction; it shews all the struts, but few of the ties, and perhaps we might even say *none* of the principal ones; it falls all to pieces unless we clamp it together, as best we can, in a more or less clumsy and immobilised way. But in life that fabric of struts is surrounded and interwoven with a complicated system of ties—"its living mantles jointed strong, with glistering band and silvery thong": ligament and membrane, muscle and tendon run between bone and bone; and the beauty and strength of the mechanical construction lie not in one part or another, but in the harmonious concatenation which all the parts, soft and hard, rigid and flexible, tension bearing and pressure bearing, make up together.'[1]

[1] Thompson, D'Arcy W., *Growth and Form*, Cambridge, 1917, p. 968.

Fifty years after the publication of Thompson's book we are in an even better position to appreciate the force of his position. For we can follow his engineer's vision right down to the molecular level. Let us take as an example the minute structure of a limb bone such as the femur. First of all we find that it is composed of two types of bone: compact and cancellous. The compact bone forms the walls of the shaft whereas the cancellous bone is to be found at each end. If a section is cut through the head of the femur (fig. 8.4) we can see that the cancellous bone consists of a large number of thin spicules. These spicules, moreover, are disposed along the lines of force which the bone experiences when we stand up.

This fact was first noted by nineteenth-century anatomists. D'Arcy Thompson tells the story of how in 1866 Culmann, a professor of engineering deeply involved in designing the jib of a crane, walked by chance into the room of his colleague Hermann Meyer,

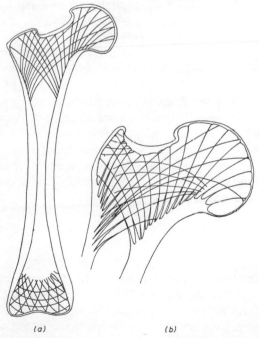

(a) (b)

Fig. 8.4 (*a*) Section through femur to show the distribution of compact and cancellous bone.

(*b*) Section through head of femur to show the arrangement of the spicules.

an anatomist. Meyer, so the story runs, was at that moment contemplating the head of a femur. Culmann on glimpsing the delicate tracery of spicules in the sectioned bone is said to have exclaimed: 'There's my crane!' It was immediately apparent to him that the lines of spicules ran precisely along the lines of stress.

The architecture of cancellous bone varies throughout the life of an individual. At birth, for example, and during infancy, the pattern of bony spicules differs considerably from that of the adult. Furthermore if a bone is fractured and badly reset, or not reset at all, its internal architecture becomes completely reorganised. It is consequently clear that the internal organisation of a bone is indeed a direct expression of the forces acting upon it.

Now it can be shown that during the development of bone the calcareous spicules are laid down along pre-existing collagen fibres. Indeed the crystals of calcium phosphate which form the material basis of the spicules can be shown to be deposited actually within the aboriginal collagen fibres.[1] These crystals are very small—about 300A long and 25A in diameter—and are orientated so that their axes are parallel to the long axis of the collagen fibre. It is clear, therefore, that the disposition of the primordial collagen fibres is responsible for the precise organisation of cancellous bone. How this initial fibrous architecture develops remains to date one of the many intriguing unsolved problems of molecular biology.

It is plain that the 'order based on order' which Schroedinger, in a very influential book,[2] noticed as characteristic of life is nowhere more apparent than in the detailed architecture of animal skeletons. Similarly fascinating instances of order based on order will be examined in the next sections where some of the structures built of $k.m.e.f.$ proteins are discussed.

6

It will be remembered from Chapter 6 that the third major architectural principle in the world of fibrous proteins is the α-helix. It will also be recalled that fibrous proteins constructed according to this plan have powers of reversible stretching denied to collagen. It is

[1] Glimcher, M. J. in *Biophysical Science: A Study Programme*, John Wiley, New York, 1959, p. 359.
[2] Schroedinger, E., *What is Life?*, Cambridge, 1944.

thus not surprising to find that the so-called *k.m.e.f.* group of proteins is not employed where tensile strength is required. That is collagen's job. It is on the other hand most suggestive to find that α-helical proteins form the molecular basis of all biological structures capable of movement.

The implications of this unity in diversity were fully grasped by W. T. Astbury—one of the founders of the modern science of biophysics. Astbury had started his scientific career by studying the structure of wool with the techniques of X-ray diffraction. His researches gradually widened to include an investigation of the molecular structure of muscle, cilia and flagella. He became convinced that these apparently quite dissimilar objects were in fact constructed of arrays of basically similar units. At an Experimental Biology Symposium in 1955 he was able to write that in his opinion, '. . . flagella, cilia and muscles . . . surely comprise a single molecular topic if ever there was one'.

We shall see that there is much truth in Astbury's insight. The implication that the reversible stretching, so characteristic of α-helices, is in some way fundamental to the movement of these organs and organelles, has, however, remained merely an implication. All the evidence at present points in the other direction. $\alpha \leftrightharpoons \beta$ transitions have never yet been observed to take place in living muscles, cilia, or flagella.

Before, however, examining some examples of Astbury's 'single molecular topic' we must devote some space to a brief consideration of his first concern: wool.

7

The protein from which wool is constructed is *keratin*. This protein is by no means restricted to wool. It also forms the basis of hair, nails, claws, hooves, quills, etc., etc. Because of the great economic importance of wool, keratin from this source has been more intensively studied than any other. However, there is every reason to believe that the conclusions drawn from a study of wool keratin can be applied, with very little modification, to describe the molecular organisation of keratins derived from other sources.

X-ray analysis of keratin has left no doubt that, fundamentally, the protein is twisted into an α-helix. However, in order to account for some of the detailed features of the diffraction pictures, Crick and others have suggested that the α-helix is itself twisted into a higher order spiral with a pitch of about 186A. It is then proposed that three of these spiralling α-helices twist around each other to form a three-stranded rope. The molecular situation is thus, in some ways, reminiscent of that obtaining in the tropocollagen molecule. In contrast to the latter molecule, however, the three strands of the keratin 'rope' are not H-bonded to each other. It is for this reason that the structure is considered in this chapter rather than in Chapter 5.

Keratin, like other α-helical proteins, can be stretched into a β-configuration. This characteristic property provides something of a stumbling-block for those who would assert a straightforward coiled-coil model. It is difficult to see how such a compact and intricate structure could undergo reversible stretching. In order to 'save the phenomena' various ingenious solutions have been proposed.[1] All of these 'solutions', however, assume that the coiled-coil model is basically true; none of them, as yet, has gained universal acceptance.

As in the case of collagen, the basic macromolecular structure of keratin becomes organised into a higher structure which ultimately becomes visible in the electron microscope. This higher structure is not, however, laid down in the ground substance between cells, but within the cytoplasm of certain highly specialised spindle-shaped cells. The keratin fibres are laid down parallel to the long axes of these cells. The cells, in turn, are orientated with their long axes parallel to the long axis of the hair or wool.

If keratin is observed under the electron microscope it can be shown to be organised into microfibrils each about 75A in diameter. These fibrils are closely packed together in the otherwise structureless cytoplasm of the spindle cell. Very high resolution electron microscopy shows that the microfibrils are themselves composed of yet smaller fibrils. We are here at the very limits of present-day electron microscopy and it is consequently rather difficult to be sure of exactly how the so-called protofibrils are disposed within the microfibril. The most generally accepted idea is that a 9+2 arrangement of protofibrils exists.[2] It is believed that nine protofibrils form a peripheral ring enclosing two central fibrils (fig. 8.5). The diameters

[1] Crewther, W. G., Fraser, R. D. B., Lennox, F. G. and Lindley, H. (1965), *Adv. in Prot. Res.*, *20*, 191.
[2] Filshie, B. K. and Rogers, G. E. (1961), *J. Mol. Biol.*, *3*, 784.

of these protofibrils is of the same order of magnitude as the three-stranded coiled-coils envisaged by the X-ray crystallographers. Thus to borrow a phrase coined, as we shall see, in another context, it may be said that the structure of wool, hair, etc. has been 'run into the ground'.

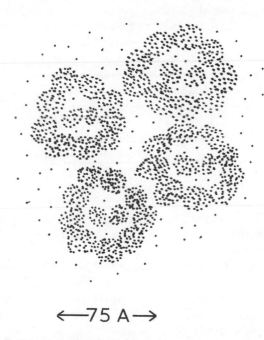

←—75 A—→

Fig. 8.5 Transverse section through keratin to show the organisation of the protofibrils. From Filshie and Rogers, *loc. cit.* (1961).

We shall meet the '9+2' organisation again, on a rather larger scale, when we come to consider the fine structure of cilia and flagella.

Before, however, leaving the subject of keratin it is interesting to note that the powers of reversible stretching possessed by this protein, whatever their molecular basis, are made use of in the hairdresser's salon. By subjecting keratin to moist heat and at the same time to stretching forces the fibre may be converted from an α- to a β-configuration. New connections then become possible and the fibre is able to 'set' into any mould provided for it.

The keratins do not themselves generate movement though they are, as we have seen, subject to reversible stretching. We have already mentioned, however, that other α-helical proteins do form important constituents of motile organs and organelles. The principal organs of movement in the animal kingdom are, of course, muscles. Amongst micro-organisms, however, minute hair-like organelles—the flagella and cilia—serve as propulsive structures. In all cases, as Astbury emphasised, whether muscle, cilium, or flagellum, the structural protein gives a typical alpha X-ray diffraction pattern.

Let us begin our examination of these structures by considering the design of flagella. There is reason to believe that these are the most primitive of all motile organs. Not only are they developed by some of the cells of higher organisms but they are also to be found on many bacteria. Cilia, on the other hand, whilst of considerable importance in many higher organisms, are not developed by the teeming world of bacteria.

The protein of the bacterial flagellum—flagellin—gives a typical α-helical diffraction pattern. Moreover, this minute whip-like projection seems to be composed almost entirely of this protein.[1] The great simplicity of the bacterial flagellum's structure led Astbury to the belief that it might best be regarded as a 'monomolecular muscle'.[2]

High resolution electron microscopy of bacterial flagella[3] shows that they are constructed from globular subunits (Plate V(a)). Each subunit is approximately 50A in diameter.

The subunits are arranged in helices of various kinds depending on the type of bacterium being studied. In one case—*Salmonella*—there are four helices each with a pitch of about 200A. This organisation is shown in fig. 8.6. In this figure the run of one of the four helices is marked by blackening its globular elements.

Fig. 8.(6b) shows an 'end-on' view of the flagellum. Whether the space in the centre remains empty or is filled with a similar or a different protein remains unknown.

The movement of bacterial flagella is similar to that of the flagella

---

[1] Hofmann-Berling, H., in *Comparative Biochemistry*, Vol. 2, Academic Press, New York and London, 1960, p. 342.

[2] In *Soc. Exp. Biol. Symp.*, IX (1955), p. 6.

[3] Lowy, J. and Hanson, J. (1965), *J. Mol. Biol.*, *11*, 293.

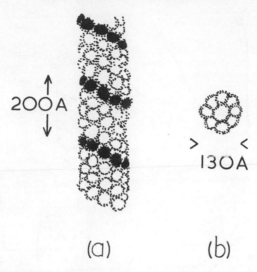

$$\uparrow$$
200 A
$$\downarrow$$

$$> \quad <$$
130 A

(a)   (b)

Fig. 8.6 Helical structure of *Salmonella* flagellum. From Lowy and Hanson,
loc. cit. (1965).

developed by animals and plants. It consists of a screw-type motion
in three dimensions. This motion is schematised in fig. 8.7(*c*). How
his movement is achieved remains, at present, a mystery.

The flagella developed by higher cells are larger and more complex
than those of bacteria. Instead of being about 130A in diameter they
average about 0·2μ, or 2,000A. Moreover, instead of the comparatively simple molecular organisation of bacterial flagella, the flagella
of higher cells display an intricate and intriguing ultrastructure.
Plate V(*b*) shows that this consists of a peripheral ring of nine fibrils
surrounding two rather more slender inner fibrils.[1]

This very interesting ultrastructure is not only found in practically
all the flagella of higher cells but is also to be found in cilia. The latter
organelles are usually shorter than flagella and, in contrast to the
corkscrew motion characteristic of flagella, lash from side to side
(fig. 8.7(*a*) and (*b*)). Amongst the protozoa all gradations between
typical flagella and typical cilia are to be found.

Close examination of the fibrils forming the ultrastructure of
cilia and flagella shows that those forming the peripheral ring are
divided into two halves by a radially orientated septum. This is

[1] In the tails of mammalian spermatozoa the peripheral fibres are sometimes
doubled in number to give a ring of eighteen.

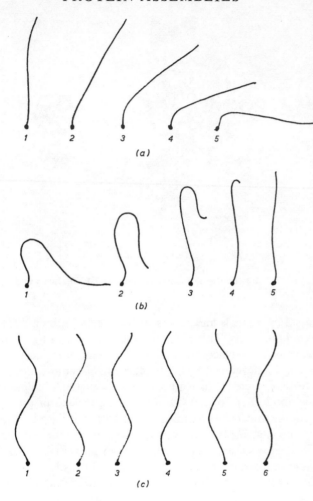

Fig. 8.7 The movement of flagella and cilia.

(*a*) Ciliary beat: effective phase.

(*b*) Ciliary beat: recovery phase.

(*c*) Flagellar beat.

The diagrams show successive instants in the movements of these organelles, and bring out the fundamental differences between the motion of cilia and flagella.

206

shown in fig. 8.8 and Plate V(*b*). The cross-sectional dimensions of the peripheral fibrils are approximately 350A × 180A. The two internal fibrils are not divided into two halves and have a more circular cross-section with a diameter of about 200A. All these fibrils are embedded in a comparatively structureless substance and the whole apparatus is contained within a membrane continuous with the cell membrane. It is very interesting to note that both the peripheral and the central fibres appear hollow in high resolution electron micrographs. Furthermore, recent work[1] on the flagellum of a species of *Chlamydomonas* has shown each of the peripheral half-fibrils to be composed of globular subunits. In cross-section there appears to be a peripheral ring of thirteen of these subunits surrounding a homogeneous core. Each of these subunits is about 40A in diameter. This corresponds to a protein with a molecular weight of about 40,000. It is clear that one of these half-fibrils resembles in many respects an entire bacterial flagellum. It is also fascinating to find that the microtubules which have recently been found to be widely distributed in cells of all types (see Chapter 12) also have a similar morphology.

The great regularity in the ultrastructure of flagella and cilia does not extend to their basal regions. In general there is some form of more or less complex basal granule (Plate V(*b*)), but this varies considerably from one organism to another. In many, but not all, cases a striated 'rootlet' fibre can be observed extending from the basal granule into the cell's cytoplasm. These rootlet fibres are from 500A to 1,000A in diameter, and the striations recur at 550A to 700A intervals. Although earlier investigators believed that they were implicated in the movement, or control of movement, of the cilium or flagellum, this is not now thought to be the case. Instead the rootlet fibres are thought to have the function their name suggests. They probably anchor the cilium to the cell; their prominent cross-banding indeed suggests a relation to collagen.

Before leaving the topic of cilia and flagella it is interesting to note a structural, and possibly also a functional, similarity between basal granules and centrioles. A transverse section through the basal region of a cilium reveals the peripheral ring of nine fibrils but no sign of the two central fibrils. We shall see in Chapter 12 that the centriole has a closely similar structure. In Chapter 12, also, we shall see that the functions of the two organelles have much in common.

In conclusion it is worth pointing out that not all cilia and flagella

[1] Ringo, D. L. (1967), *J. Ultrastruct. Res.*, *17*, 266.

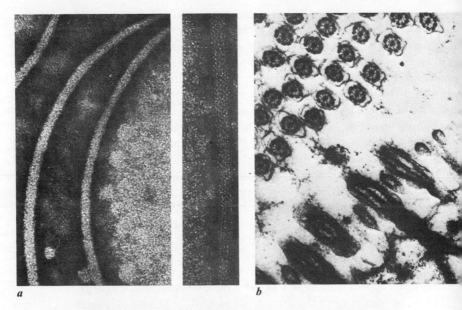

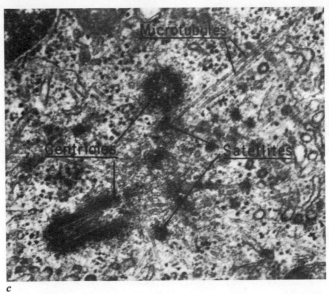

are motile. Amongst non-motile cilia it is very interesting to find that several types have developed a sensory function. Of these the most well known are the outer-segments of the rods and cones of vertebrate retinae. These photosensitive regions are known to develop from cilia springing from the surface of the sensory cells. More will be said of these interesting structures in Chapter 11. Many other sensory cells are provided with sensitive 'hairs'. These hairs, which are modified cilia, are to be found in the olfactory organs, in the taste-buds, in the lateral-line sense receptors of fish, and in certain auditory and mechano-receptors.[1] These projections, which possess all the characteristic ultrastructural features of cilia are, moreover, the sensitive parts of the sensory cells.

It is clear that the organisational level represented by cilia and flagella is an extremely fundamental one in the architecture of the body.

9

Even more basic to the design of bodies belonging to members of the animal kingdom are muscles. We have seen that Astbury likened the bacterial flagellum to a monomolecular muscle; it follows that muscles may, in some respects, be regarded as highly complex arrays of flagella-like units.

---

[1] Vinnikof, J. A. (1965), *Symp. on Quant. Biol.*, 30, 293.

V In this plate some examples of flagella, cilia and related structures are shown.

(*a*) this is a very high resolution electron micrograph of a bacterial flagellum prepared by a negative contrast technique. The micrograph shows that the flagellum has a globular substructure. The bacterium is *Pseudomonas fluorescens*; the magnifications are (*a*) 111,000 × and (*b*) 172,000 ×.

(*b*) this shows the cilia of a mussel's gill. The bottom half of this electron micrograph (magnification 20,000 ×) shows the basal regions of the cilia and in the top half the cilia have bent over so that they are cut in section. The characteristic 9+2 arrangement of internal fibres is well shown and, in addition, it can be seen that each cilium is surrounded by a typical unit membrane.

(*c*) this electron micrograph shows both centrioles and microtubules. The similarity of centrioles to the basal regions of cilia and flagella is evident. The micrograph is of an Ascites tumour cell and is magnified 54,000 ×.

(a) *courtesy of J. Lowy (1965)*, J. Mol. Biol., 11, *308;* (b) *courtesy of P. Satir;* (c) *courtesy of G. de Thé, reprinted by permission of The Rockefeller University Press from* J. Cell Biol. (*1964*), 23, *265–75.*

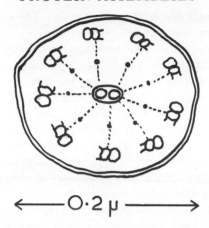

$\longleftarrow$ O·2 µ $\longrightarrow$

Fig. 8.8 A transverse section of a cilium reveals an interesting ultra-structure. Each of the nine peripheral filaments is divided into two parts and to the slightly smaller of these are attached two 'arms'. In some cases secondary filaments may be seen between the peripheral ring and the central filaments. Furthermore, running between the peripheral filaments and the central sheath are a number of 'spokes'.

Vertebrate muscles are, traditionally, divided into three sorts: skeletal (or striped), visceral (or smooth) and cardiac. The vertebrates, however, although they loom large in the minds of humans, as *Homo sapiens* and most of his domestic animals belong to the group, are in fact only a rather small segment of the animal kingdom. Of the well over a million animal species only about 40,000 are vertebrates. It is thus not surprising to find that the rather sharp tripartite distinction mentioned above does not run, without exception, throughout the whole range of the animal kingdom. Nonetheless certain broad generalisations can be made. Fast-acting muscles are usually striped; slow-acting muscles, capable of more sustained contraction, are frequently found to be unstriped, or smooth.

Because the 'proper study of mankind' has long been held to be 'man' the greatest volume of research has, in the past, been directed towards an understanding of vertebrate skeletal muscle. In recent years the field of interest has widened somewhat, and much significant and valuable work has been done on the muscles of invertebrates.

It is still, however, probably true to say that more is known about vertebrate skeletal muscle than any other type. It is in this tissue that molecular biologists are beginning to perceive the nexus between chemical and mechanical change. It is to this tissue, therefore, that the remainder of this chapter will be devoted.

Let us concentrate our attention on the molecular architecture of a single vertebrate striped muscle. It is of no consequence which we choose—the biceps, the psoas, the gastrocnemius, etc.—all are equally suitable.

First it is found that the muscle is entirely enclosed by a connective tissue membrane. This is continued at each end to form the tendons by which the muscle is attached to the bone. The essential substance of the muscle consists of fibres. If a muscle is dissected out, its fibres teased apart and observed under the microscope, they will each be seen to be crossed by a large number of dark bands, or stripes. It is for this reason that skeletal muscle is often referred to as striped, or striated, muscle. We are now at the optical microscopist's level.

The muscle fibre is the unit of skeletal muscle. It is not a typical cell as it contains several nuclei. It seems to be formed by the coalescence of several precursor cells. The cytoplasm of a muscle fibre is called *sarcoplasm*. Within it are to be found myoglobin molecules (Chapter 6) on which oxygen is stored; mitochondria (Chapter 11) within which proceed the metabolic reactions which yield the energy-rich phosphate bonds on which contraction depends; the sarcoplasmic reticulum (Chapter 12) which is believed to

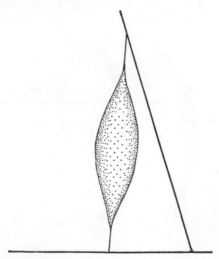

Fig. 8.9 Diagrammatic representation of a skeletal muscle and its attachments.

211

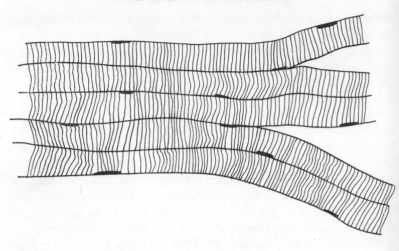

Fig. 8.10 A small piece of skeletal muscle teased apart at its tip. Five muscle fibres are shown, each of which exhibits prominent cross striations and contains several nuclei.

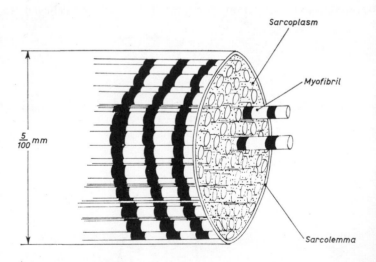

Fig. 8.11 The characteristic elements of a muscle fibre are the myofibrils. The figure shows that it is these which confer a striped appearance on the muscle.

212

initiate and control the processes of contraction; the enzymes and coupling devices whereby the energy of the energy-rich phosphate bonds is fed into the contractile machinery; and last, but very far from least, the contractile proteins themselves in the form of myofibrils.

The myofibrils being the ultimate contractile elements of the muscle fibre are thus of very great interest. Each is no more than about 1 or 2μ in diameter. Hence they can only just be distinguished by the optical microscope. Analysis of their structure has thus depended on the development and use of more powerful techniques—in particular electron microscopy.

In addition to being responsible for the contractility of skeletal muscle the myofibril is also responsible, as is shown in fig. 8.11, for its characteristic cross striations. It has already been mentioned that cross striations are in some way connected to a muscle's ability to contract rapidly. It will thus be sensible to examine the nature of these cross striations more closely.

Figure 8.12 shows a small portion of a single myofibril. It can be seen that it consists of a sequence of bands or, more correctly, as the myofibril is cylindrical, discs. These bands, or discs, have been given names. One of the bands can be shown to absorb polarised light to a greater extent when the plane of polarisation is in one direction than when it is in another. This band is, in other words, anisotropic, and is called, in consequence, the A-band. The other band absorbs polarised light to an equal extent whatever its plane. In other words this second band is isotropic with respect to polarised light. In

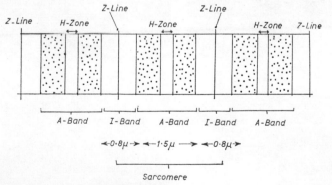

Fig. 8.12 It has long been known that a myofibril consists of a regularly repeating sequence of zones, bands and lines.

a

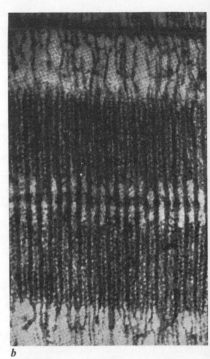

b

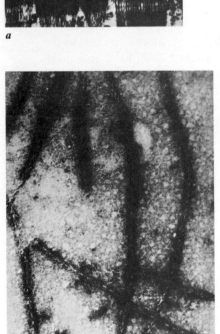

c

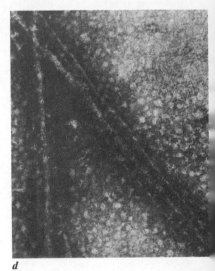

d

214

consequence it is called the I-band. The two bands also differ in their staining properties. The A-band easily takes up stains like haemotoxylin, whereas the I-band is relatively unstainable.

In addition to the succession of A- and I-bands the myofibril shows other transverse markings. In the centre of each I-band a thin line—the Z-line—is visible. In the centre of each A-band a light area is visible. This is called the H-zone, or H-band. The H-zone, unlike the other transverse bands, varies in extent according to the degree of contraction of the myofibril. When the myofibril is fully relaxed the H-zone is large; on the other hand when it is fully contracted the H-zone is much reduced in extent and may have disappeared altogether.

As fig. 8.12 shows, the segment of myofibril between one Z-line and the next is called a sarcomere. We shall see below that it can be regarded as the unit of contraction.

What lies behind this highly characteristic and highly regular transverse striping? Do we have a situation similar to that which we found in collagen? Are the striations the outward and visible sign of the sub-microscopic organisation of the contractile proteins?

The answer to this last question appears to be—yes. Plate VI(b) is an electron micrograph of a sarcomere. Fig. 8.13 schematises this Plate. It is evident that the banding visible in the optical microscope is due to the arrangement of a number of filaments within the

Plate VI Some electron micrographs of skeletal muscle and of the proteins extractable from this type of muscle.

(a) this is an electron micrograph (magnification 22,000 ×) of a thin section of striated muscle. The 'A', 'I', 'Z' and 'H' bands are clearly shown. The fibrous nature of the muscle's contractile elements is also evident.

(b) the magnification has been increased to 75,000 ×. The arrangement of the thick (myosin) and thin (actin) filaments is clear. At the top of the micrograph a portion of the Z-line can be seen.

(c) this electron micrograph is of F-actin to which has been added a quantity of heavy meromyosin. The resulting complex has been negatively stained and magnified 57,000 ×. The meromyosin appears to attach itself at regular intervals along the actin thread forming arrowhead-like structures.

(d) isolated thick (myosin) and thin (actin) filaments can be seen in this negatively stained electron micrograph (magnification 117,000 ×) to be still attached to each other. The attachment between the two filaments appears to be via the protuberances of the thick filaments.

(a) and (b) courtesy of H. E. Huxley: The Cell, Vol. IV, Part 1, Academic Press Inc. (London) Ltd., 1962; (c) and (d) courtesy of H. E. Huxley (1963), J. Mol. Biol., 7, 281.

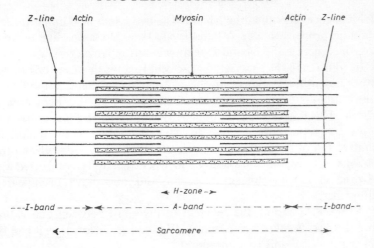

Fig. 8.13 Distribution of myosin and actin within a sarcomere.

sarcomere. These filaments vary in diameter. It can be seen that some are relatively thick, whilst others are much thinner.

By making use of specific extractants and by other means the molecular constitution of these two types of filament may be ascertained. The thick filaments can be shown to consist of several hundred molecules of a protein called myosin, and the thin filaments to consist of another protein called actin.

Careful examination of Plate VI(*b*) shows that the thick filaments are not smooth surfaced. Quite the contrary: they seem to be covered with knobs and protuberances of all sorts. These often appear to bridge the gap between the thick and the thin filaments.

Next let us increase the magnification a step further and examine the actin and myosin molecules themselves. This can be done by extracting them from the muscle fibre and examining the extract either by physico-chemical techniques or by electron microscopy.

Both these techniques have been used to investigate the nature of the myosin molecule. Recent electron micrographs of myosin show it to be a long thin molecule (about 1,600A) with a prominent bulge at one end.[1] This confirms the results of earlier chemical work. This work had shown that if the molecule was subjected to the proteolytic enzyme, trypsin, it could be split into two parts. One part, called light meromyosin (LMM), was long, slender, and possessed a very

[1] Huxley, H. E. (1964), *Proc. Roy. Soc. B.*, *160*, 442.

high content of protein in the α-helical configuration; the other part, heavy meromyosin (HMM), was, in contrast, compact and globular. It was shown, furthermore, that the ability to hydrolyse ATP and thus extract energy from its energy-rich bonds, was confined solely to the HMM moiety.

The current picture of the myosin molecule is shown in fig. 8.14. The LMM region is believed to consist of three α-helices coiled around each other—a conformation reminiscent of keratin.[1]

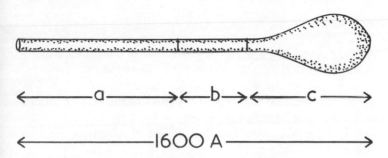

Fig. 8.14 The current picture of myosin suggests that it has three regions: (a) LMM, (b) a region sensitive to trypsin, and (c) HMM.

Actin seems to be a rather simpler molecule than myosin. Again, both electron microscopy and chemical analysis have been used in its investigation. It seems that in the thin filaments of striated muscle actin exists in the form of a twisted double string of 'beads' (fig. 8.15). This form of actin is called fibrous, or F-actin. The individual 'beads' of the fibres can be separated from each other by appropriate chemical techniques and are known as globular, or G-actin. The G-actin globules are about 55A in diameter.

If isolated HMM units are added to a solution containing F-actin and the result examined in the electron microscope, it is found that the HMM units attach themselves along the length of the F-actin in a very regular manner. It will be remembered that, in the sarcomere, the thick filaments apparently connect with the thin filaments by numerous small protuberances. Thus the foregoing observation

[1] Very recently Slayter and Lowey (*Proc. Nat. Acad. Sci. Wash.*, 58, 1611, 1967)) have shown by a new electron microscopical technique that the globular HMM part of myosin consists of two subunits. These investigators thus believe that the rod-like LMM tail of the molecule consists of two, not three, super-coiled alpha-helices. It is suggested that the two alpha-helices stabilise each other by strong side-chain interactions.

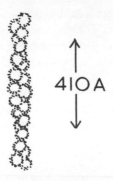

Fig. 8.15 Actin, as it exists in the muscle fibre, is believed to consist of two long strings of globular elements twisted lightly together.

supports the idea that it is the HMM parts of the myosin molecules which form these protuberances. Hence fig. 8.16 shows the modern concept of the molecular structure of one of the sarcomere's thick filaments.

Fig. 8.16 is, of course, a hypothetical section through a thick filament. The filament in reality is cylindrical and, in consequence, the HMM protuberances protrude all over its surface. This corresponds to the appearance of the thick filament in the electron microscope.

We have now completed our description of the molecular basis of the transverse striations visible in skeletal muscle. Clearly the anisotropy of the A-band is due to the concentration in this band of numerous rod-like myosin molecules. The density of the band is due to the presence of both actin and myosin. Where actin is present on its own—the I-band and the H-zone—the fibre is much less opaque. The Z-lines which divide one sarcomere from the next seem to be formed of a complex meshwork of actin fibres. It follows that the actin in each sarcomere is anchored to the Z-lines at each end.

In spite of long continued research the means by which this very

Fig. 8.16 Optical section through one of a myofibril's thick filaments. The myosin molecules are arranged so that their HMM moieties project from the surface. Notice that the centre of the thick filament is devoid of such protuberances.

interesting and intricate molecular architecture produces movement remains obscure. There is indeed good evidence that contraction of a sarcomere occurs by a sliding of the thin filaments towards each other between the thick filaments. This has been called, for obvious reasons, the *interdigitating* hypothesis of muscular contraction. Exactly how this movement of the thin filaments with respect to the thick filaments is brought about remains, however, unknown.

It seems probable that the HMM protuberances are very intimately involved in the sliding of the thick and thin filaments over each other. Perhaps these projections make and remake connections with the neighbouring actin filaments, thus, in some way, pulling the actin filaments which, it will be remembered, are attached to each end of the sarcomere, towards each other. In this connection it is probably very significant that HMM is an ATP-ase. For it seems certain that the energy essential for mechanical movement is derived from the energy-rich bonds of ATP.

A number of theories have been proposed to explain how phosphate-bond energy is fed into the contractile machinery of the myofibril. To date, however, none of these theories have gained general acceptance. The processes involved are probably very complicated. Some other aspects will be considered in Chapter 12. A detailed understanding in molecular terms of muscular contraction will, however, be of very great value both to the science of biology and to its applications in medicine and elsewhere.

10

This chapter has shown that assemblies of globular and fibrous proteins form an important structural and functional level in the architecture of life. Frequently these quaternary structures have exceedingly important biological activities. We noticed that this is rapidly becoming clear for the globular proteins discussed in the earlier part of this chapter, and it is already well documented for the fibrous proteins discussed later. The emergence of new structure and, concomitantly, new function is perhaps best demonstrated by the unity in diversity of flagella, cilia and muscles. At the molecular level this heterogeneous collection of organs and organelles shows a quite remarkable structural uniformity. This suggests that they may all share a common mechanism for transducing chemical into mechanical energy. Indeed recent work by Satir suggests that a sliding filament mechanism may well be responsible for the movements of the cilia and flagella of higher cells.[1]

However, no matter how intricate and interesting such assemblies may become, and macromolecular assemblies consisting of more than one molecular species—lipoprotein membranes, nucleoprotein viruses—may be very complex indeed, none of them can be said to be independently alive. The latter term will be defined, admittedly rather arbitrarily, in Chapter 12. It seems that the living state emerges from the loose interaction of a large number of different molecular species cabined closely together in a watery environment. The living state, also, requires a source of energy, and the means to trap and use it. Both these essentials are nowadays dependent on the development of those two-dimensional lipoprotein assemblies which we call biomembranes. Hence in the next chapters of this book attention is directed away from proteins and protein assemblies and refocused on lipids, biomembranes and bioenergetics.

[1] In *Symposium on the Contractile Process* held in New York, December, 1966.

9

Lipids, Lipid Assemblies and Biomembranes

1

In the preceding five chapters we have concentrated our attention on proteins and the structures formed from proteins. In the architecture of the body, however, other types of molecule are also employed. Frequently these latter types of molecule interact with proteins to form biological structures. Nucleic acids, which we shall describe in Chapter 13, combine with proteins to form, for example, ribosomes and viruses. However, perhaps the most important of these non-protein molecules so far as the *structure* of the animal body is concerned are the lipids. We shall see in Chapter 12, where we discuss cells, that an important part of much of the structure visible in the electron microscope is lipid.

2

Lipids are a rather heterogeneous collection of molecules. They are united by only one common characteristic: insolubility in water. Of the several types of lipid found in biological structures only two are of major importance: steroids and phospholipids. Various other types—cerebrosides, gangliosides, etc.—are to be found usually in smaller amounts.

3

The most important structural steroid is cholesterol. Its formula is shown in fig. 9.1.

Fig. 9.1 shows that cholesterol consists of a compact 'nucleus' formed of three six-membered rings and one five-membered ring. This group of rings is called the steroid nucleus. To this nucleus are attached a methyl group, a hydroxyl group and, at the top of fig. 9.1, a lengthy side chain.

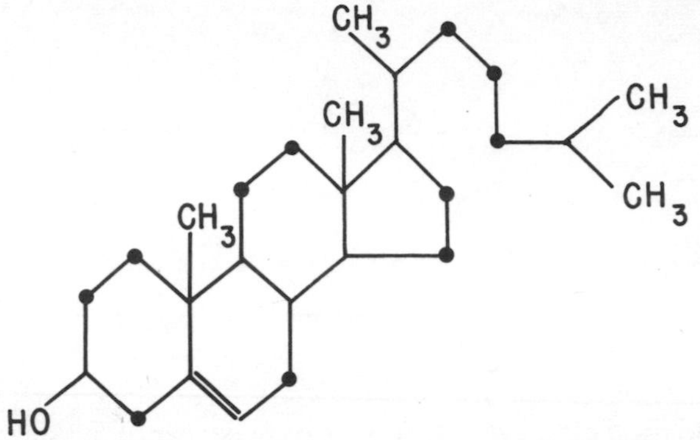

Fig. 9.1 The structure of cholesterol. CH_2 groups have been represented by dots.

4

The most well known and important phospholipids are derivatives of triglycerides. Triglycerides differ greatly in structure from steroids, being formed by the union of a trihydroxy alcohol—glycerol—with three fatty acids. This union is accomplished by a condensation reaction whereby three molecules of water are eliminated between the fatty acids and the glycerols.

Fig. 9.2 shows the formation of a triglyceride. The fatty acids are long chains of CH_2 groups with an occasional $-CH=CH-$ 'unsaturated' linkage. The structure of a triglyceride (fig. 9.2) shows that it is incapable either of ionisation or of forming hydrogen bonds. It follows that triglycerides are completely insoluble in water.

Triglycerides themselves do not play an important part in biological architecture. Derivatives of the triglycerides, on the other hand, are of considerable importance in this connection. These derivatives are called phospholipids or phosphatides. The reason for this nomenclature is not far to seek: they all contain a phosphate group.

The phosphate group replaces one of the fatty acid residues of a triglyceride. Thus fig. 9.3 shows the simplest of the phospholipids.

Examination of fig. 9.3 immediately shows a very important feature in which phospholipids differ from triglycerides. The phosphate group is capable of ionisation. Hence this part of the molecule is soluble in water. Fig. 9.3 may suggest that this potential hydrophilia will be completely masked and overshadowed by the

LIPIDS, LIPID ASSEMBLIES, BIOMEMBRANES

(a) *A saturated fatty acid*

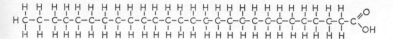

(b) *Glycerol*

CH₂OH
CHOH
CH₂OH

(c) *The formation of a triglyceride from a molecule of glycerol and three molecules of fatty acid*

Glycerol   Fatty acid

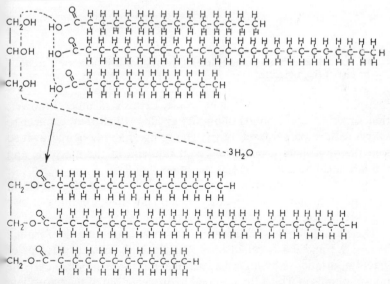

A triglyceride

Fig. 9.2 The figure shows how a triglyceride is formed by eliminating the elements of water between glycerol and three fatty acid molecules.

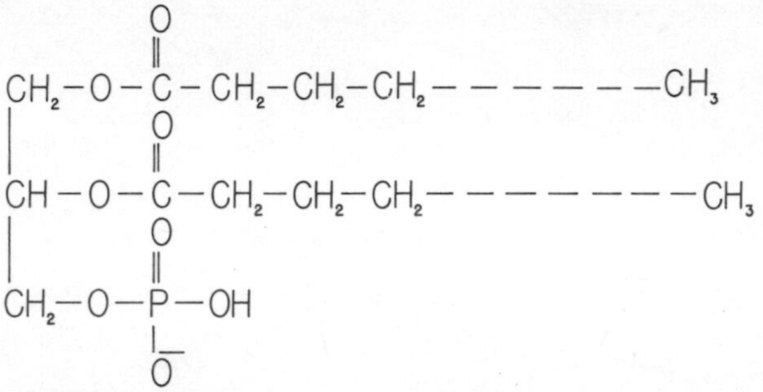

$$CH_2-O-\overset{\overset{\displaystyle O}{\|}}{C}-CH_2-CH_2-CH_2------CH_3$$
$$CH-O-\overset{\overset{\displaystyle O}{\|}}{C}-CH_2-CH_2-CH_2-------CH_3$$
$$CH_2-O-\overset{\overset{\displaystyle }{|}}{\underset{\underset{\displaystyle O^-}{|}}{P}}-OH$$

Fig. 9.3 Phosphatidic acid. At physiological pHs the phosphate group is electrostatically charged in the manner shown.

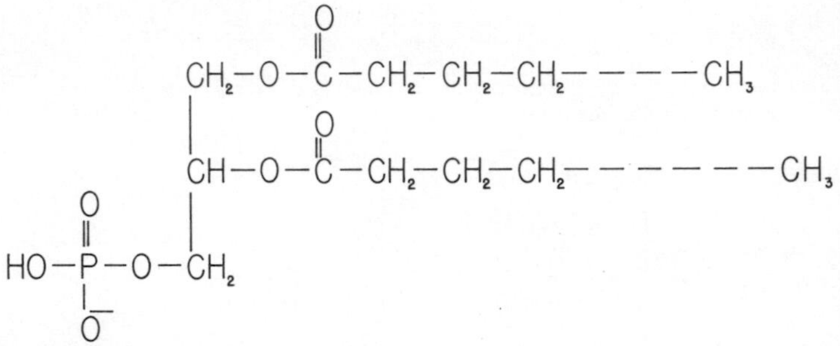

$$CH_2-O-\overset{\overset{\displaystyle O}{\|}}{C}-CH_2-CH_2-CH_2----CH_3$$
$$CH-O-\overset{\overset{\displaystyle O}{\|}}{C}-CH_2-CH_2-CH_2-----CH_3$$
$$HO-\overset{\overset{\displaystyle O}{\|}}{\underset{\underset{\displaystyle O^-}{|}}{P}}-O-CH_2$$

Fig. 9.4 The phosphate group is free to rotate so that it faces away from the rest of the molecule.

hydrophobia of the rest of the molecule. Let us remember, however, that single covalent bonds allow the groups which they connect to swivel with respect to each other. Hence fig. 9.3 may be redrawn so that the phosphate group projects at one end of the molecule and the fatty acid chains project at the other (fig. 9.4).

Fig. 9.4 shows that phospholipid molecules are hydrophobic at one end and hydrophilic at the other. This dual solubility is, we shall see below, of very great importance.

The phospholipid of which we have been examining the formula in figs. 9.3 and 9.4 is called phosphatidic acid. In fact, it is not of great importance in biological structures. Far more important are the phospholipids in which the terminal hydrogen atom of the phosphate group is replaced by one of a number of different nitrogen-containing groups. The most important of these derivatives are shown in Table 9.1.

TABLE 9.1 *Common Phospholipids*

A general formula for a phospholipid may be written in the following way:

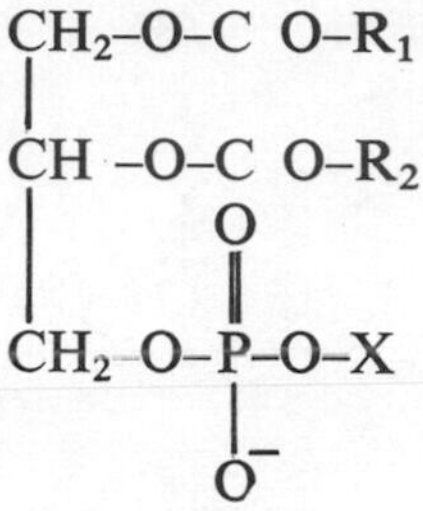

$$CH_2-O-C\ O-R_1$$
$$CH\ -O-C\ O-R_2$$
$$\underset{O}{|}$$
$$CH_2\ O-P-O-X$$
$$\underset{O^-}{|}$$

In this formula R_1 and R_2 are fatty acids. X, however, is variable and determines the particular phospholipid:

Name	Abbreviation	X
Phosphatidic acid	PA	—H
Phosphatidyl choline (lecithin)	PC	$-CH_2-CH_2-\overset{+}{N}(CH_3)_3$
Phosphatidyl ethanolamine (cephalin)	PE	$-CH_2-CH_2\ \overset{+}{N}H_3$
Phosphatidyl serine	PS	$-CH_2-\underset{\overset{|}{\overset{+}{N}H_3}}{CH}-COO^-$
Phosphatidyl inositol	PI	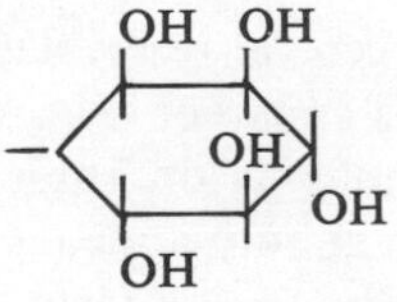 inositol ring with OH groups

TABLE 9.1 (*continued*)

In some cases the phospholipid is found to have lost one of its fatty acids and it is then referred to as a lysophosphatidyl–X:

Lysophosphatidyl X

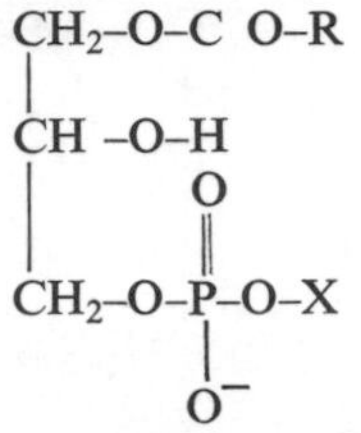

$$
\begin{array}{l}
CH_2\!-\!O\!-\!C\ O\!-\!R \\
\;|\\
CH\ \!-\!O\!-\!H \\
\;|\qquad\quad O\\
\;|\qquad\quad \|\\
CH_2\!-\!O\!-\!P\!-\!O\!-\!X \\
\qquad\qquad |\\
\qquad\qquad O^-
\end{array}
$$

In other cases one of the fatty acids is connected by an ether linkage to the rest of the molecule. This type of phospholipid is called a plasmalogen:

Plasmalogen X

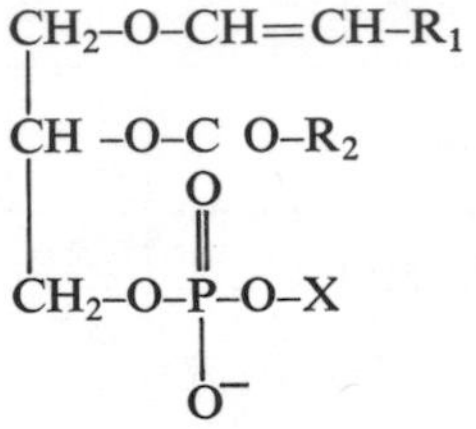

$$
\begin{array}{l}
CH_2\!-\!O\!-\!CH\!=\!CH\!-\!R_1 \\
\;|\\
CH\ \!-\!O\!-\!C\ O\!-\!R_2 \\
\;|\qquad\quad O\\
\;|\qquad\quad \|\\
CH_2\!-\!O\!-\!P\!-\!O\!-\!X \\
\qquad\qquad |\\
\qquad\qquad O^-
\end{array}
$$

The most commonly occurring of the phospholipids shown in Table 9.1 are phosphatidyl choline (lecithin) and phosphatidyl ethanolamine (cephalin). The other phospholipids occur less frequently.

Rather different from the phospholipids of Table 9.1 are the derivatives of sphingosine. Sphingosine, unlike the triglycerides we discussed above, possesses an amino group (fig. 9.5).

In biological systems it is found that attached to the amino group (NH_2) is a fatty acid, and attached to the CH_2OH group is a phosphate radical and one of the nitrogen-containing groups (X) of Table 9.1.

The general resemblance of sphingomyelin to the other phospholipids is apparent. Fig. 9.6 shows, moreover, that it shares with the phospholipids of Table 9.1 the important characteristic of being soluble in both aqueous and organic solvents.

Finally, to complete this brief résumé of the lipids of structural

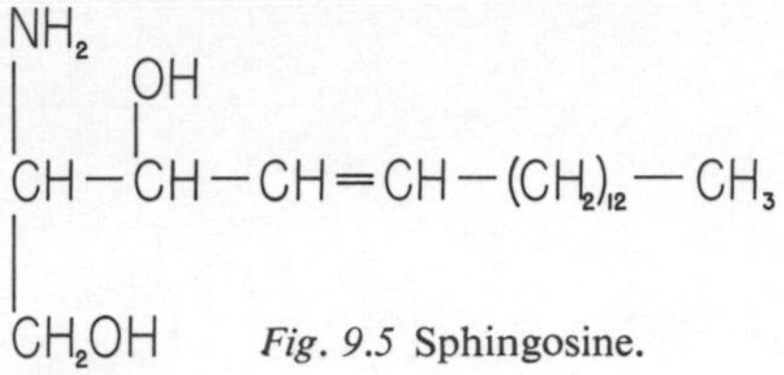

$$NH_2$$
$$|\quad OH$$
$$CH-CH-CH=CH-(CH_2)_{12}-CH_3$$
$$|$$
$$CH_2OH$$

Fig. 9.5 Sphingosine.

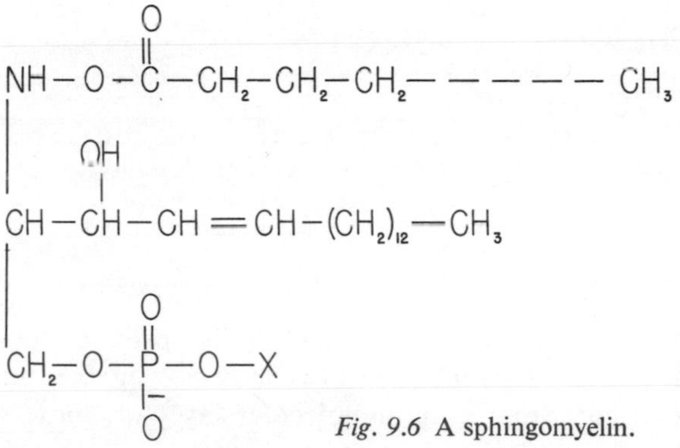

$$O$$
$$||$$
$$NH-O-C-CH_2-CH_2-CH_2-----CH_3$$
$$|\qquad OH$$
$$|\qquad |$$
$$CH-CH-CH=CH-(CH_2)_{12}-CH_3$$
$$|\qquad\qquad O$$
$$|\qquad\qquad ||$$
$$CH_2-O-P-O-X$$
$$|-$$
$$O$$

Fig. 9.6 A sphingomyelin.

importance, mention must be made of cerebrosides and gangliosides. These lipids do not contain a phosphate group and hence cannot be classified as phospholipids. Both types, however, are derivatives of sphingosine and can thus be best considered at this point. Cerebrosides are formed by adding a sugar such as galactose to sphingosine (fig. 9.7) and gangliosides are very complex entities consisting of sphingosine linked through galactose to glucose, a hexosamine and neuraminic acid.

5

The fact that phospholipids have hydrophobic and hydrophilic ends has already been emphasised. These solubility properties cause phospholipids to arrange themselves characteristically at air-water, or oil-water, surfaces. Phospholipids also form characteristic structures within aqueous and organic phases.

At an air-water, or oil-water, interface phospholipids orientate themselves so that their charged ends project into the water surface,

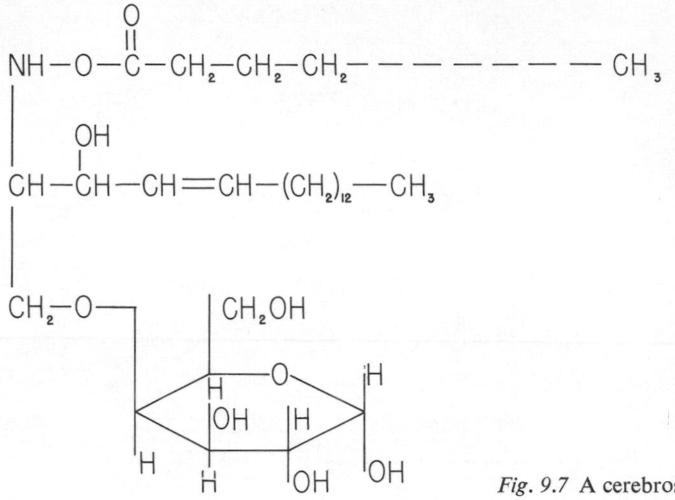

Fig. 9.7 A cerebroside.

and their hydrophobic fatty acid 'tails' project into the air or organic phase. This arrangement is shown in fig. 9.8. Such a line-up is said to constitute a monomolecular layer or, more succinctly, a monolayer.

In the main bulk of an aqueous or an organic phase phospholipids form minute globules known as micelles. In an aqueous phase their charged ends will face outwards, rendering the micelle soluble; in an organic phase the reverse arrangement again confers solubility. The organisation of phospholipid micelles is shown in fig. 9.9.

Thus we see that the dual solubility properties of phospholipid molecules cause certain types of multimolecular organisation.

6

So far in this chapter we have noted that lipids form important elements of certain biological structures but we have not yet said what these structures are. The fact that phospholipids very readily form monolayers has probably already suggested that the structures in question are membranes.

Membranes are ubiquitous structural elements in animal cells (fig. 12.5). They are also deeply involved in the biochemical and biophysical activities occurring within cells. All cells seem to have a

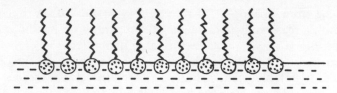

Fig. 9.8 A monolayer of phospholipid molecules. The phospholipids are symbolised by a circle representing the charged, hydrophilic, end and a zig-zag line representing the hydrophobic fatty acid chains.

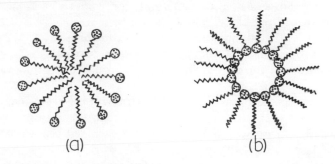

(a)   (b)

Fig. 9.9 Phospholipids form micelles of two sorts, depending on the nature of the surrounding liquid. If the liquid is polar, like water, the charged phosphates face outwards (a); if it is non-polar, like benzene, they face inwards (b).

boundary membrane at their periphery which acts as a permeability barrier. A great deal of work has been devoted to analysing the nature of this permeability barrier. It has been shown[1] that the boundary membrane is preferentially permeable to lipid-soluble molecules. The simplest explanation of this observation is to suppose that part of the membrane is composed of lipid. In order to pass through the membrane, molecules would have perforce to pass through a layer of lipid. This condition obviously favours lipid-soluble molecules.

If the cell's boundary membrane contains lipids it should be possible to extract them with organic solvents. First, however, it is essential to obtain isolated membranes to extract. Subjection of entire cells to organic solvents might well yield lipids, but there is no

[1] Collander, R. (1949), *Physiol. Plant.*, *3*, 45.

knowing from which part of the cell they originated. Fortunately, however, a reasonably pure membrane preparation is not difficult to obtain. Blood may be obtained in large quantities from slaughterhouses. Red blood cells can be burst, or haemolysed, by subjecting them to hypotonic saline solutions. The haemoglobin escapes and can be washed away from the broken membranes. The latter, known as red cell ghosts, form a reasonably pure and quantitatively adequate source of membranes for analysis.

If the lipids extracted from red cell ghosts are analysed most of the species mentioned earlier in this chapter are to be found.[1] Red cell ghosts are also important for another reason. The surface area of red blood cells is known with reasonable accuracy. Hence, if the total quantity of lipid extractable from red cell ghosts is determined it should be possible to calculate whether it is sufficient to form a continuous layer around the surface of the cell.

This determination was initially carried out by Gortner and Grendel[2] in 1925. In a classical experiment these two workers showed that there was sufficient lipid in each red cell to form a double layer around its perimeter. This work has been recently repeated[3] using the more sophisticated techniques of today and shown to be, in the main, valid.

Thus the concept of a bimolecular, rather than a monomolecular, layer became orthodox amongst biologists interested in membranes. This concept is schematised in fig. 9.10.

It is clear that a bimolecular layer is well suited to the task of forming a lipid barrier between two aqueous solutions. The protoplasm of cells may, of course, be regarded as an aqueous solution. Thus we are led to the idea that the charged ends of the phospholipid molecules abut the aqueous exterior and interior of cells, while the hydrophobic fatty acid chains form an oily interior to the membrane.

Permeability and lipid content are, however, not the only membrane characteristics which can be measured. Determination of parameters like surface tension and electrical capacitance indicate that the bimolecular lipid layer is coated with a covering of protein. This protein is probably in the α-helical configuration

[1] Except cerebrosides.
[2] Gortner, E. and Grendel, F. (1927), *J. Exp. Med.*, *41*, 439.
[3] Ways, P. and Hanahan, D. J. (1964), *J. Lipid Res.*, *5*, 319.

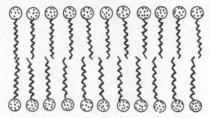

Fig. 9.10 A bimolecular layer of phospholipid molecules.

and seems to cover both surfaces of the membrane. There is also evidence that carbohydrate molecules may form part of some biomembranes.

The general picture of the cell membrane which we have built up in the foregoing account was crystallised by Davson and Danielli in 1943.[1] We can see that the whole structure is held together by electrostatic forces. Not only are the phospholipid molecules held in position by such forces but it is also believed that electrostatic interactions between phospholipids and amino-acid residues are responsible for holding the protein layers in position. The whole structure is thus highly labile and highly fragile. In this respect fig. 9.11 showing a Davson-Danielli type membrane is misleading: the structure looks too solid and permanent.

7

Knowing the dimensions of the molecules constituting a Davson-Danielli membrane, it is possible to calculate an approximate width. This turns out to be about 80A. A membrane of this dimension is far too thin to be visible in the optical microscope. Belief in its existence rested on the evidence outlined in the previous section until, in the nineteen-fifties, the electron microscope became generally available to biologists.

It is frequently found that the solution of a biological problem depends upon the selection of a suitable preparation or organism. The electron microscopy of biomembranes is no exception to this

[1] Davson, H. and Danielli, J. F., *The Permeability of Natural Membranes*, Cambridge University Press, 1943.

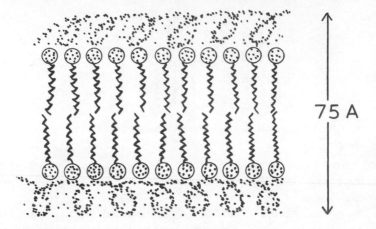

Fig. 9.11 Main features of the molecular architecture of biological membranes as envisaged by Davson and Danielli. Cholesterol, which is present in some membranes, has been omitted. The stippled spirals represent the putative protein layers of the membrane.

rule. An ideal preparation for the electron microscopist would be one in which cell membranes are concentrated and packed close together. A preparation which closely approaches this ideal has proved to be the myelin sheath of vertebrate axons.

That axons may be distinguished into two types—myelinated and unmyelinated—has been a familiar fact to microscopists for nearly a century. Axons belonging to the first type are surrounded by a fatty sheath, those belonging to the second type lack this sheath. The substance of the fatty sheath is called myelin: hence the nomenclature. A portion of a myelinated nerve is shown in fig. 9.12.

Running along the centre of the myelin sheath is the axon. In unmyelinated nerves this is naked. Fig. 9.12 shows that the sheath is interrupted at intervals. These interruptions are called the nodes of Ranvier. As we shall see later in this chapter the nodes have an important part to play in the transmission of nerve impulses. In addition they have a structural significance. Each of the segments into which they divide the myelin sheath is in fact developed from a single cell, called a Schwann cell.

That myelin had an interesting ultrastructure had been known for some years before the lens of electron microscopy was brought to

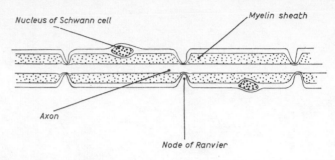

Fig. 9.12 Segment of a myelinated axon.

bear on the problem. X-ray diffraction and polarisation microscopy had suggested that myelin was composed of regular layers of membranes, stacked one above the other, and each about 80A thick. Chemical methods showed that these membranes were composed of lipid and protein.

It is thus not surprising to find that electron microscopists interested in the problem of membrane structure should, initially, have concentrated much attention on nerve myelin.

Two lines of research were destined to bear fruit. Firstly, Gasser[1] in a series of studies showed that the axons of unmyelinated neurons lay embedded in an associated Schwann cell. He demonstrated that they lay in deep troughs in this cell. Having in mind the fact that the membranes by which the viscera are suspended in the body cavity are called *mesenteries* Gasser decided to name these deep clefts *mesaxons*. The second fruitful line of research focused on the development of the myelin sheath around myelinated axons. B. B. Geren[2] investigated the development of myelin around the axons of embryonic chicks. Her findings, when taken together with those of Gasser, are most illuminating. At the beginning of the developmental process she found that the axon and the Schwann cell are related in very much the same way as that found for unmyelinated nerves by Gasser. However, there was one point of difference: only *one* axon was associated with a Schwann cell. The process of development seems to consist of the Schwann cell slowly rotating around the axon. This slow rotation is accompanied by growth of the mesaxon. This, as

[1] Gasser, H. S. (1952), *Cold Spring Harbour Symposium on Quantitative Biology*, *17*, 32.
[2] Geren, B. B. (1954), *Experimental Cell Research*, 7, 558.

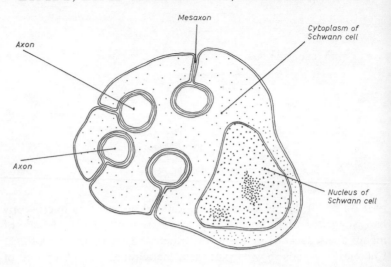

Fig. 9.13 The relationship of unmyelinated axons to a Schwann cell. The cell and nuclear membranes are represented by double lines. The mesaxon cleft is about 150A wide.

fig. 9.14 shows, transforms the mesaxon from a straight cleft into a tight spiral around the axon.

Close examination of Plate VII(*b*) shows that the myelin spiral is apparently composed of light and dark zones. The dark zones, moreover, alternate in intensity. Both dark lines are believed to represent positions where two membranes abut on each other. The darker line is believed to be the line of join of the interiors of two adjacent membranes, while the less dense line, called the *intraperiod* line, is regarded as the line of join of the outer surfaces of two membranes. This distinction has suggested to some workers that the chemical constitution of the exterior and interior of cell membranes differs.

The myelin spiral, we have seen, develops from the boundary membrane of a Schwann cell. Plate VII(*b*) shows that the spiral is very tight and may consist of many layers. It is clear that myelin provides an excellent opportunity for establishing the average dimension of a cell membrane. Measurements of the repeat distance of the period or the intraperiod line give values of about 180A.[1] We have seen that

---

[1] The dimensions observed in the electron microscope have been confirmed by X-ray analysis. Finean, J. B. (1958), *Exp. Cell Res.*, suppl. 5, 18.

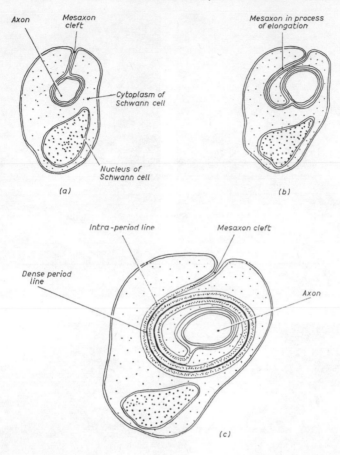

Fig. 9.14 Stages in the formation of myelin. In (*a*) a single axon lies at the bottom of a mesaxon cleft in a Schwann cell. In (*b*) the Schwann cell has begun to rotate and the growing mesaxon cleft is wound around the axon, (*c*) shows a later stage in the development when the mesaxon cleft is tightly spiralled around the axon. The fatty sheath so formed constitutes myelin.

the space between two intraperiod lines is filled by two layers of cell membrane. We are thus led to conclude that the Schwann cell membrane is no thicker than 90A.

Electron microscopy of other cell membranes suggests that 90A is a little high. In general, cell membranes seem to be 75–80A in

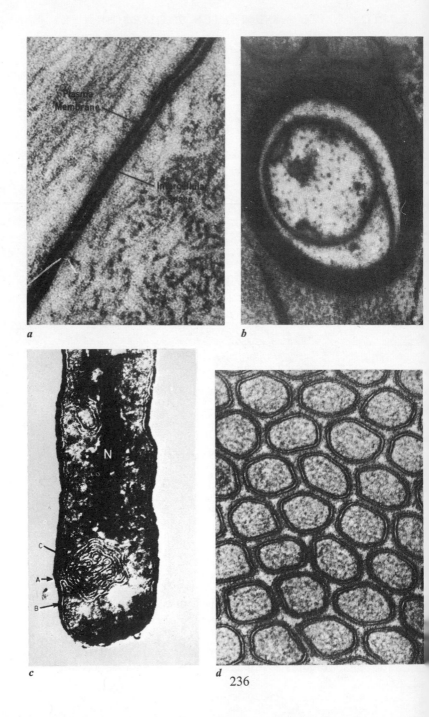

width.[1] This dimension accords admirably with the Davson-Danielli model described above. Because this type of membrane seems to be so universally distributed in cells it has been called by Robertson[2] the 'unit membrane'.

8

Although the unit membrane is widely accepted as the most likely structure for biological membranes there have been a number of alternative suggestions. The most attractive of these is the suggestion that biomembranes may have a micellar structure. Fig. 9.15 shows the nature of such a possible membrane structure.

We have already mentioned (fig. 9.9) that phospholipids very readily form micelles in aqueous solvents. It is easy to see that the micellar membrane of fig. 9.15 could without too much difficulty arise from the bimolecular structures we have considered above. It

---

[1] Sjöstrand (1963) has presented evidence to show that membranes in different parts of the same cell vary in thickness from 60A to 100A. *J. Ultrastruct. Res.*, *9*, 561.

[2] Robertson, J. D. (1960), *Progr. in Biophys. and Biophys. Chem.*, *10*, 354.

VII Biomembranes.

(*a*) this shows the cell membranes of two neuroglial cells of the annelid worm *Aphrodite*. The trilaminate structure of each membrane is clearly evident, as is the existence of a definite intercellular space filled with an amorphous material. Magnification 122,000×.

(*b*) this electron micrograph (magnification 76,000×) is of a transverse section through the myelin sheath of a nerve. In the centre of the sheath is the axon itself and at the top left-hand corner the origin of the mesaxon cleft can be seen. The granular material outside the sheath is the cytoplasm of the Schwann cell.

(*c*) a thin section through a bacterium (*Mycobacterium* sp.) shows the distinction between cell wall and cell membrane. The cell wall (*A*) is dense and comparatively thick. The cell membrane (*B*) is much less opaque and possesses the familiar 'sandwich' structure. At *C* an internal system of membranes, clearly derived from the cell membrane, is shown. Magnification 93,000×.

(*d*) this electron micrograph (magnification 83,000×) is of a transverse section across the microvilli of intestinal cells. The trilaminate structure of biomembranes is particularly well shown in this position.

(a) and (d) *courtesy of D. W. Fawcett:* The Cell: Its Organelles and Inclusions, Philadelphia, W. B. Saunders Co., 1966; (b) *courtesy of J. D. Robertson;* (c) *courtesy of T. Imaeda and M. Ogura (1963),* J. Bact., 85, 153.

is also clear that the membrane of fig. 9.15 would have the same dimensions as Robertson's unit membrane.

Evidence for the existence of micellar membranes comes principally

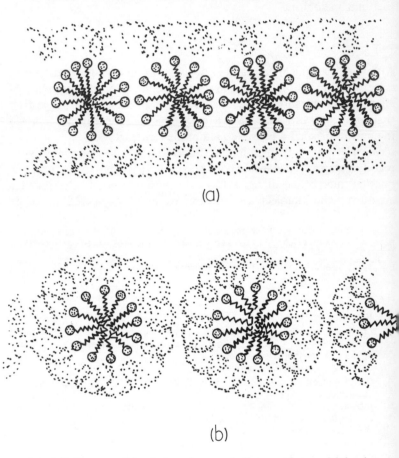

(a)

(b)

Fig. 9.15 Two possible designs for a micellar membrane. Molecular symbolism the same as in fig. 9.11.

from studies with the electron microscope.[1] It has, however, by no means been established that the images obtained are not in fact due to that bugbear of microscopists: preparative artefact. It is interesting to remember, in this connection, that the early optical microscopists

[1] See van Deenan, L. L. M., *Progress in the Chemistry of Fats and other Lipids*, 8, Part 1. Pergamon Press, London (1965).

feeling their way towards the cell theory believed, initially, that living matter was composed of globules. This heresy is mentioned again in Chapter 12.

The existence of micelles is difficult to prove or disprove with the electron microscope. If they exist, however, they would seem to have considerable consequences for the permeability properties of the membrane. For between the micelles charged pores might well be present. It is not difficult to imagine that such pores could exert a major control over the ingress and egress of materials from the cell.

In conclusion, however, it is well to recall our caution on p. 231. Biomembranes are highly labile structures. It is quite possible that in different circumstances the same membrane is sometimes a bimolecular sheet and sometimes a micellar mosaic.

9

The intimations of universality in Robertson's unit membrane theory tend to divert attention from the important fact that different membranes differ considerably in chemical constitution. Table 9.2 shows marked differences in amino-acid/phospholipid/cholesterol ratios in a selection of biological membranes. Analysis of the phospholipids of different membranes also shows considerable variation. Cerebrosides, for example, are the major phospholipid of myelin but have not been demonstrated in any other membrane.

TABLE 9.2

Protein and lipid composition of some biological membranes (molar ratios)

Membrane source	Amino-acid	Phospho-lipid	Cholesterol
Myelin	264	111	75
Erythrocyte	500	31	31
Micrococcus lysodeikticus	524	29	0
Streptococcus faecalis	441	31	0

(Adapted from Korn, E. D. (1966), *Science, 153*, 1496)

Sphingomyelin is well represented in red cell membranes, and is present to a lesser extent in myelin; it is, however, altogether lacking in bacterial and mitochondrial membranes.[1]

This diversity of chemical constitution reminds us that membranes are probably far from being mere passive scaffoldings supporting the dynamic activities of the living process. It is likely that they *do* function as supports and surfaces upon which reactions can proceed, but it is just as probably true that they are, perhaps at the same time, deeply implicated in many vital processes. In Chapter 11 we shall see that the visual pigments responsible for the eye's ability to detect light are part of the membranous structure of the photoreceptor cell. In the same chapter we shall see that the co-enzymes responsible for cellular respiration are probably keyed into the mitochondrial membranes. In Chapter 12 we shall find that the synthesis of proteins, at least in animal cells, is intimately associated with a system of membranous sacs and channels called the endoplasmic reticulum.

However, perhaps the most intensively investigated function of biomembranes is the function we discussed initially: that of acting as permeability barriers. The importance of a permeability barrier around the surface of cells does not need stressing. That the physico-chemical constitution of a cell's interior should be kept constant within narrow limits is, in most cases, of the utmost importance. It will be recalled, for instance, from Chapter 8 that the quaternary structure of haemoglobin is disrupted at pHs outside the usual values. It will also be recalled, from Chapter 7, that enzyme activity is critically dependent on the presence of activator ions. Many other examples could be cited. In sum, the constitution of the cell's interior critically affects the multitude of interlocking and interdependent reactions proceeding within it. This constitution is largely under the control of the boundary membrane.

In animal cells, as we shall see in Chapter 12, the interior of the cell is subdivided by membranes into a number of compartments. Again, it seems likely that the membranous walls of these compartments can exert considerable control on the reactions occurring within.

The means whereby membranes are able to govern the passage of

---

[1] Tables showing the lipid constitutions of different membranes are to be found in Korn, E. D. (1966), *Science*, *153*, 1491, and in van Deenen, L. L. M. (1965), *loc. cit.*

materials into and out of the cell, or its compartments, are still poorly understood. It remains true to say that biologists have not yet begun to understand the movements of the membrane during phagocytosis and pinocytosis at the molecular level. More progress has been made towards an understanding of the direct permeation of materials through the membrane. Many substances appear to diffuse through membranes under the influence of normal physico-chemical forces. The passage of other materials appears to depend upon a supply of energy from the metabolic machinery of the cell. Membrane biophysicists thus distinguish passive from active transport. For some materials it is difficult to decide which of the two types of transport obtains. In order to reach such a decision, the flow of material across the membrane has to be compared with that which would be expected if normal physico-chemical forces alone were acting. The branch of physical science which allows the scientist to predict a flow given the physico-chemical parameters is called irreversible thermodynamics.

10

Irreversible, or non-equilibrium, thermodynamics is too technical a subject to be described in this book.[1] It can be shown, however, that many of the flows of matter and energy across membranes are interconnected. Thus the active transport of one chemical species across a membrane affects the trans-membrane distribution of all the others. Now it is found that in the majority of cells sodium ions are actively extruded. It follows that the distribution of all the other ions across the cell membrane is affected.

Ions, as we noticed in Chapter 3, are electrostatically charged. It should not surprise us, therefore, to find that an uneven distribution of these charged bodies is reflected by an electrical potential difference across the cell membrane. The potential difference across most cell membranes has a value of between 50 mV and 60 mV. The outside of the membrane is positively charged compared with the inside.

In certain cells, known as excitable cells, the normal potential across the membrane—called, in these cells, the resting potential—is subject to sudden and transient alterations. If an excitable cell is

[1] A good introductory account may be found in Denbigh, K. G., *The Thermodynamics of the Steady State*, Methuen, London (1958).

stimulated, the resting potential may disappear to be replaced by a potential difference of the opposite sign. In other words, the membrane is repolarised. Instead of being about 55 mV positive on the outside compared with the inside, the polarity momentarily reverses so that the outside becomes about 50 mV negative to the inside. This repolarisation is only transient and the normal value of the resting potential re-establishes itself after a few milliseconds. The whole phenomenon is known as an *action potential*.

Action potentials are shown by all nerve and some muscle cells. It seems that the root cause of the action potential is an abrupt alteration in the sodium permeability of the nerve or muscle cell membrane. Instead of being relatively impermeable to sodium, the membrane suddenly becomes fully permeable to this ion. In consequence sodium ions which, it will be remembered, are normally continuously extruded from the interior, cascade inwards. This sudden inrush completely outweighs the small outward movement caused by the sodium pump. It is this mass movement which is responsible for the observed repolarisation.[1]

The most important biological feature of an action potential is that it is capable of self-propagation. Repolarisation of any particular small section of a nerve cell's membrane initiates a similar phenomenon in the immediately adjacent region. This in turn stimulates the next region, and so on. In a conventional, but nevertheless vivid, simile the propagation of an action potential along a nerve cell membrane is likened to the spread of a flame along a gunpowder trail.

To develop this simile a little, we may notice that the transmission of the flame along a gunpowder trail depends upon the chemical energy stored in the gunpowder. In the same way, transmission of an action potential along a nerve cell membrane depends upon chemical energy stored in the form of an uneven distribution of ions across the membrane. At root, as we have seen, this uneven distribution depends upon the activity of the sodium pump.

There is however, an important difference between our gunpowder trail and the nerve cell membrane. Once a flame has sped along the gunpowder trail no second flame can pass. The trail is burnt out, blackened and of no further use. This is not the case with the nerve

[1] In order to give these ideas greater reality it may be stated that an action potential is associated with an inward movement of 20,000 sodium ions through $1\mu^2$ of membrane: Hodgkin, A. L. (1957), *Proc. Roy. Soc. B.*, *148*, p. 4.

cell membrane. Immediately the action potential, or nerve impulse, has passed, the pumping mechanism reasserts itself and sodium is once more passed to the outside. In a very short space of time, measured in milliseconds, the resting potential is re-established. A second impulse can now be initiated and will be transmitted along the membrane. The small period during which the membrane is inactive is called the refractory period.

The transmission of action potentials provides the body with a means of rapid signalling between its parts. In general the rate of impulse transmission is proportional to the diameter of the axon. Thus, in the invertebrates, in places where rapid conduction is required, giant axons have developed. In some cases giant axons become very large indeed. The nerves which control the escape reflex of the squid, for example, possess axons up to 0·6 mm. in diameter. These axons, it is not surprising to find, have provided the nerve physiologist with excellent preparations in which to study the physical basis of the nerve impulse.

Great size, however, brings with it its own disadvantages. A nerve trunk can obviously not contain many fibres of 0·6 mm. diameter. What is gained in rapidity is lost in quantity. The optic nerve, for example, of the human eye is about 2 mm. in diameter. It follows that it could contain only four, or so, giant fibres. In consequence the human brain would be supplied with rather little information about the visual scene. Instead we find that the human optic nerve is composed of several hundred thousand axons. These are correspondingly small. The problem of conduction rate has, however, been solved in another way.

Fig. 9.12 showed that the myelin sheath around a myelinated axon is interrupted at intervals by nodes. The fatty substance of the myelin insulates the portion of the axon between the nodes. This internodal region is, in consequence, shielded from the influences which trigger action potentials. The only exposed and consequently stimulable regions of the axonal membrane are at the nodes. It follows that the impulse is believed to 'jump' from node to node. It is clear that this so-called 'saltatory' conduction will greatly increase the rapidity of impulse transmission. It is found that the fastest myelinated fibres conduct impulses considerably more rapidly than the unmyelinated giant fibres of invertebrates. In the mammals, nerve messages may be conducted by this system at velocities of over 100 metres/second.

It is clear from the foregoing account that lipoprotein membranes play many important parts in the architecture of living bodies. In particular, as we have seen, they form the structural basis of the animal body's communication system. Lipoprotein membranes are also very deeply implicated in processes even more fundamental to life on the surface of this planet: the processes of bioenergetics. The organelles essential to life's energy transactions are largely composed of lipoprotein membranes, and it is found that the enzymes and co-enzymes on which these processes depend are keyed into these membranes. Indeed this localisation of the primary events of bioenergetics in or on membranous assemblies of enzymes has greatly complicated the study of these vital phenomena. Nevertheless, considerable advances in this field of study have been made in recent years. Accordingly it is to bioenergetics that the next two chapters are devoted.

10

Bioenergetics

1

The distinction between animate and inanimate nature was for many centuries tied closely to the concept of energy. We still use the terms 'quick' and 'dead' and our first unconscious distinction between living and non-living forms tends to be that the former display some kind of movement whereas the latter do not. We find it difficult to believe that the energy driving the living body is not somehow different in kind from the external forces which affect inorganic materials. However, the scientific revolution of the last three centuries leaves no doubt that a distinction between animate and inanimate creation is a false distinction. We are all 'parts of the maine'.

Ultimately 'life-as-we-know-it' depends on the sun's radiant energy. The constant stream of solar photons bombarding the turning planet is the primordial source of all living activity.[1] As Szent-Györgyi[2] puts it, 'when a photon ejected by the sun interacts with an electron of a molecule on our globe, then the electron is raised to a higher energy level to drop back, as a rule within 10^{-8} to 10^{-9} seconds, to its ground state. Life has shoved itself between the two processes, catches the electron in its high energy state and lets it drop back to the ground level within its own machinery, using the energy thus released for its own maintenance.' Szent-Györgyi illustrates his concept by a diagram similar to fig. 10.1.

When Szent-Györgyi writes of life 'shoving itself' into the path of the falling electron he clarifies an extraordinarily complex affair in a single vivid phrase. Nonetheless the phrase can be criticised; in an important way it begs the question. For life has no independent

[1] Gaffron, H. in *The Origins of Prebiological Systems*, edit. Fox, W., Academic Press, New York and London, 1965, p. 437.
[2] Szent-Györgyi, A. (1959), *Faraday Soc. Disc.*, 27, 111–14.

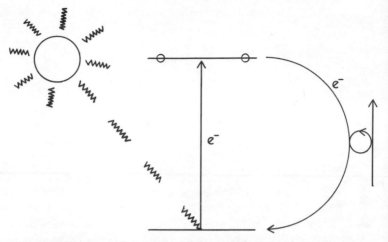

Fig. 10.1 This symbolism is adapted from Szent-Györgyi: *Introduction to a Sub-molecular Biology*, Academic Press, New York and London, 1960, p. 18. It shows that when a solar photon of appropriate energy is absorbed by an atom or molecule an electron (e^-) is raised from a low to a high energy level. Normally it falls back to its ground state in a very short space of time (10^{-8} secs.). Some living organisms have developed a mechanism for harnessing the electron's fall. This mechanism (represented by a small circle in the figure) traps some of the energy liberated by the falling electron and uses it for the organism's purposes. These purposes are symbolised by the arrow on the right-hand side of the diagram.

energy 'entire of itself'. The situation might be better figured by another simile. We have all seen how a heavy rainstorm beating on the tarmac of a road creates a shifting pattern of activity as the drops splash back. In the same way the storm of solar photons creates the shifting pattern of activity over the surface of the globe which we know as life.

Fig. 10.1 is nonetheless extremely useful as it concentrates our attention on the essence of bioenergetics. It points up the fact that life's energy, like much of the energy of our modern technology, is based on the movement of electrons. The body, however, unlike the artefacts of modern technology, is not based on metals and the metallic bond, but on carbon compounds and the covalent bond. Thus the electron movements on which the organism's energetics depend are infinitesimal movements between atoms, not surges along metallic conductors.

We saw, in Chapter 3, that some atoms are more electronegative than others (Table 3.2). In other words some atoms have a greater attraction for electrons, a greater electron affinity, than others. Table 3.2 shows that one of the most electronegative atoms is oxygen. Indeed oxygen is the best known of the electronegative atoms. When it attracts electrons from another atom the latter atom is said to be *oxidised*. On the other hand oxygen, receiving these extra electrons, or electron, is said to be *reduced*. The electron movements in oxidation-reduction (redox) reactions are the movements on which all the activities of living things are based. Hence it is important to consider this type of reaction rather more closely.

2

The best known example of a redox reaction is the oxidation of hydrogen by oxygen to form water:

$$2H_2 + O_2 \rightarrow 2H_2O$$

We discussed this reaction in Chapter 7. It will be remembered that a great deal of energy is liberated in the form of heat and light when the reaction occurs. In other words the reaction is highly exothermic. Now where does all this energy appear from? We said in Chapter 7 that in the water molecules the atoms were in a lower energy state than when they existed independently. But can we discern a structural reason for this increased stability?

We saw in Chapter 2 that the energy associated with an electron was a function of its position in the structure of the atom. The electrons in oxygen's valency shell are in a lower energy state than the lone electron circling hydrogen's nucleus. Consequently when hydrogen and oxygen react, hydrogen's electron moves far over into oxygen's sphere of influence (fig. 3.18). In this position it is in a considerably lower energy state. The difference in the energy levels, when summed over all the atoms reacting, expresses itself as the observed violent explosive reaction.

As Table 3.2 shows, oxygen is not the only highly electronegative atom. Chlorine is, for example, equally electronegative. When it reacts with hydrogen to form hydrochloric acid an exactly analogous electron movement occurs:

$$H_2 + Cl_2 \rightarrow 2HCl$$

Once again hydrogen's electron is pulled far over towards the chlorine molecule. Because the reaction is so similar the terms 'oxidisation' and 'reduction' have been extended to describe it. Chlorine is said to have oxidised hydrogen and, vice versa, hydrogen is said to have reduced chlorine.

Thus we see that the terms 'oxidisation' and 'reduction', originally developed to describe reactions in which hydrogen and/or oxygen were involved, have had their denotation extended. They now cover all reactions in which electron movements of the type described occur.

3

If redox reactions are basically movements of electrons it should, in principle, be possible to measure them by using electrical recording instruments. For, after all, an electric current is nothing more than a flow of electrons in a wire. This idea has proved practical.

If a solution of reductant and a solution of oxidant are connected together by a wire, electrons are found to flow from the reductant to the oxidant. This is as expected, for the oxidant (for example, oxygen or chlorine) has a high electron affinity, whereas the reductant (for example, hydrogen) has a low electron affinity. By making use of the piece of apparatus shown in fig. 10.2 it is possible to measure the strength of this current.

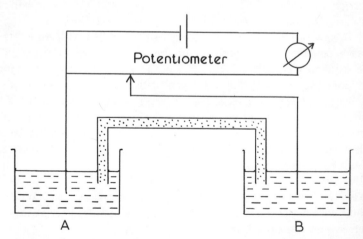

Fig. 10.2 The redox potential of a solution may be measured by the apparatus shown in the figure. A contains a standard solution and B a solution whose redox potential is unknown. Into both solutions dips a platinum electrode. Completing the circuit is a tube filled with agar (stippled in the figure).

Fig. 10.2 shows that a wire dipping into a solution whose electron affinity is arbitrarily taken as zero (hydrogen electrode) is connected to the wire of a potentiometer. A wire dipping in the solution whose electron affinity is to be tested is also connected to the wire of the potentiometer. By adjusting the position of the contact on the potentiometer wire the flow of electrons from the standard solution towards the unknown solution can be exactly balanced by the opposing electron flow generated by the battery. When this null point is found the strength of current can be calculated. As we have defined the solution in *A* as having zero electron affinity, the strength of the current is proportional to the electron affinity of the solution being tested in *B*.

It is clear that if we keep the solution in *A* the same and test a number of different solutions in *B* we can arrange the electron affinities of the latter in order. Those with greater electron affinities will be capable of attracting electrons from those lower in the scale. In other words those with greater electron affinities will be capable of oxidising those with lesser electron affinities. This scale of electron affinities is called the *redox potential* scale. It is not difficult to relate the difference in redox potential of two chemical species to the amount of energy liberated when the two species interact.

Before leaving this account of the nature of redox potentials it is important to be clear about one point of possible confusion. We have seen that a redox potential measures the electron affinity of a chemical species. However it is frequently convenient to look at matters rather the other way around. Clearly those substances with low electron affinities might equally well be regarded as substances with high 'electron pressures'. A chemical species with a high electron pressure will be able to 'force' electrons on to species with lower pressures. We might say, for instance, that hydrogen has a higher electron pressure than oxygen and hence can force its electron on to the latter atom. The electron pressure of a chemical species is thus a measure of its reducing power. But more important than this, the concept of electron pressure brings matters into line with the gravitational analogy we discussed in Chapter 2. For the electrons in a chemical species with a high electron pressure might be said to be in positions of high potential energy. As an electron 'falls' from a 'high' to a 'low' position its potential energy decreases. This gravitational analogy has already been made use of in fig. 10.1 and will be employed in several other figures in this chapter. The confusion arises when we forget that the substances on to which the electron 'falls', the substances at the bottoms of these figures, have the *higher* redox potential. The confusion disappears when we bear in mind that redox potentials measure electron affinities.

4

After this brief digression into the method by which electron affinities, or redox potentials, may be measured we can return to the main thread of our discussion. The multifarious phenomena of life are at root actuated by electron movements occurring between atoms undergoing redox reactions. For this to happen atoms at opposite ends of the redox potential scale have to be brought into contact. But, in turn, for this to happen these atoms must first of all exist.

Life on the surface of this planet is by no means a small-scale affair. The total mass of living matter in the biosphere is of the order of $n \times 10^{17}$ gm. where n is a small number. The total quantity of carbon built into the bodies of green plants during the history of the Earth is in the region of 10^{26} gm. which approaches one-fiftieth of the weight of the entire globe. The point here is that the colossal scale on which life is lived would long since have exhausted any indigenous sources of oxidative energy. Indeed there is only one energy source which could supply this gigantic demand over the several billion years of geological history. This source, of course, is the uncontrolled nuclear fusion furnace which is the sun.

Solar photons, as we have already noticed, are trapped and used to raise electrons from low to high energy states. When atoms possessing electrons in these high energy states come into contact with electronegative atoms like oxygen we have, as we have seen, a classical redox reaction situation. Our next task, therefore, must be to examine the methods organisms have evolved to trap photons and make use of their energy to raise electrons into higher orbitals.

5

The development of an effective means of trapping and utilising the energy of solar photons probably marked a decisive break-through in the early development of life.[1] Lynn White, in a fascinating book

---

[1] See *The Origin of Life on Earth*: *the proceedings of the first Moscow conference*, Pergamon Press, London, 1959.

on the development of medieval technology,[1] provides an analogy. He presents evidence for the belief that the great complex of social relations and forms of thought which made up the fabric of feudal society was dependent on the development of an efficient stirrup. 'Antiquity', he writes, 'imagined the centaur; the early Middle Ages made him master of Europe.' Something similar might be said about the development of the chlorophyll molecule. That life should gain a firm and, we hope, permanent foothold on the surface of the planet was dependent on the 'invention' of this molecule.

Like Lynn White's stirrup, however, chlorophyll was probably not without its precursors. We shall see below that the chlorophyll molecule is strikingly similar to haem. Haem, as we have noticed in several earlier chapters, is a ubiquitous chemical group. Not only is it an important constituent of haemoglobin and myoglobin but it is also essential to the function of the almost universally distributed cytochromes. If we investigate the biosynthesis of haem and chlorophyll we find that the initial steps are common to both molecules. It seems probable that haem is the earlier molecule[2] and chlorophyll a more recent modification. By recent, in this context, is meant not earlier than about 2,500 million years ago.

Let us now look at the chemical structure of these key molecules. Chlorophyll and haem are both modifications of a chemical structure known as porphin. Porphin, as fig. 10.3 shows, is a very beautiful structure. It consists of four five-membered pyrrole rings joined together into a larger ring system by CH, or methene, bridges. It can be seen, moreover, that the porphin molecule is built of an extensive system of alternate single and double covalent bonds. It follows from our discussion in Chapter 3 that there is widespread electron delocalisation. In fact the Pullmans[3] have shown that there are 26π electrons contributed by 24 different atoms. This extremely large system of π electrons is probably responsible for some of the important biological properties of porphin derivatives. Finally the extensive delocalisation ensures, as we noticed in Chapter 3, that the whole porphin molecule is planar. Like a thin disc it fits into the

[1] *Medieval Technology and Social Change*, Lynn White, Jr., Clarendon Press, Oxford, 1962.

[2] Granick, S. in *Evolving Genes and Proteins*, ed. Bryson and Vogel, Academic Press, New York and London, 1965, pp. 67–88.

[3] Pullman, A. and Pullman, B., *Quantum Biochemistry*, Interscience, New York and London, 1963.

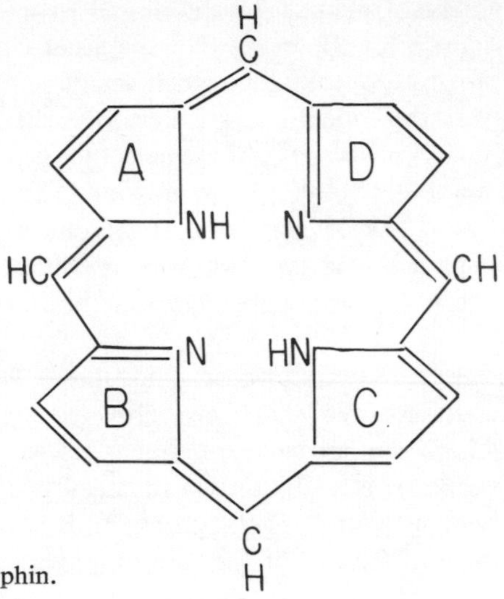

Fig. 10.3 Porphin.

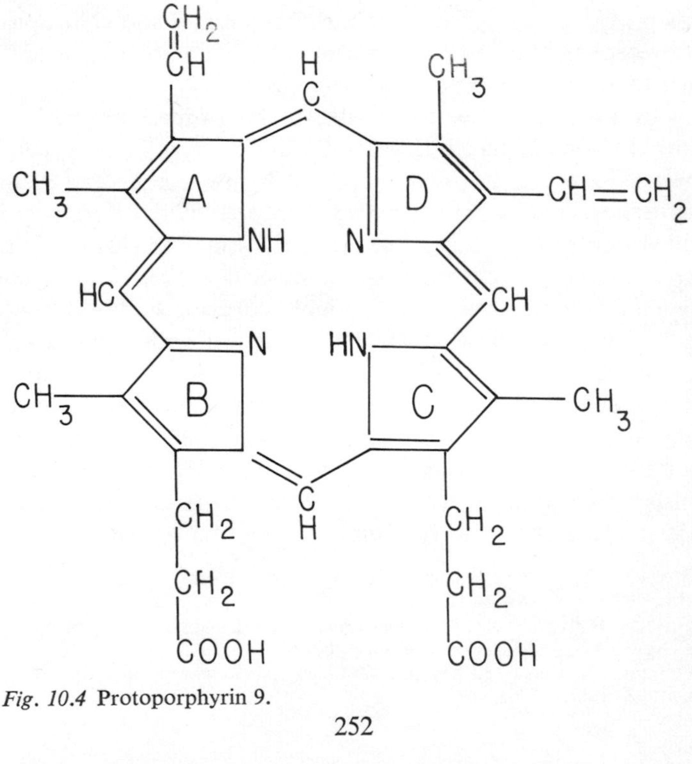

Fig. 10.4 Protoporphyrin 9.

252

crevices which have been shown to exist for it in myoglobin and haemoglobin.[1]

In biological systems the porphin group is always modified by the addition of side chains. The most common of these modifications are to be found in a structure called protoporphyrin 9 (fig. 10.4) from which both haem and chlorophyll are derived.

The haem of haemoglobin, myoglobin and the cytochromes[2] can be derived from protoporphyrin 9 by inserting an atom of iron in the centre of the main ring system (fig. 10.5).

The iron atom is believed to displace two protons from the pyrrole nitrogens and is hence held in position by ionic forces. The haem molecule, it will be noticed, has, like protoporphyrin 9, a hydrophobic and a hydrophilic end. The carboxylic acid groups shown at the bottom of fig. 10.5 are able to ionise and hence render this end of the molecule soluble in water. The hydrocarbon groups at the top of the molecule in fig. 10.5 have no such ability and consequently render this end of the molecule hydrophobic. It will be remembered from our account in Chapter 6 that both the myoglobin and haemoglobin molecules have 'oily' clefts into which haem can fit. The different solubilities of opposite ends of the molecule ensure its correct orientation in the cleft.

The modification which protoporphyrin 9 undergoes to form chlorophyll is slightly more complicated. Fig. 10.6 shows that in addition to the insertion of a central magnesium atom the ring system has undergone several modifications. Most important of these are, first, that the $-CH_2CH_2COOH$ chain attached to ring C is altered and closed up with the methene carbon to form an extra five-membered ring and, second, that the other $-CH_2CH_2COOH$ group, on ring B, is joined to a lengthy (twenty carbon) alcohol called phytol. The first modification considerably alters the properties of the ring system, the second modification is probably of importance in attaching the chlorophyll molecule to a chloroplast lamella (Chapter 11).

In general, however, it can be seen that the structures of chlorophyll and haem are very similar. In spite of this similarity it is found that chlorophyll is several thousand times more effective than haem

---

[1] A crevice is also believed, on less secure evidence, to house haem in the cytochrome molecules.

[2] Cytochrome a_3 is an exception to this statement. This has $-HC=O$ in place of $-CH=CH_2$ on ring A.

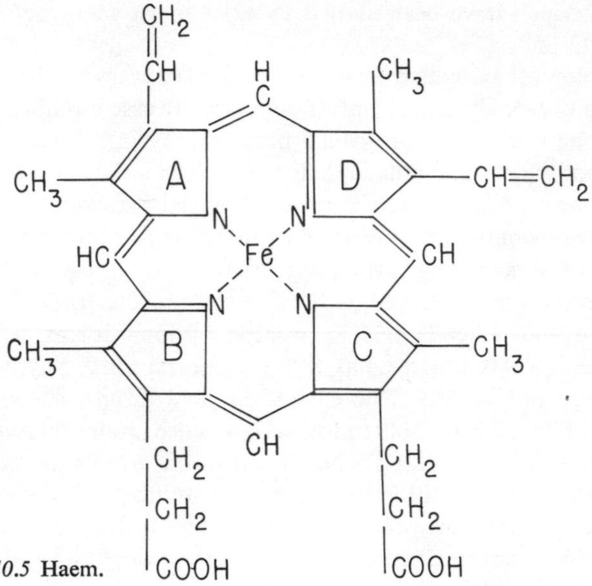

Fig. 10.5 Haem.

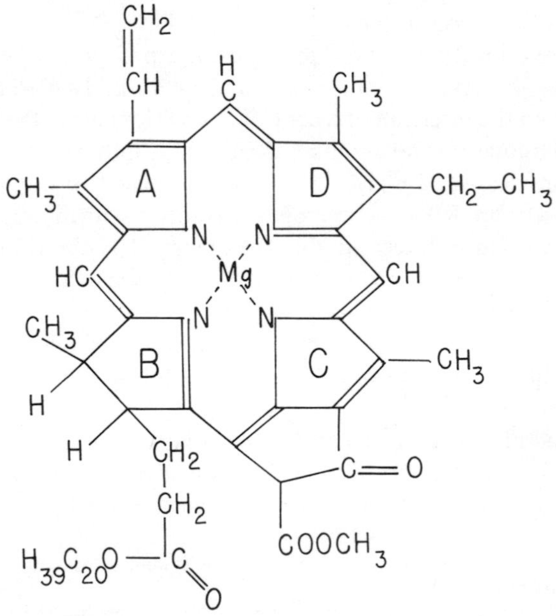

Fig. 10.6 Chlorophyll.

254

in trapping solar photons. This increased efficiency is largely due to the substitution of magnesium for iron in the centre of the ring system.[1] Moreover, the absorption occurs in the visible spectrum— hence the green colour of chlorophyll-containing plants. This is no accident, for the major part of the radiant energy reaching the planet's surface from the sun is concentrated in this part of the spectrum.[2]

The physical basis of the absorption of a photon by an atom or molecule was outlined in Chapter 2. We saw that the photon's energy was absorbed in raising an electron from a low to a high orbital. Chlorophyll has many electrons capable of this elevation. It is believed that any one of the delocalised (π) electrons may be raised on receipt of a photon bearing a suitable energy packet. The electron in its high orbital is said to be in an excited state. This is symbolised by *. Thus the transition of a π electron to a higher orbital is symbolised as $\pi \rightarrow \pi^*$ or, more succinctly, $\pi\pi^*$. The reverse process whereby an electron falls back to its ground state and in the process emits energy is symbolised as a $\pi^*\pi$ transition.

It is certain that the major absorption bands of the chlorophyll molecule are due to $\pi\pi^*$ transitions.[3] There are, however, other possibilities. For example, an electron orbiting a single atom, usually nitrogen or oxygen, may be raised on receipt of a suitable photon to one of the π^* orbitals. Accordingly such transitions are symbolised as $n\pi^*$ transitions. $n\pi^*$ transitions are considerably rarer than the $\pi\pi^*$ type, but when they occur they are much longer lasting. There are a number of other possible ways in which photons may be absorbed by chlorophyll. At present, however, the precise events in the initial 10^{-8} seconds after the absorption of a photon are far from being fully understood.

6

We have seen above that the development of the chlorophyll molecule provided living organisms with an efficient means of absorbing solar photons. It is emphasised in fig. 10.1 that when the

[1] Calvin, M. in *Perspectives in Biology and Medicine*, 1962, pp. 147–72.
[2] The wave-length of the electromagnetic radiation constituting the visible spectrum ranges from about 4,000A to about 7,000A.
[3] Clayton, R. K. in *Photophysiology*, Vol. 1, edited by Giese, A. C., Academic Press, New York and London, 1964, pp. 155–97.

excited electrons fall back to the ground state their fall is coupled to a mechanism designed to synthesise covalent bonds. We must now turn our attention to this mechanism.

In Chapter 3 we discussed the concept of energy-rich bonds. We noticed that the most important of the molecules possessing such bonds was ATP. Hydrolysis of ATP yields ADP+P_i and about 7 kcal. of energy.[1] This energy is used by organisms for the multitudinous energy-requiring activities of their lives. Thus one important way in which the energy liberated by electrons falling from high to low orbitals could be used would be in the synthesis of ATP from ADP and P_i. We find that this is indeed what happens in the green plant.

7

The mechanism by which ATP synthesis is coupled to the fall of electrons is called cyclic photosynthetic phosphorylation or, rather more compactly, cyclic photophosphorylation. Its main features are schematised in fig. 10.7.

Fig. 10.7 shows that when chlorophyll (chl) receives a solar photon of appropriate energy one of its electrons is raised to an excited orbital. Instead, however, of dropping back to the ground level in the chlorophyll molecule the electron is withdrawn from chlorophyll altogether. This leaves chlorophyll positively charged. Remembering our discussion in the earlier part of this chapter we can say that chlorophyll has been oxidised. Putting it yet another way we can borrow the terminology of solid state physics and say that chlorophyll has been left with a hole. These, of course, are all different ways of saying the same thing: that chlorophyll has lost an electron.

The electron having escaped from chlorophyll is transferred first to Vitamin K, or FMN[2], and then, through a number of cyto chromes, back to chlorophyll. When the electron arrives once more at chlorophyll it neutralises its positive charge. Or, to use our alternative terminology, chlorophyll is reduced or its hole is filled.

Fig. 10.7 shows that the electron is not so much transferred from co-factor to cytochromes to chlorophyll, but cascades over these

---

[1] P_i is biochemist's shorthand for inorganic phosphate (H_3PO_4).
[2] FMN: the initials stand for flavine mononucleotide.

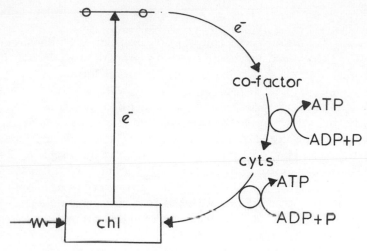

Fig. 10.7 Cyclic photophosphorylation.
  chl=chlorophyll.
  co-factor=FMN, or Vit K.
  cyts=cytochromes.
For further explanation see text.

molecules. Its potential energy continually decreases. The co-factor and the co-enzymes are interposed to fragment its fall into more manageable fractions. Manageable for what purpose? Fig. 10.7 shows that between co-factor and cytochrome, and between cytochrome and chlorophyll, a coupling mechanism exists. This connects the electron's fall to the synthesis of ATP from ADP and P_i. In short, the electron is geared into a mechanism which produces energy-rich phosphate bonds ($\sim$P).

8

Energy-rich phosphate bonds form the common energy currency of living organisms. They are extremely convenient, for the terminal phosphates are easily hydrolysed and their energy liberated. However, like pounds, shillings and pence, energy-rich bonds suffer from the disadvantage of being only too easily used up. Sensible citizens store their wealth in less readily accessible forms than money bags beneath the mattress. Similarly the living cell stores the major part of its energy in a less labile form than the ATP molecule. The most important energy stores in the living organism are the covalent bonds holding carbohydrate molecules together.

Carbohydrate molecules consist of the elements carbon, hydrogen and oxygen joined together in various proportions. Glucose, for example, can be shown to have the empirical formula $C_6H_{12}O_6$; sucrose, $C_{12}H_{22}O_{11}$; and starch, $C_n(H_2O)_m$ where n and m are both large numbers. It follows that if the living organism is to store its energy in the form of the covalent bonds of carbohydrate molecules, carbon, hydrogen and oxygen must somehow be assimilated from the environment. How does the organic world solve this problem?

The solution is striking in its simplicity. Carbon dioxide is reduced. Hydrogen is used to effect the reduction. In order to bring about this reduction, hydrogen is first attached to a co-enzyme—NADP.[1] In other words, NADP is reduced to NADPH. With appropriate enzymes the hydrogen may be eased off NADP on to a derivative of CO_2. In essence, CO_2 has been reduced.

Enzymes, it will be remembered, do not affect the direction of a reaction, only its speed. It follows that the affinity of NADP for hydrogen must be even less than that of CO_2. Indeed, NADP has a very low affinity for hydrogen; to put it another way, it has a very low redox potential. In consequence it is by no means easy to add hydrogen to NADP in the first place.

Several different mechanisms of various levels of complexity have been developed to achieve this end. It will be seen below that the complexity is connected with the raw material which the organism uses as a hydrogen source.

9

In the simple case of the anaerobic sulphur bacterium *Chromatium*, hydrogen gas itself can act as the hydrogen source. Hydrogen molecules are able to reduce NADP to NADPH and this, in turn, with the aid of ATP, is able to reduce CO_2[2] to yield carbohydrate molecules. Thus, if the enzyme systems of *Chromatium* are released from the cell, and provided with ATP and hydrogen gas, carbohydrates are synthesised *in vitro*. In other words, if *Chromatium* is supplied with hydrogen gas the sole function of light is to provide the energy

[1] NADP: the initials stand for nicotinamide adenine dinucleotide phosphate.
[2] This, as was mentioned above, is shorthand. As will be outlined later, the compound reduced by NADPH is not CO_2 itself but a molecule derived from it.

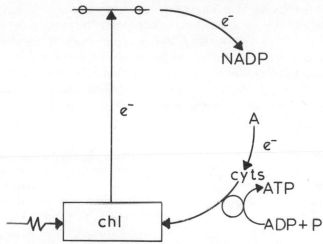

Fig. 10.8 Some bacteria are able to reduce NADP using thiosulphate or succinate (A) as a source of electrons.

necessary to synthesise ATP. This can be achieved by the cyclic photophosphorylation mechanism already described.

However, in general, hydrogen gas is not available to act as a hydrogen source. At best it is present in only very small amounts. Certainly the innumerable organisms populating the biosphere could not subsist on so meagre a diet. It follows that some other source of hydrogen has to be found.

It is found that some bacteria can make use of succinate and that others utilise thiosulphate. In both cases, however, it can be shown that the electron affinities of the sources are rather greater than the electron affinity of NADP. It follows that there is no tendency for electrons to move from succinate or thiosulphate on to NADP. In other words, succinate or thiosulphate will not normally reduce NADP. Here then is a problem. How are these bacteria able to use electrons of such a low potential to reduce NADP where the electrons are at a higher potential?

It is obvious that in order to reduce NADP the potential of electrons originating in succinate or thiosulphate has to be raised. The energy necessary to accomplish this work is believed to be extracted by chlorophyll from solar photons. The sequence of events as it is understood[1] at present is shown in fig. 10.8.

[1] Whateley, F. R. and Losada, M. in *Photophysiology*, Vol. I, edited by Giese, A. C., Academic Press, New York and London, 1964, pp. 111–54.

Fig. 10.8 shows that electrons from the source (succinate or thiosulphate) symbolised as 'A' pass first over the cytochromes and then on to chlorophyll. As they fall from cytochrome to chlorophyll they are coupled to a mechanism designed to synthesise ATP from ADP and P_i. This part of the diagram should be compared with fig. 10.7. The chlorophyll on to which the electron finally passes may be regarded as positively charged. The positive hole, we may imagine, has been left by an electron expelled from chlorophyll on receipt of a solar photon. This phenomenon we have already discussed under the heading of cyclic photophosphorylation. The electron from 'A' thus finds a place reserved for it in the chlorophyll skeleton, perhaps in the π pool. Very quickly, however, it, or another electron—and there is no way of labelling or distinguishing between elementary particles like electrons—is raised to an excited orbital by absorption of another photon. From this high position it is able to fall back on to NADP reducing it in the process to NADPH.

It may puzzle the reader to find that after tracing the path of an electron we end up by saying that it reduces NADP and instead of writing $NADP^-$ we write NADPH. This puzzle is resolved when it is remembered that the substrate we symbolised by 'A' may be either succinate or thiosulphate. Both these are ions formed ultimately by the ionisation of a parent acid:

$$\text{succinic acid} \rightleftharpoons H^+ + \text{succinate}^-$$

Hence when we remove an electron from succinate we are left with an excess of H^+ ions in solution.[1] When the electron reaches NADP we can see that the negative charge engendered will be neutralised by the attraction of an H^+ ion giving NADPH.

Now although succinate and thiosulphate are rather more common than hydrogen gas they are nevertheless far from being the commonest materials on the surface of the planet. The large-scale existence of life on earth depends on the electron source 'A' being widely distributed in large quantities. Few materials are more common or widespread on the surface of the globe than water. If H_2O could be used as an electron source, prospects for the continuing development of life on earth would be assured. In parenthesis, it is interesting to notice that the technology of *H. sapiens* may also depend ultimately on the use of water as an energy source. It is at least arguable that when the earth's fossil fuels have been exhausted nuclear fusion

[1] The physical reality of H^+ ions was discussed at the end of Chapter 3.

reactions making use of water's hydrogen atoms can alone ensure the survival of human civilisation.

Some two thousand million years ago a method for using water molecules as sources of electrons was devised. Today the surface of the planet is covered with a green interface in which electrons derived from water are energised by incoming solar photons and on falling back to their ground states bring about the reduction of NADP.

The transference of electrons from water molecules to NADP is more difficult than their transference from succinate or thiosulphate to NADP. If we recall our discussion of the water molecule in Chapter 3, it will be remembered that the electron contributed by each hydrogen is pulled far over into oxygen's sphere of influence. This follows from the fact that oxygen is a highly electronegative atom. In consequence, as we saw earlier in the present chapter, the electrons in the water molecule have a particularly low potential energy. It requires considerable ingenuity to raise electrons from their low potential in the water molecule to the much higher potential they would have in the NADPH molecule.

Some figures bring the problem into focus. The energies of the photons absorbed by chlorophyll are dependent on their wavelengths (Chapter 2) and hence, knowing the absorption spectrum of chlorophyll,[1] easily computed. It turns out that these photons average about 45 kcal./Einstein.[2] Now, knowing the redox potentials of water and NADP, it is possible to compute the difference between the potential energies of an electron on each molecule. This potential energy difference works out at about 58 kcal./mole. This, then, is the problem. How is an electron movement requiring at least 58 kcal. to be effected by a photon possessing only 45 kcal. of energy?

The obvious solution is to use more than one photon. This is precisely the solution which the green plant is believed to have adopted. In a nutshell, the electron is believed to be raised from water to NADP in two steps, each of which requires the absorption of a photon. The electron flow is schematised in fig. 10.9.

Fig. 10.9 shows that two distinct pigment systems are believed to

[1] Green plants contain two principal chlorophylls: chlorophyll a and chlorophyll b. Chlorophyll a absorbs maximally at 6,800A and chlorophyll b at 7,050A. Both these wave-lengths are at the red end of the visible spectrum; consequently the light transmitted and reflected appears green in colour.

[2] An Einstein is defined as N photons, where N is Avogadro's number ($6 \cdot 023 \times 10^{23}$)—see Introduction. An Einstein, in other words, is a *mole* of photons.

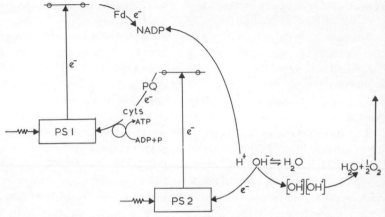

Fig. 10.9 Green plants can reduce NADP using water as a source of electrons. For further explanation see text.

be involved in the transference of electrons from water to NADP. Pigment system 1 (PS 1) contains a form of chlorophyll *a* which absorbs maximally at the relatively long wave-length of about 7,000A. Pigment system 2 (PS 2), on the other hand, possesses a form of chlorophyll *a* absorbing at a rather shorter wave-length, and probably quantities of chlorophyll *b* and other light-sensitive pigments.

The means by which this rather complicated and as yet incompletely understood system is believed to raise electrons from water to NADP is schematised in fig. 10.9. First of all, on the right-hand side of the figure, we see that water is normally ionised, slightly, into H^+ and OH^- ions. It is believed that the electron source is the hydroxyl (OH^-) ion. The electron drops from this ion on to PS 2. On receipt of a solar photon it, or another electron, is raised into an excited orbital. The potential of this electron is, however, still not high enough to reduce NADP. It thus falls from its high position first, it is believed, on to an acceptor—plastoquinone (PQ)—and from there via cytochromes to PS 1. It is raised from PS 1 by the absorption of another photon to a yet higher energy level. From this eminent position it falls first on to an acceptor called ferrodoxin (Fd) and from ferrodoxin on to NADP. The H^+ ion, left far behind in the electron's eventful journey, or an equivalent H^+ ion, neutralises the negative charge engendered by the electron on NADP giving NADPH.

262

In addition to producing the indispensable NADPH, the electron's passage also results in the manufacture of one energy-rich phosphate bond. But more important than this is the fact that the extraction of an electron from a hydroxyl ion results in the production of oxygen. For when an electron is removed from a hydroxyl ion the radical left behind has only seven electrons in its valency shell. This means that one of the valency orbitals contains an unpaired electron. In consequence the radical is extremely reactive and quickly unites with a similar radical to form water and oxygen. Thus the perfection of a method for using water as a source of electrons carried with it, as a by-product, the liberation of gaseous oxygen.

10

We have now briefly reviewed the mechanisms by which certain organisms are able to utilise the energy of solar photons to bring about the reduction of NADP and the phosphorylation of ADP. We have mentioned that NADPH is essential for the reduction of CO_2 which is the first step in the synthesis of carbohydrate molecules. The energy-rich bonds of ATP provide the energy necessary to drive this synthesis.

The synthesis of carbohydrate molecules proceeds by an intricate series of reactions. It is found that these reactions can occur perfectly well in the dark so long as NADPH and ATP are supplied. The task of the light-trapping mechanism of chlorophyll-containing organisms is thus to provide adequate supplies of these two molecules.

The unravelling of the series of reactions which underlie the synthesis of carbohydrate molecules has formed one of the most brilliant episodes in modern biochemistry. To mark its completion Melvin Calvin was awarded the Nobel prize for chemistry in 1961.[1] No attempt to outline these synthetic reactions will be made. Time and space do not permit, and the discussion would divert us too far from the central concern of this chapter. Fig. 10.10, however, shows the basic flow diagram and the points at which CO_2 enters and NADPH acts.

Fig. 10.10 shows that the hydrogen on NADPH is used to reduce

[1] Calvin's Nobel Lecture provides an outstandingly clear account of this work. The Lecture is reprinted in *Nobel Lectures in Chemistry* (*1942–1962*), Elsevier, 1964.

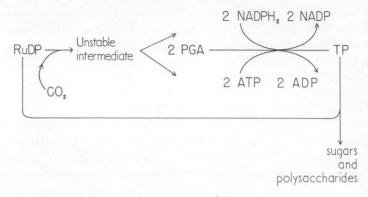

Fig. 10.10 Basic features of the 'dark reaction'.
RuDP=Ribulose diphosphate.
PGA=Phosphoglyceric acid.
TP=A triose phosphate (phosphoglyceraldehyde).
About $\frac{1}{6}$th of the TP generated in the above cycle is used to form sugars and polysaccharides, the remaining $\frac{5}{6}$ths recycles to form RuDP again.

PGA to yield TP. Starting with TP, sugars and polysaccharides can be synthesised if ATP is present to supply the necessary energy. Fig. 10.10 also shows that the electron whose adventures we have followed from its origin in a water molecule has now been dropped on to TP and from TP on to a carbohydrate molecule. Its potential energy in the TP, or in the carbohydrate, molecule will not be so great as it was on NADPH; it will, however, still be considerably greater than it was in the water molecule.

11

We have seen that a necessary consequence of extracting electrons from the ubiquitous water molecule was the liberation of gaseous oxygen. Thus we see the irony of things. For, in liberating oxygen, photosynthetic (autotrophic) organisms have provided conditions in which heterotrophic organisms could evolve. In liberating gaseous oxygen, plants and their allies have doomed themselves to a future of being eaten, grazed, chewed and nibbled. For, as Szent-Györgyi puts it,[1] animals have neither the time nor the wherewithal

[1] Szent-Györgyi, A., *Introduction to a submolecular biology*, Academic Press, New York and London, 1960.

to trap the energy of solar photons so 'they let the plants do it and then eat the plant, or eat the cow which has eaten the plant'. Indeed, as was very early perceived, 'all flesh is grass'.

Once the carbohydrate molecule, synthesised with such pains by the plant, is within the animal's body the business of respiration can begin. At root, this is the business of dislodging the electron from its high position in the carbohydrate molecule and allowing it to fall over a series of co-enzymes back to its ground state in the water molecule. Respiration, of course, is not the prerogative of animals. It happens also in photosynthetic organisms. In the latter, however, the carbohydrate molecules from which the electron is dislodged were synthesised at an earlier stage in the life of the same organism. The animal kingdom, however, is obliged to parasitise the plant kingdom, for these vital molecules.

The final task in this chapter is thus to examine the means by which organisms can tap the energy liberated when an electron falls from a carbohydrate back down to oxygen.

12

In Chapter 7 we briefly outlined the part played by co-enzymes in biochemical reactions. In the earlier parts of the present chapter we have described how electrons 'fall' from cytochrome to cytochrome, etc. In earlier parts of this book we have discussed the nature of cytochrome c. At this point we can draw some of these disparate threads together.

First, then, more than one cytochrome is known. Second, cytochromes are co-enzymes. Third, not only are cytochromes involved in the electron flow mechanisms associated with photon-trapping, but they are also deeply implicated in respiration.

Cytochromes are, however, not the only co-enzymes involved in respiration or, for that matter, photosynthesis. In addition to the cytochromes, two other molecules act as important co-enzymes in respiration. These are NAD and FAD. The initials stand for nicotinamide adenine dinucleotide, and flavine adenine dinucleotide. Unlike the cytochromes which, it will be remembered, are haem proteins, both NAD and FAD are smallish molecules (fig. 10.11).

Co-enzymes, it will be remembered, are acceptor molecules. In the case of the respiratory co-enzymes hydrogen is accepted as in fig. 7.7.

(a) Nicotinamide adenine dinucleotide (NAD)

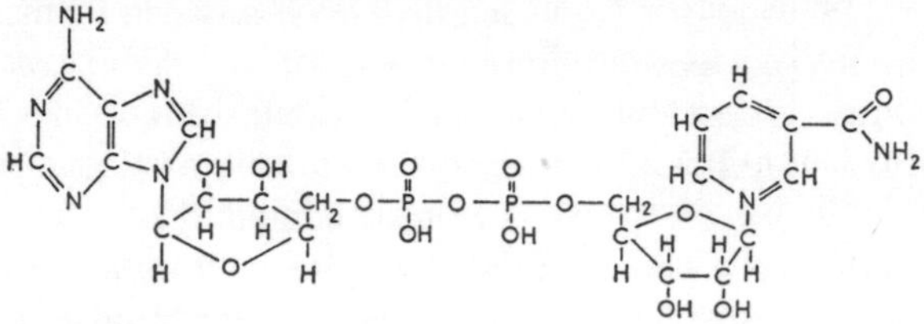

(b) Flavine adenine dinucleotide (FAD)

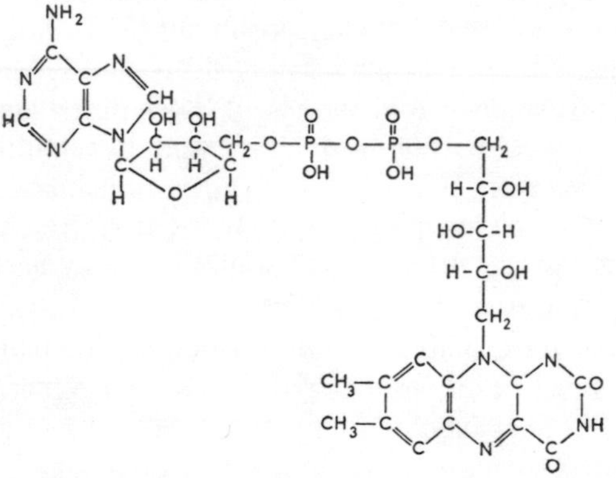

Fig. 10.11 The molecular structure of two important co-enzymes. NADP, which is of such importance as an electron acceptor in photosynthesis, differs from NAD only in the possession of an additional phosphate group joining the two nucleotides together.

A hydrogen belonging to a carbohydrate, or the breakdown product of a carbohydrate, is transferred to a co-enzyme. This transference will be catalysed by a specific dehydrogenase enzyme.

However it will also be recalled from Chapter 7 that enzymes cannot alter the direction of a reaction but only the rate at which it occurs. It follows that the co-enzyme to which the hydrogen is transferred must have a higher electron affinity (higher redox potential) than the donor molecule.

The electron affinities (redox potentials) of the various respiratory co-enzymes can be measured. In consequence they can be arranged on a scale so that co-enzymes higher in the scale will attract electrons away from those lower in the scale. The scale thus shows the direction in which hydrogen atoms and electrons should move. That they *do* move in this direction is ensured by appropriate enzymes.

If we make use of the symbolism introduced in Chapter 7 (fig. 7.8) the movement of hydrogen over the respiratory co-enzymes may be schematised in the following way:

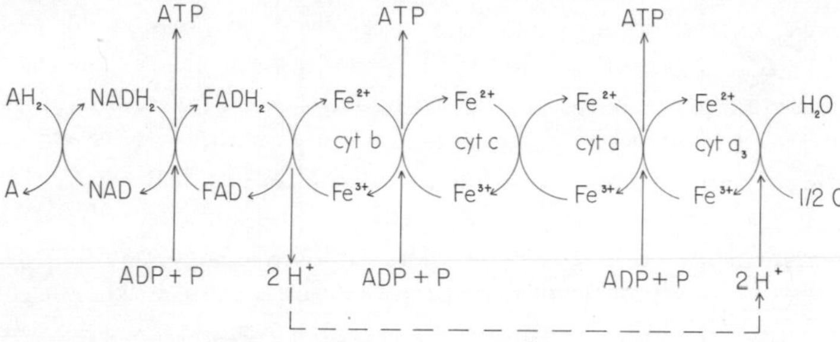

Fig. 10.12 The respiratory chain. For explanation see text.

Fig. 10.12 shows that hydrogen is passed from the donor molecule, A, first to NAD and then to FAD. From FAD onwards the hydrogen atom is split into two parts. The positively-charged hydrogen ion diffuses out into the circumambient solution and the electron flows down over a series of cytochromes to oxygen. The negative charge on oxygen is neutralised by the absorption of a hydrogen ion from solution. The final result is a water molecule.

The wheel has come full circle. The water molecule is reconstituted. The electron has returned, after many adventures, to its minimal energy level. But life, to requote Szent-Györgyi, has meanwhile, very effectively, 'shoved' itself under the electron's fall.

The cascade of electrons from A to oxygen is shown in fig. 10.12 to be broken up into a number of rapids. Certain of these rapids are harnessed to machinery designed to phosphorylate ADP. These points are marked in the figure. The resultant high-energy bonds, as in the case of those formed as a result of trapping photons, are made use of for many purposes. In the animal they are used not only for biochemical synthesis but also for muscular contraction, nerve conduction, glandular secretion, etc.

Finally it is possible to schematise the electron flow from A to oxygen in a rather different way. Fig. 10.13 draws once again on the analogy between the potential energy of an electron and gravitational potential energy. It will be remembered that this analogy has been implied already in the diagrams of photon trapping. That it is *only* an analogy must be remembered. Using it, however, makes the essentials of the situation more evident to our intuition.

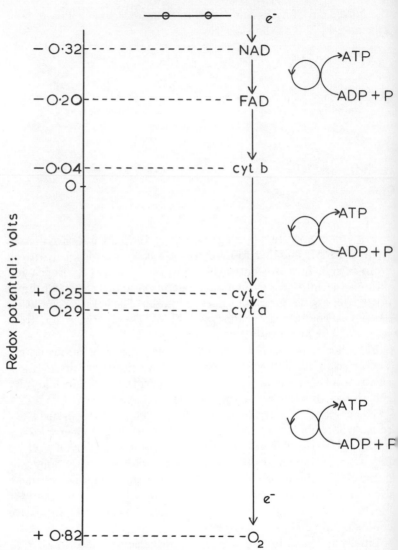

Fig. 10.13 The co-enzymes of the respiratory chain are arranged on a redox potential scale. An electron (in fact it is believed that two electrons make this journey in tandem) is shown falling from one co-enzyme to the next. Between certain co-enzymes a coupling device exists, as yet poorly understood, which traps some of the energy liberated in the electron's fall and uses it for the phosphorylation of ADP. Note that the redox potential scale is inverted: the greatest redox potentials are at the bottom of the figure.

The foregoing account of the essentials of bioenergetics will probably have left the reader with an admiration for the ingenuity of living machinery. It will probably also have left him with an inkling of the complexity of events at this molecular and sub-molecular level. Function, we have suggested, implies structure. On quite *a priori* grounds it would, indeed, seem that such intricate processes demand some framework in or on which to occur.

The initial events in photosynthesis, for example, result in the production of a strong reductant (NADPH) and a strong oxidant (oxygen). It is essential that these two be kept apart else, coming together, they vitiate the whole carefully organised machinery by the reproduction of water. Similarly the flow of electrons over the series of respiratory co-enzymes and its coupling, at certain points, to the phosphorylation of ADP would seem to imply some form of spatial organisation.

Our expectations are not disappointed. In the next chapter we shall find that the initial events in photosynthesis, and the electron flow in respiration, do in fact occur within intricately organised structures.

11

Some Energy Transducers

1

Energy is transformed from one form to another at many points in the living organism. In the green plant, as we saw in the last chapter, the energy of solar photons is transformed into phosphate bond energy and/or reducing power. In animals, plants and micro-organisms redox potential energy is transformed into the energy of energy-rich phosphate bonds. In most animals photoreceptors are capable of using the energy of incident photons to initiate impulses in optic nerves. There are, of course, many other instances of energy transduction. Some we have already mentioned: for example, the transformation of phosphate bond energy into mechanical energy in the myofibril. Others, for which we have no space: for example, the production of electric shock by the electroplaxes of the electric eel, or the production of light by the firefly.

The first three cases of energy transduction mentioned above occur in highly specialised organelles. Although photosynthesis, respiration and photoreception seem, superficially, very dissimilar processes, we find that the transducing organelles in which they occur display marked similarities. In each case the organelle is composed of an intricately interwoven system of biomembranes.

The flow of energy through the biosphere commences, as we saw in Chapter 10, with photosynthetic organisms. It will be logical, therefore, to commence our outline by discussing what is known of the structure of chloroplasts.

2

In the photosynthetic bacteria chlorophyll appears to be concentrated in organelles known as chromatophores which do not possess a well-organised ultrastructure. In the plant kingdom, however, where the technically more difficult operation of raising electrons from

270

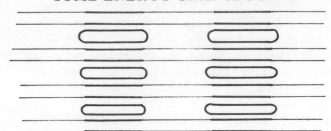

Fig. 11.1 An interpretation of the membranous structure of a chloroplast's grana.

water to NADP occurs, chlorophyll is always found to be associated with a system of lipoprotein membranes.

In the most primitive members of the plant kingdom—the blue-green algae—the lipoprotein membranes are extended throughout the cytoplasm of the cell. In all higher plants, however, the membranes are organised into an intricate and highly ordered structure—the chloroplast. As was mentioned in Chapter 10 this is, in fact, only to be expected. The complexity depicted in fig. 10.9 demands some sort of spatial organisation.

Chloroplast structure varies from one plant group to the next.[1] In all cases, however, an essential feature is the presence of stacks of phospholipid membranes. The organisation of the membranes within the chloroplast of a higher plant is well shown in Plate VIII(c)

The membrane systems within a chloroplast seem to consist of a number of flattened sacs.[2] These sacs have been called thylakoids: a word derived from a classical root meaning 'sac'. The arrangement of the thylakoids differs in chloroplasts obtained from different plants. Although the thylakoids appear separated and distinct from each other in electron micrographs it is believed[3] that, in fact, they are all interconnected.

Plate VIII(c) shows that in certain positions the thylakoids appear to approach each other more closely and become more densely stained. The periodic membrane stacks so formed are called 'grana'. It is rather difficult to see exactly how they are constructed. Menke, however, has suggested, and most investigators accept his interpretation, that the grana are due to smaller thylakoids interpolated among the large. This interpretation is shown in fig. 11.1.

[1] See *The Cell*, Vol. 2, ed. Brachet and Mirsky, Academic Press, New York and London, 1961.
[2] Menke, W. (1962), *Ann. Rev. Plant Physiol.*, *13*, 27–44.
[3] Heslop-Harrison, J. (1966), *Sci. Progr.* (*Oxford*), *54*, 519–41.

It has proved possible to separate the thylakoids from the background material or stroma of the chloroplast. When this is done it can be shown that when they are illuminated these isolated membrane systems evolve oxygen. The evidence, however, suggests that CO_2 is not at the same time taken up. Indeed CO_2 fixation can be shown to occur in the absence of chlorophyll. This can be done by supplying a chlorophyll-free extract of chloroplasts with ATP, NADPH and CO_2 labelled with a radioactive carbon atom. It can then be demonstrated that the radioactive carbon becomes incorporated into newly synthesised carbohydrates.

It looks as though the electron transfer from water to NADP is associated with the membrane system, and the reduction of CO_2 to form carbohydrates occurs in the stroma. That chlorophyll itself is affixed to the lipoprotein membranes is well established. Very probably the longish phytol chain attached to the porphyrin (fig. 10.6) forms the means by which chlorophyll attaches itself to the lipid core of the membrane. There is good evidence that chlorophyll is concentrated in the grana of chloroplasts which possess such regions.

It is possible that the thylakoids of the grana function in some way to separate, and keep separate, the primary oxidant and reductant which, as we saw in Chapter 10, are the initial products of photosynthesis. It is clear that some mechanism or structure must serve this function, else oxidant and reductant would merely gravitate together, negating the whole process.

Several suggestions have been made about the way in which the chlorophyll is organised in or on the grana membranes. Studies with polarised light have been carried out in an attempt to detect molecular organisation. These studies have so far proved inconclusive.[1] Rather more fruitful have been investigations involving high resolution electron microscopy.

Electron microscopists using the techniques of negative staining and metal shadowing (Chapter 12) have shown that the grana thylakoid membranes have a globular substructure.[2] The globules seem to be about $180A \times 150A \times 100A$ in size. They have been shown to contain a hundred, or so, chlorophyll molecules and a number of carotenoids, phospholipids and cytochromes. Because these granules have been shown capable of carrying out the light-induced splitting

[1] Granick, S. in *The Cell*, Vol. 2, ed. by Brachet and Mirsky, Academic Press, New York and London, 1961.
[2] Park, R. B. and Biggins, J. (1964), *Science*, *144*, 1009.

272

of water leading to the liberation of oxygen they are called quanto-somes. It is believed that the thylakoid membrane in the region of the grana is composed of a close-packed array of quantosomes. More recently still, evidence that the quantosome itself consists of four 90A globular subunits has been presented.[1] The significance of this observation is not yet clear.

The existence of a globular substructure in the thylakoid membrane becomes even more interesting in the light of suggestions that a similar substructure exists in mitochondrial membranes. The possibility that this latter substructure exists will be discussed in the next section. Before leaving the topic of quantosomes, however, it must be emphasised that their dimensions are considerably greater than the phospholipid micelles mentioned in Chapter 9 (fig. 9.15). These two types of globule should not be confused.

3

Chloroplasts are, of course, restricted to the green plant. This is not the case with mitochondria. These organelles are found in both the plant and animal kingdoms. If anything they are slightly more numerous in animal cells than in plant cells.

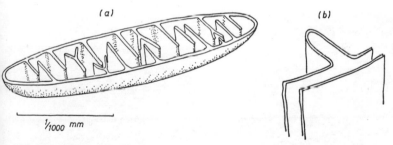

(a) (b)

$\frac{1}{1000}$ mm

Fig. 11.2 (*a*) Longitudinal section of a mitochondrion to show its internal structure.

(*b*) A portion of the wall magnified to show that it consists of typical lipoprotein biomembranes.

Mitochondria, like chloroplasts, vary considerably, not only from animal group to animal group, but from one cell to another in the same organism. The ultrastructure of some typical mitochondria is shown in Plate VIII. Fig. 11.2 shows an interpretation of the electron micrographs.

[1] Park, R. B. (1965), *J. Cell. Biol.*, **27**, 151–61.

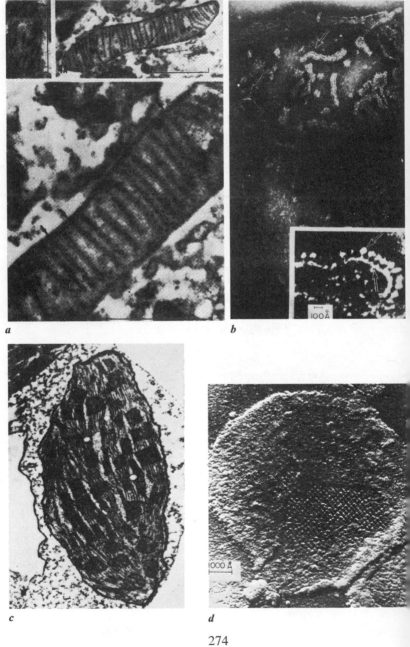

a

b

c

d

As in the case of chloroplasts the interior of the mitochondria is criss-crossed by membranes. The membrane systems of the mitochondrion are, however, rather simpler to understand than those of the chloroplast. Fig. 11.2(*b*) shows that the mitochondrion is bounded by a double membrane. The inner of these membranes projects as fingerlike processes (plant mitochondria) or platelike partitions (animal mitochondria). These processes or partitions are called cristae.

Although some of the earlier workers believed mitochondria to be associated with a cell's hereditary mechanism, it has been known since the nineteen-twenties that their major function lies in the field of bioenergetics. It is nowadays believed that the respiratory co-enzymes which we discussed in Chapter 10 are attached to the cristae. The enzymes catalysing other parts of energy metabolism, for example those concerned with the Krebs cycle and the oxidation of fatty acids, do not appear to be firmly attached to the membranes. These latter enzymes are to be found in the mitochondrial 'sap' between the cristae.

It was mentioned in the preceding section that some workers

VIII This plate shows some of the organelles involved in the processes of bio-energetics.

(*a*) mitochondria. In the top left-hand corner a mitochondrion from the liver of a rat is shown (magnification 18,000 ×). The other two electron micrographs are of a mitochondrion from the kidney of a mouse (magnification 14,800 × and 44,500 ×). The arrows in the lower micrograph emphasise that the cristae are continuous with the inner of the two boundary membranes.

(*b*) examination of mitochondria in the electron microscope when they have been prepared by a negative staining technique shows that the cristae are covered with minute particles. The arrows point to regions where these particles are particularly evident (magnification 48,000 × and 245,000 ×).

(*c*) maize chloroplast magnified 11,300 ×. This electron micrograph shows the membranous structure of the chloroplast of a higher plant exceptionally well. The dark rectangular stacks of membranes constitute the grana.

(*d*) a single lamella from the interior of a chloroplast. This lamella has been prepared for electron microscopy by shadowing with metal atoms. The interesting mosaic visible in one part of the membrane is believed to consist of arrays of quantosomes (see text).

(a) *courtesy of A. J. Dalton (1957)*, Society of Experimental Biology Symposium, 10, *148;* (b) *courtesy of H. Fernandez-Moran, reprinted by permission of The Rockefeller University Press from* J. Cell Biol. *(1964)*, 22, *73;* (c) *courtesy of A. E. Vatter;* (d) *courtesy of R. B. Park (1964)*, Science, 144, *1009.*

believe the mitochondrial membranes to have a globular substructure. The evidence for this substructure again arises from high resolution electron microscopy. The evidence for mitochondrial substructure, however, is not so strong as that for chloroplast quantosomes.

One of the techniques used by electron microscopists, initially to investigate the structure of viruses, is called negative staining. It will be briefly discussed in Chapter 12. In certain circumstances, if mitochondria are negatively stained globular elements can be seen covering the cristae. These globules are about 90A in diameter and are attached to the cristae by 'stalks' about 50A in length and 40A in breadth. When mitochondria are prepared by the more conventional techniques of fixing, embedding, sectioning and staining, these globules are not observed. Their real existence is thus, at the time of writing, still somewhat in doubt. It must be stated, however, in defence of the globules, that negative staining of other membrane systems does not produce the same effect.

Granting, provisionally, a real existence to the globules, the next question is: do they have any functional significance in the mitochondrion? It is suggested that they do have such a significance.

If mitochondrial membranes are disintegrated and the resulting fragments subjected to high-speed centrifugation, the sediment at the bottom of the centrifuge tube is found to contain a quantity of minute particles. Biochemists are able to show that these particles possess all the respiratory co-enzymes necessary to transport hydrogen from a metabolite to oxygen (fig. 10.12). Accordingly these particles have been called electron-transport particles (ETP) or, more simply, elementary particles (EP).

Now, if the dimensions of the EPs are determined, it is found that they are closely similar to the dimensions of the 90A globules seen by the electron microscopists. It is, in consequence, tempting to identify the one with the other. It is tempting to suggest that the globules seen in negatively stained mitochondria are complexes of respiratory co-enzymes. They would, in other words, be rather analogous to, though considerably smaller than, the quantosomes of chloroplast membranes.

It is clear, however, that an identification of the electron microscopists' globules with the biochemists' EPs is at the moment speculative and premature. There are several possibilities. It may be that the EPs are in fact the stalked granules; it may be that EPs are normally part of the structure of the crista membrane and are

276

forced out in the extreme conditions of negative staining; or it may be that EPs and stalked granules are in no way related.

4

The third and last group of energy-transducing structures to be considered in this brief survey are the photoreceptor cells of animals. It is appropriate to consider them in this chapter as they share common architectural features with the two energy transducers we have considered above. In other words the photosensitive regions of photoreceptor cells are again composed of systems of interweaving lipoprotein membranes.

It was mentioned in Chapter 8 that the photosensitive tips of vertebrate rod and cone cells are developed from non-motile cilia. This mode of origin is also to be found in the photosensitive regions of coelenterate, echinoderm and protochordate eyes. Development from cilia, however, does not occur in the eyes of arthropods,

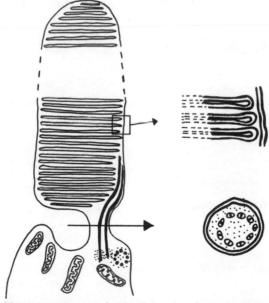

Fig. 11.3 The outer segments of rod cells consist of a stack of membranous discs. The outer segment is connected to the rest of the cell by a fine stalk which still retains the internal structure of a typical cilium minus the two central filaments. On the right-hand side of the figure a few discs are shown at a higher magnification.

277

mollusca, annelids and platyhelminthes. R. M. Eakin[1] believes that this distinction is of sufficient importance to justify the drawing of phylogenetic conclusions. It is proposed, in this section, to outline the structure of a photoreceptor belonging to both main groups. We shall discuss the structure of the rod cell outer segment of vertebrate retinae, and the retinula cells of the arthropod compound eye.

The rod cell outer segment is represented diagrammatically in fig. 11.3. It can be shown to originate by elaboration and modification of a non-motile cilium springing from the rod cell surface. The process of development appears to consist of growth and invagination of the ciliary membrane. In consequence the outer segment appears, in the electron microscope, to consist of a stack of discs.

There is good evidence that the visual pigment—rhodopsin—is present in the membranous discs. Rhodopsin is formed of a protein—opsin—joined to a pigment group—retinene.[2] Whilst little is yet known about the structure of opsin the structure of retinene is well understood. It is very interesting to find that it, like chlorophyll, is a highly conjugated molecule (fig. 11.4).

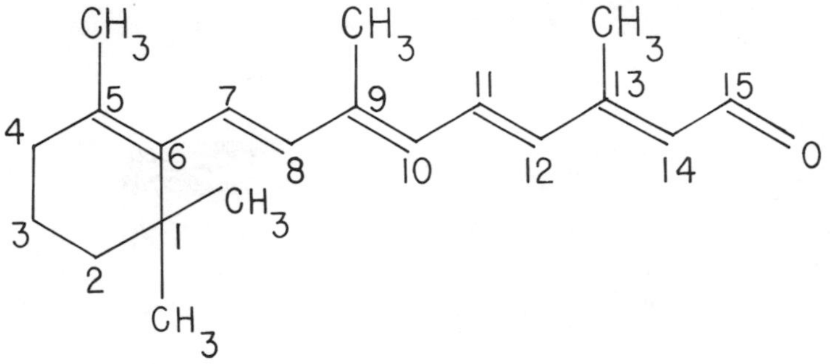

Fig. 11.4 All-trans retinene.

There is good evidence that retinene in the dark-adapted retina is bent into the so-called 11-cis isomer shown in fig. 11.5.

The 11-cis isomer is in a higher energy state than the all-trans isomer of fig. 11.4. A photon of light is believed to release the 'catch' holding 11-cis retinene in its contorted form and the molecule immediately straightens to give the all-trans form.

[1] Eakin, R. M. (1965), *Sympos. on Quant. Biol.*, *30*, 363.
[2] Retinene in fact comes in two varieties: $retinene_1$ and $retinene_2$. The small difference between the two is located in the six-membered ring.

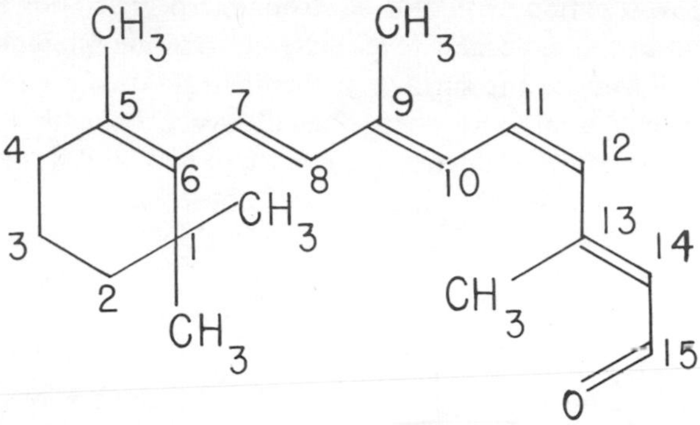

Fig. 11.5 11-cis retinene.

Photoreception is known to be an extremely sensitive process. It is plausibly suggested[1] that a single rod can detect a single photon of light. How such sensitivity is achieved is still a mystery. It seems probable, however, that the initial process which results in a straightening of retinene's conjugated chain causes the latter to break off its union with opsin. This in turn leads, through yet unknown processes, to electrical events which initiate action potentials in a fibre of the optic nerve.

Not only is rhodopsin involved crucially at the critical point of photoreception but it also appears to be essential to the structural integrity of the membrane system. Retinene is synthesised in the body from Vitamin A to which, indeed, its structure is very closely similar. It has been shown that rats fed on a diet lacking Vitamin A become blind. Investigation of their retinae reveals the fact that their rod and cone outer segments have completely degenerated.[2]

It will be remembered from Chapter 6 that one of the important stabilising factors of myoglobin and haemoglobin was the haem group. It is perhaps not too audacious a speculation to suggest that retinene has an analogous function in the rhodopsin molecule. It would follow from this suggestion that lack of retinene would cause the rhodopsin molecule to become unstable. In turn, if rhodopsin is part of the membranous structure, the rod discs would begin to disintegrate. In short, for lack of retinene the animal's sight is lost.

The structural elements of the arthropod compound eye are superficially very dissimilar to the rods and cones of vertebrate

[1] Hecht, S., Shlaer, S. and Pirenne, M. H. (1942), *J. Gen. Physiol.*, *25*, 819.
[2] Dowling, J. E. and Wald, G. (1960), *Proc. U.S. Acad. Sci.*, *46*, 587.

retinae. Investigation with the electron microscope, however, has shown that at the molecular level there are striking analogies.

As is well known, the surface of the arthropod compound eye is broken up into a large number of small facets. Beneath each facet are the photoreceptor elements. Each facet, or lens, and its underlying

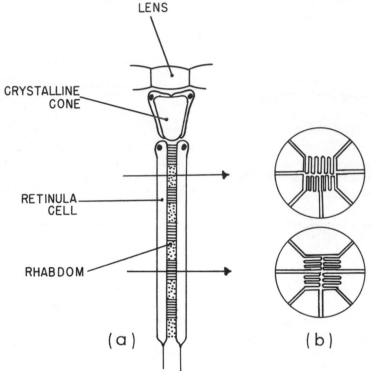

Fig. 11.6 (*a*) Longitudinal section of a crab ommatidium.

(*b*) Transverse section of the ommatidium at different levels. Note that the rhabdomeres project at right angles to each other at these two different levels. For further explanation see text.

Re-drawn from Waterman, T. H. and Horch, K. W. (1966) *Science*, *154*, 467.

elements is called an ommatidium. Isolating each ommatidium from its neighbours is a layer of pigmented cells.[1] Longitudinal and cross sections through a typical arthropodan ommatidium are shown in fig. 11.6.

[1] The distribution of pigment in these cells can be altered so that visual acuity and sensitivity, which are to some extent inversely related, can be altered.

As fig. 11.6 shows, the photosensitive part of the arthropodan ommatidium consists of a group of seven or eight retinula cells. These cells are arranged to form a long thin cylinder. The lens and the crystalline cone funnel light into the centre of this cylinder. Now it is found that the centre of the cylinder is composed of minute fingerlike projections arising from the retinula cells. These projections are, in fact, expansions of the lipoprotein membranes of their respective retinula cells. They range from 500A to 1,000A in diameter. Together they make up the substance in the centre of the cylinder of retinula cells, a substance which has been called the rhabdom.

The fingerlike projections of the retinula cells are called rhabdomeres. It is very interesting to find that in many arthropods—in particular the decapod crustacea and some insects—the rhabdomeres are arranged in alternating groups at right angles to each other. This organisation is shown in fig. 11.6(a) and (b). The significance of this observation is connected with the ability of some arthropods to detect the plane of polarised light. This ability is often of great behavioural importance to the crustacean or insect. In short, patterns of rhabdomeres are believed to form the basis of an efficient polarimeter.[1]

The visual pigments of arthropods are not so well known as those of vertebrates. This relative lack of knowledge is due to the much smaller size of most arthropod eyes compared to those of the larger vertebrates. Rhodopsin, however, identical to vertebrate rhodopsin, has been identified in the eye of the lobster. It is believed that the visual pigments are concentrated in the rhabdomere membranes.

From this brief account it can be seen that in spite of the vast differences between the eyes of vertebrates and arthropods there exists at the molecular level a striking similarity. In both cases, systems of membranes bearing photopigments are presented to the incoming photons. In both cases receipt of one or more photons results ultimately in the propagated membrane repolarisation which we call the action potential.

5

The full significance of the intricate molecular architecture described in this chapter is not yet clear. The fact that throughout the living world the processes of bioenergetics frequently occur in association

[1] Waterman, T. H. and Horch, K. W. (1966), *Science*, *154*, 467.

with complex patterns of membranes suggests that some common underlying mechanism exists. Recalling our observations in Chapter 9 it seems not improbable that this common mechanism depends on the ability of biomembranes to control the fluxes of materials and energy along their thermodynamic gradients. In this way, perhaps, energy can be stored and transformed from one form into another. Perhaps, too, patterns of biological membranes allow some of the phenomena studied by solid state physicists to occur. There is some evidence to show that such phenomena do occur in chloroplasts.

Further research into the molecular biology of these important organelles will enable scientists, first, to understand how they work and, second, to gain some control over their working. Indeed it may not be too speculative to suggest that in the foreseeable future similar, or perhaps improved, organelles may be manufactured in the laboratory and, perhaps, used where microminiaturised energy transducers or batteries are required. The Americans have a name for this possible technology: *bionics*.

$$12$$

Cells

1

The idea that the bodies of the larger plants and animals are subdivided into minute compartments called cells is one of the major concepts to arise from the work of nineteenth-century biologists. The cell theory may, perhaps, be regarded as the outcome of applying the developing prowess of European technology to the age-old studies of anatomy and physiology. For the history of the discovery and analysis of animal and plant cells is closely dependent on the history of the development of the microscope. Furthermore the continuing analysis of cell structure and function nowadays depends to a great extent on the art of the electrical engineer. Thus we shall see that the development of the electron microscope has in recent years, led to an enormous increase in our knowledge of cells.

2

Schleiden and Schwann are generally credited with initiating the cell theory. In 1839 Schwann[1] published a seminal book in which he writes as follows: 'One may include under the name *cell-theory*, in the wider sense, the exposition of the statement that there exists a general principle of construction for all organic products, and that this principle of construction is cell formation.'

Schleiden and Schwann, however, were by no means the first microscopists to observe cells. In fact knowledge of the existence of cells antedates these two workers by nearly two centuries. Robert

---

[1] *Mikroskopische Untersuchungen uber die Uebereinstimmung in der Struktur und dem Wachstein der Tiere und Pflanzen*, Berlin 1839. The English translation was published in 1847, with the title *Microscopical researches into the accordance in structure and growth of animals and plants*, by the Sydenham Society, London.

Hooke,[1] in 1665, gave the following account of the cells which he had observed in cork to the members of the Royal Society:

'. . . I could exceedingly plainly perceive it to be all perforated and porous, much like a honey comb but that the pores of it were not regular; yet it was not unlike a honey comb in these particulars.

'First, in that it had a very little solid substance, in comparison to the empty cavity that was contained within . . . for the Interstitia, or walls (as I may so call them) or partitions of those pores were near as thin in proportion to their pores, as thin films of wax in a Honey comb (which enclose and constitute the sexangular cells) are to theirs.

'Next, in that the pores or *cells*, were not very deep, but consisted of a great many little Boxes, separated out of one continued long pore, by certain Diaphragms.'

It is no accident that cells were first discovered in plant material. One of the most important differences between the bodies of plants and animals lies in the nature of the molecules of which they are built. Whereas the main structural material of the animal's body is protein, that of the plant is a complex carbohydrate—cellulose. Cellulose forms thick walls around cells. These walls were easily visible to Hooke in 1665, as the quotation indicates. The animal cell, however, possessing no cellulose possesses no such easily visible wall. Hence it is not surprising that the first animal cells to be seen were the blood corpuscles which, floating freely in the blood plasma, are quite separate from each other. It seems probable that the blood cells were first observed by Swammerdam, who died in 1680. His book, *Biblia Naturae*, in which he describes these cells, was not, however, published until 1737–8.

The realisation that the bodies of animals, like those of plants, were built of vast congeries of cells was, at the beginning of the eighteenth century, still far in the future. Even today, looking at a slice of unstained animal tissue with an average microscope, it is difficult to be sure that what one is looking at is cellular material. The early microscopists, beset by all the troubles of inferior instruments, may be excused if they failed to recognise the cellular nature of the animal body. Indeed so great was the difficulty of this investigation that, due to their inadequate microscopes, they sometimes mistook diffraction effects and other artefacts for structures actually existing in the tissues. Before the true nature of the body's minute structure

[1] *Micrographia*, London, 1665. Quoted by J. R. Baker in *Q.J.M.S.*, *89* (1948), 108.

was established at least two fallacious theories developed to channel men's energies in the wrong direction. The most tenacious of these theories was developed by microscopists in the late eighteenth and early nineteenth centuries. J. R. Baker[1] calls it the 'Globule Theory'. Globulists believed the fine structure of the animal's body to consist of globules, usually spherical or ovoid, never angular. History is said never to repeat itself. Nevertheless, it is interesting to recall that in Chapter 9 we saw that some electron microscopists believe that cell membranes consist of minute globules. Again the microscopist is working at, or very near, the limits of his instrument's resolution. History may not repeat itself, yet the parallel is striking!

The nineteenth-century globulists were, of course, not so very far from the truth: yet their theory quite possibly hindered discovery of the facts. For the great defect of the globular theory lay in the indefiniteness of the globule concept itself. Not only were globules to be observed in nearly all the tissues of the body, but they were also visible in milk; not only in freshly killed and prepared animals, but also in animals long dead, when, according to Leeuwenhoek (1686), they consisted of a 'thin transparent oyl-like substance'. Evidently the term 'globule' stretched to cover a multitude of dissimilar things: from straightforward preparative artefacts, to fat droplets, to cells. Clearly, before a valid theory of the ultimate units in the body's anatomy could be developed, it was essential to clarify the exact connotation of the term by which this unit was to be designated.

This clarification was not quickly forthcoming. Many years were to elapse before the painstaking researches of many men established the modern concept of the cell. A sense of the intellectual ferment in the early years of the nineteenth century, when anatomists in many countries felt their way towards the cell theory, may be gained from the following passage in which George Eliot describes the ambition of young Dr Tertius Lydgate:

'This great seer (George Eliot refers to the great French anatomist Bichat) did not go beyond the consideration of the tissues as the ultimate facts in the living organism, marking the limit of anatomical analysis; but it was open to another mind to say, have not these structures some common basis from which they have all started, as your sarsnet, gauze, satin and velvet from the same cocoon. Here

[1] Baker, J. R. (1948), *Q.J.M.S.*, *89*, 114.

would be another light, as of oxy-hydrogen, showing the very grain of things and revising all former explanations.'[1]

The establishment of the modern concept of the cell was at the beginning hindered by the fact that the plant material on which most of the early work was done suggested that the most important single feature of a cell was its wall. The cytoplasm and nucleus which make up practically the whole of the animal cell are in many plant cells pressed against the cellulose wall to form a quite inconspicuous layer. Botanical research, however, soon made it clear that the nucleus played a most important part in cell development. So that when a similar structure began to be observed in animal cells the stage was set for the wide-ranging generalisation of the modern cell theory.

In 1838 Schwann went to dinner with Schleiden. As they dined, Schleiden outlined the importance of the nucleus in the development of plant cells. Schwann, a zoologist, had been working on the nerves of the tadpole and had observed the nuclei of the notochordal cells. 'I at once', he says, 'recalled having seen a similar organ in the cells of the notochord, and in the same instant I grasped the extreme importance that my discovery would have if I succeeded in showing that this nucleus plays the same role in the cells of the notochord as does the nucleus of plants in the development of plant cells.'[2] Thus was the cell theory born.

By 1893 it had gained general acceptance. In this year Hertwig was able to write:

'Animals and plants, so diverse in their external appearance, agree in the fundamental nature of their anatomical construction; for both are composed of similar elementary units, which are generally only perceptible to the microscope.'

It is clear from this brief historical summary that at the end of the nineteenth and the beginning of the twentieth centuries cells were regarded as the units of which the bodies of plants and animals were built. The hidden analogy is, presumably, to the bricks from which a house is built, or the wheels and springs which form the mechanism of a clock.

In the twentieth century the concept of the cell has continued to develop. The bodies of plants and animals are unquestionably alive: can the cell thus be regarded as the unit of life?

[1] George Eliot, *Middlemarch*.
[2] Quoted by J. R. Baker (1949), *Q.J.M.S.*, *90*, 103.

There are many organisms whose bodies are not subdivided into cells. Yet these organisms are also unquestionably alive. Do the inhabitants of the teeming world of micro-organisms thus destroy the idea that the cell is the unit of life? We seem to have only two alternatives: either we abandon our belief that the cell is the unit of life, or we assimilate micro-organisms into the cell theory by suggesting that their entire bodies are but single cells. In other words, by suggesting that the entire micro-organism is in some way akin to a single cell in the body of a higher plant or animal.

Which alternative we choose is to some extent a matter of taste. If we extend the term 'cell' to include the entire bodies of micro-organisms in addition to the compartments into which the bodies of higher forms are subdivided we reduce its connotation. The bodies of some of the protozoa are, for example, far more complicated than the typical metazoan or metaphytan cell. On the other hand the bodies of bacteria and their allies are far simpler than the cells of higher organisms. Yet it can be argued that the loss in connotation is amply made up by the gain in generality. The bodies of micro-organisms do have some things in common with the cells of higher organisms—as we shall see later in this chapter. Moreover, if this extension of denotation is accepted, then it is probably justifiable to regard the cell as the unit of life. Furthermore we should consider that most important of all criteria—common usage. Microbiologists commonly refer to the organisms which they study as 'cells'. As an instance of this habit the title of one of the classical books on the subject may be quoted: *The Chemical Kinetics of the Bacterial Cell*.[1]

If the arguments set out above are accepted it follows that our definition of a cell is much reduced in content. This is inevitable. Logicians assure us that denotation and connotation are inversely related. If the denotation, or coverage, of a term is extended, then its connotation, or content, is diminished. Thus having extended our term to cover not only the compartments observable within the bodies of higher organisms, but also the total bodies of micro-organisms, it is not surprising to find that its connotation is reduced. Indeed it seems to be reduced to the following very simple definition: a cell is any living, or once living, entity surrounded by a continuous lipoprotein membrane.

[1] Hinshelwood, C. N., *The Chemical Kinetics of the Bacterial Cell*, Oxford, 1946.

The definition, of course, now turns on what is meant by the term 'living'. There have been innumerable attempts throughout history to define the meaning of this term. It would require a separate book, or books, to review and assess them all. Instead let us simply state here a convenient and possible definition. Let us define a living organism as an entity capable of extracting energy from its environment and capable of using this energy to ensure the perpetuation of its own kind.

There are, of course, objections to this, as to practically any other definition. The difficulty is the difficulty common in biology of fixing a dividing line in a continuous series. In the evolution of the vertebrates, for example, it is impossible to say, except entirely arbitrarily, where, in a series of fossil forms, mammals begin and reptiles end. Similarly forms which are unquestionably alive connect, by an uninterrupted series, with those which are unquestionably not alive. Where the line is drawn between animate and inanimate nature becomes, as our knowledge increases, increasingly arbitrary. The definition suggested above implies that the dividing line is drawn above the viruses. These infective particles are unable to perpetuate themselves, or to increase in numbers, in the absence of cells.

We can thus see that the level of organisation represented by the cell is extremely important. To be alive according to the above definition entails a highly complex and highly integrated set of chemical processes. These intricate, inter-related and co-ordinated processes depend on the reactant molecules being held together, in close proximity, perhaps even in particular spatial relations with one another, within the lipoprotein 'bag' which is the cell.

If the arguments and definitions of the above paragraphs are accepted then we can see the sense in which the cell can be called *the* unit of life. For it would seem that all living things either are cells, or have developed from cells and are composed of cells. In Virchow's phrase, 'Omnis cellula e cellula'.

4

Although some cells, like the giant algal cell *Chara*, are visible to the naked eye, the vast majority are of microscopic dimensions. In our brief sketch of the development of the cell theory we noticed how dependent this development was on the evolution of the microscope.

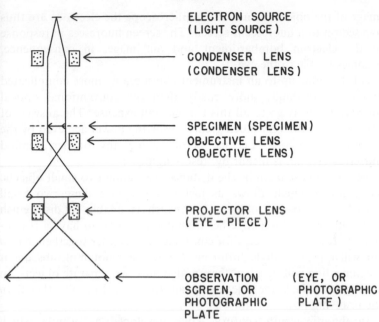

ELECTRON SOURCE
(LIGHT SOURCE)

CONDENSER LENS
(CONDENSER LENS)

SPECIMEN (SPECIMEN)
OBJECTIVE LENS
(OBJECTIVE LENS)

PROJECTOR LENS
(EYE – PIECE)

OBSERVATION   (EYE, OR
SCREEN, OR   PHOTOGRAPHIC
PHOTOGRAPHIC   PLATE)
PLATE

Fig. 12.1 The optical principle of the electron microscope is analagous to that of the light microscope. After Swanson, C. P., *The Cell*, Prentice-Hall, New Jersey, 1960, p. 8.

The recent upsurge in cell biology has in turn depended heavily on the evolution of a new type of microscope: the electron microscope.

The design of an electron microscope is analogous to that of an optical microscope (fig. 12.1). Instead of light rays, however, electron rays are used. This introduces several complications. Most of these arise from the fact that electrons are very easily absorbed by matter. Thus, because electron rays will not pass any useful distance through air, the tube of the electron microscope has to be evacuated. If electrons are absorbed by air they will, *a fortiori*, be absorbed by glass. It follows that specimens to be examined in the electron microscope cannot be mounted on glass slides. Instead the specimen is placed on a small copper grid. But, more importantly, electrons will not pass through, far less be refracted by, glass lenses. Some other means of focusing electron beams must therefore be devised. Fortunately electrons, unlike photons, carry negative charges. It follows that electron beams can be refracted, or bent, by electromagnetic 'lenses'. Finally, electrons are invisible. In order to see an image of the object in an electron microscope the electrons are thus focused on to a fluorescent screen. The screen fluoresces in response to the electron bombardment and an image, in consequence, becomes visible to the eye.

All this adds up to an instrument considerably more complicated and correspondingly more costly than the conventional optical microscope. Why go to all this trouble and expense? The answer, of course, lies in the very much greater resolving power achieved by the electron microscope. Let us, before going any further, remind ourselves of what is meant by 'resolving power'.

Let us suppose d cm. is the distance separating two small objects. Then a lens which allows us just to distinguish these two small particles as separate objects, but which is unable to distinguish between objects closer together than d cm., is said to have a resolution, or resolving power, of d cm. Objects set closer together than d cm. will appear as single diffuse entities and no amount of subsequent magnification will 'resolve' the smudge into two separate objects. In consequence the latter objects are said to be set closer together than the resolving power of the lens.

In the nineteenth century Abbé developed a formula which relates the resolving power (d) of a lens to certain other parameters:

$$d = \frac{0 \cdot 61\lambda}{n \sin i}$$

where λ=the wave-length of the radiation employed,
  n=refractive index of the material in which the object is situated,
  i=half the angle of aperture of the lens.

The denominator of Abbé's expression—$n \sin i$—is conventionally called the numerical aperture of the lens. It is clear that the greater the numerical aperture the smaller will be d: in other words the greater will be the resolving power of the lens. In the best modern optical microscopes the numerical aperture is slightly greater than unity. The only other variable in Abbé's formula is λ, the wave-length of the radiation employed. If visible light is used we can take 5×10^{-5} cm. as an average value for λ. If we substitute the above values for λ and for the numerical aperture into Abbé's equation we can obtain a figure for d. It turns out that the best modern optical microscopes have a resolving power of about $0 \cdot 3\mu$.

This value for the resolving power can be improved if light of shorter wave-length, for example, ultra-violet light, is used. The improvement in resolution obtained by this method is not, however, very great. If, on the other hand, electrons are used a spectacular improvement results. The waves associated with electrons have a very much shorter wave-length than those of visible or ultra-violet light. In fact, the precise wave-length of electron-waves varies somewhat with the energy of the electron. For most biological work electrons with an energy of about 60 kV are used. Electrons possessing this energy can be shown to be associated with waves having a length of about 5×10^{-10} cm. Reference back to the preceding paragraph shows how very much shorter this is than the average length of the waves constituting visible light.

If we substitute 5×10^{-10} cm. into Abbé's formula leaving, for the moment, the value of the numerical aperture as slightly greater than one, we can obtain a value for the resolving power of an electron lens:

$$d_{EM} = 2 \cdot 5 \times 10^{-10} \text{ cm.} = 0 \cdot 025 A.$$

It is clear that the resolving power of an electron microscope is many orders of magnitude greater than that of the best optical microscope. It is instructive to recall, at this point, that the carbon-carbon covalent bond distance is $1 \cdot 54 A$. It would seem that the microscopic world could hide no secrets from the probing beam of the electron microscope.

The reality, however, is otherwise. The microscopic world still tenaciously guards many of its secrets. Electrical engineers, in three decades, have not yet matched the achievements of glass lens grinders over three centuries. The numerical apertures of the best electron lenses still remain at much less than unity. Chromatic aberration, spherical aberration, and astigmatism are all limiting factors. Nonetheless, the best modern electron microscopes guarantee a resolution of better than 5A. This is more than adequate for most biological investigations.

Unfortunately for the molecular biologist detail down to 5A cannot yet be distinguished in biological material. This is due to technical difficulties in the preparation of specimens for electron microscopy.

We emphasised above that electrons are very easily absorbed by matter. It follows that the first requirement in specimen preparation is that the biological material should be exceedingly thin. Second, biological material is composed of atoms which all have more or less the same atomic weight. Hence electrons will pass through, or be scattered by, the specimen quite indiscriminately. In other words the resulting image will have no contrast. It will not be possible to tell which parts of the cell consist of protein, or lipoprotein, structures and which parts consist of structureless, homogeneous fluids.

It is clear, therefore, that certain preparative procedures are necessary before a biological specimen can be observed in the electron microscope. The most important of these are to ensure that the material is thin and that certain heavy atoms have been added to it to increase its contrast.

Of the various methods nowadays available for the preparation of biological material it is believed that the method of negative staining gives the best resolution.[1] This technique depends upon the biological material being initially very thin. Thus it was first used for the study of viruses. More recently it has been applied to the investigation of many other specimens including isolated whole cells. In essence the technique consists in embedding the specimen in a 'stain' consisting of heavy atoms, for example sodium phosphotungstate, or uranyl acetate. When the specimen is put into the electron microscope the electron beam is scattered by the 'stain' but passes relatively unhindered through the lighter atoms of the biological specimen. The specimen is thus outlined by the dark material of the stain. Many elegant electron micrographs have been obtained by this technique (Plate X(b)).

However, for many specimens negative staining is not feasible. Thus the most widely used technique is a straightforward development of the classical histological techniques of fixing, embedding, sectioning and staining. For electron microscopy sections, of course, have to be extremely thin—usually less than 500A. Such very thin sections cannot be obtained if the tissue is embedded, as is conventional, in wax and sectioned on the steel knife of an orthodox microtome. Instead small fragments of the tissue are embedded in a plastic such as methacrylate or araldite. Later the plastic is hardened by polymerisation. The very firm block which results can be sectioned on an ultra-microtome. Steel blades are not sharp enough for this work and carefully prepared glass knives are usually used. The very thin

[1] Valentine, R. C., and Horne, R. W., in *The Interpretation of Ultrastructure*, edited by Harris, R. J. C., Academic Press, New York and London, 1962, p. 264.

sections obtained are customarily stained with a solution containing heavy atoms—OsO_4, $KMnO_4$, $Pb(OH)_2$. The heavy atoms are found to attach themselves to certain cell structures. Thus when the specimen is placed in the electron microscope a pattern of electron-opaque regions like those shown in Plate IX(b) becomes visible.

The two methods described above are not the only methods available for preparing specimens for electron microscopy. They are, however, the most widely used. Other methods include shadowing the specimen with heavy atoms, and freeze-etching.

5

Cells, as we have already stressed, vary greatly in size and complexity. The largest cells are larger than the smaller metazoa, the smallest cells are smaller than the larger viruses. In our quest for the 'unit of life', for the simplest entity which is living as we have defined the term, the latter cells are obviously of great interest. These minute cells form the bodies of a group of organisms which, because they resemble the organism causing pleuropneumonia in cattle, are called 'pleuropneumonia-like organisms' or, more concisely, PPLOs.

The smallest PPLOs average about $0 \cdot 1\mu(1,000A)$ in diameter. This is quite a bit smaller than the size of some of the larger viruses. The vaccinia virus, for example, is over 3,000A in diameter. At $0 \cdot 1\mu$ PPLOs are far too small to be seen by the optical microscope. They have, however, been examined in the electron microscope. Many of their biochemical properties have also been elucidated. A diagram of the probable organisation of these minute cells is shown in fig. 12.2.

Fig. 12.2 shows that PPLOs are surrounded by a continuous, flexible, lipoprotein membrane and thus, according to our definition, may be regarded as true cells. They are, of course, very much simpler than the cells making up the bodies of the metazoa and the metaphyta. Nevertheless they possess all the necessary biochemical machinery to grow and multiply in the absence of other cells. They possess, for example, an enzyme complement capable of catabolising glucose to pyruvate, and thus extracting some of the former molecule's energy. They contain genetic machinery in the form of DNA, RNA and ribosomes sufficient to allow reproduction and perpetuation of the species.

The volume of the smallest PPLOs is about $1 \times 10^{-3}\mu^3$. The volume

293

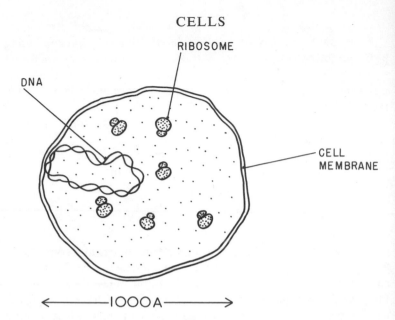

RIBOSOME

DNA

CELL
MEMBRANE

←————IOOO A————→

Fig. 12.2 Organisation of the smallest PPLO. This minute cell is bounded by a lipoprotein membrane and contains DNA, ribosomes and soluble proteins, etc.

of the smallest bacterium is about $1 \times 10^{-2}\mu^3$. The larger bacteria, however, range up to $7\mu^3$. This volume overlaps that of some of the smallest protozoa.[1] The volume of the larger protozoa, however, like the well-known *Amoeba proteus*, may exceed $1 \times 10^6\mu^3$. This is considerably greater than the volume of many of the cells composing the metazoan body. Thus we see that from the smallest PPLOs, which overlap the larger viruses, to the highly specialised cells of the protozoa and metazoa there is an unbroken chain of cell size.

There does not, however, appear to be quite so unbroken a chain of cell complexity. The bacterial cell is hardly any more complex than that of the PPLO. The metazoan or metaphytan cell, on the other hand, shows a great increase in structural complexity. Indeed, as we shall see below, there seems to be quite a sharp distinction between these latter cells and the cells of bacteria and PPLOs.

One of the best known of the larger bacteria is *Escherichia coli*. Indeed *E. coli* is probably one of the most completely known of all living organisms. This will become clear in the last three chapters of

[1] Hyman, L. *The Invertebrates: Protozoa through Ctenophora*, McGraw-Hill, New York, 1940, p. 48.

294

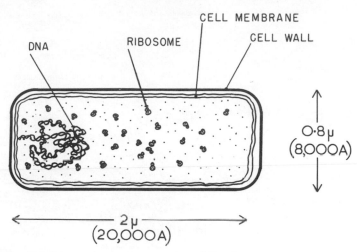

Fig. 12.3 Diagrammatic representation of *E. coli*.

this book. *E. coli* is a harmless micro-organism inhabiting the human large intestine. Its structure is schematised in fig. 12.3.

Fig. 12.3 shows that the main difference between *E. coli* and the PPLOs is the possession by the bacterium of a relatively rigid cell wall covering the flexible cell membrane. This protective wall is composed of a complex of protein, lipid and carbohydrate molecules.

Bacteriologists classify bacteria into two large groups labelled *gram positive* and *gram negative*. These two groups may be distinguished by observing how their members react to a staining technique introduced by Gram. Gram positive bacteria are coloured violet by Gram's technique, gram negative bacteria, on the other hand, quickly lose the violet colour and may be counterstained, usually red, by other dyes. It is rather extraordinary to find that this apparently trivial distinction between bacteria has a deeper significance. It appears that the division into gram positive and gram negative groups coincides with a division into two groups whose members differ in many fundamental properties. Thus, to return to our example, *E. coli* is a gram negative bacterium and in company with other gram negative bacteria shows little sign of any organised ultrastructure within its cell. However membranous ultrastructure is to be discovered within the cells of gram positive bacteria. In *Bacillus subtilis*, for instance, a definite whorl of membranes, called

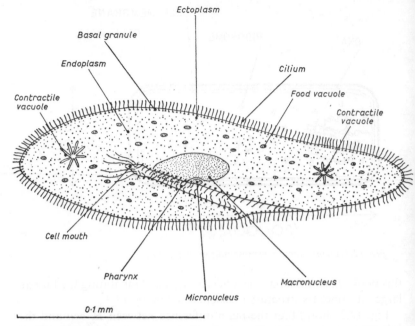

Fig. 12.4 *Paramecium:* an example of a complicated organism consisting of but a single cell.

a mesosome or chondroid, can be detected within the cell by the electron microscope. Furthermore it has been shown that this system is a centre of redox activity.[1] It may thus, perhaps, be regarded as a primitive precursor of the mitochondria of higher cells.

When we ascend to the next stage in cell size we find a very great increase in visible complexity. Most important of all, it is found that the cells of protozoa and algae (with the exception of the blue-green algae), and of the metazoa and the metaphyta, possess a distinct nucleus.

The DNA molecule(s) of bacteria frequently forms a more or less homogeneous mass (fig. 12.3), but it is never separated from the bulk of the cell by a membrane. In higher cells, on the other hand, it is found that a distinct membrane divides a DNA-containing nucleus from a DNA-deficient cytoplasm.[2] This important distinction forms

[1] Sedar, A. W. and Bunde, R. M. (1965), *J. Cell. Biol.*, **27**, 53.
[2] The cytoplasm of eukaryotic cells is not *totally* lacking in DNA. Mitochondria, chloroplasts, and perhaps other organelles, contain small quantities of this nucleic acid.

the basis of a classification of cells into two groups: the *prokaryota* and the *eukaryota*. The former lack, and the latter possess, a well-defined nucleus.

The eukaryotic cells of the protozoa and metazoa are sometimes very complex. The unicellular bodies of protozoa vary greatly from one group of these organisms to the next. The large cell of *Amoeba proteus* is superficially very simple; the cells of many members of the order Ciliophora, on the other hand, often possess an extraordinarily intricate structure. In, for example, *Paramecium* (fig. 12.4), by no means the most complex member of the order, many distinct structures develop in the cell which carry out functions analogous to those

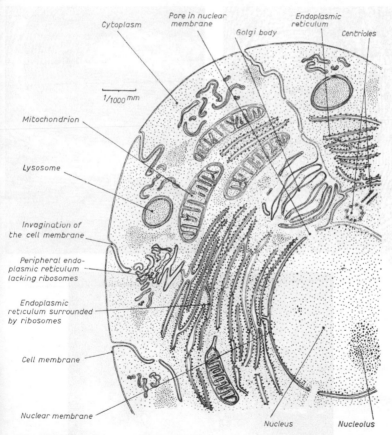

Fig. 12.5 The electron microscopists' picture of a generalised metazoan cell.

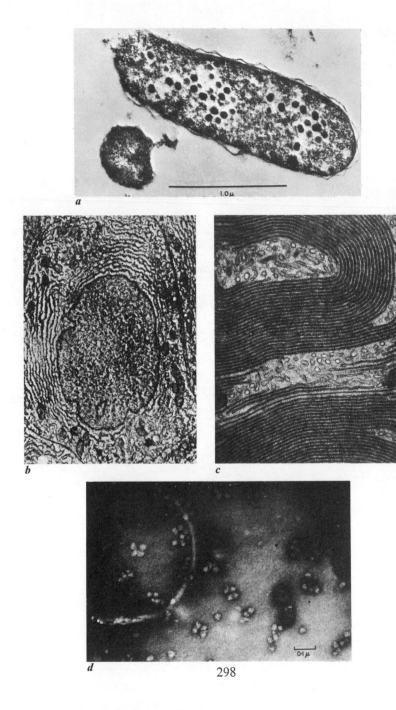

of the organs of higher animals. These distinctly differentiated regions of the cytoplasm are, accordingly, called *organelles*.

There is, however, unfortunately no space in this book to review the many fascinating structural features of protozoan cells. Instead the last section of this chapter is devoted to a brief survey of the ultrastructure of the eukaryotic cells of the metazoa.

6

In fig. 12.5 an attempt has been made to represent an electron micro-scopist's impression of a generalised metazoan cell. It is clear that much of the structure revealed by the electron microscope is com-posed of membranes. This prevalence of membranes in eukaryotic cells was mentioned in Chapter 9. It will also be recalled from Chapter 9 that biomembranes are believed to have functional, as well as structural importance.

Let us start our outline discussion of metazoan cells at the peri-phery and work inwards. We have already emphasised the importance of the cell's boundary membrane in controlling the ingress and egress

e IX Some cells and cellular organelles.

(*a*) a thin section of *E. coli*. Note that the bacterial protoplasm has shrunk away from the cell wall. The dark circular masses within the cell are stages in the growth of T4 phage with which this bacterium has been infected.

(*b*) this is an electron micrograph (magnification 5,200×) of a gland cell in the intestine of a mouse. In the centre of the cell is a large nucleus and sur-rounding this, in the cytoplasm, lamellae belonging to the endoplasmic reticulum are visible. The minute grains attached to the reticulum are ribosomes. The large sausage-like objects are mitochondria.

(*c*) this electron micrograph (magnification 8,800×) shows the well-developed endoplasmic reticulum to be found in the pancreatic cells of a bat. In these cells the membranous elements of the reticulum are covered with ribosomes.

(*d*) ribosomes can be extracted from cells and studied in isolation. In this electron micrograph the ribosomes have been negatively stained. It is clear that they tend to clump together into small groups. These groups have been called polysomes.

(a) *courtesy of E. Kellenberger;* (b) *courtesy of J. Taxi (1963),* Science Progrès —La Nature; (c) *courtesy of D. W. Fawcett:* The Cell: Its Organelles and Inclusions, *Philadelphia, W. B. Saunders Co., 1966;* (d) *courtesy of H. S. Slayter, reprinted by permission of The Rockefeller University Press from* J. Cell Biol. (1963), 7, 654.

of materials. We also noted in Chapter 9 that in some cells the boundary membrane develops into specialised structures. It will be recalled that the tightly twisted spiral of myelin, and the membrane stacks of photoreceptor cells, are both derived from the cell membrane. In many secretory and absorbitive cells, also, the peripheral membrane becomes elaborated. If, for example, the epithelial cells covering one of the villi of the small intestine are examined carefully in the optical microscope, faint vertical striations may be observed along their outer borders. This faint striping is said to constitute a 'brush

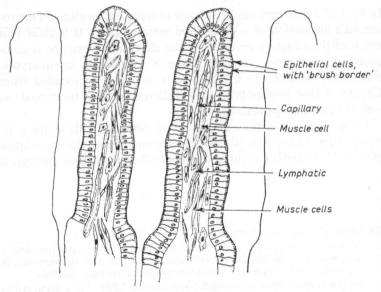

Epithelial cells, with 'brush border'

Capillary

Muscle cell

Lymphatic

Muscle cells

Fig. 12.6 The mucous membrane of the small intestine is developed into finger-like projections known as villi.

border' (fig. 12.6). Examination of these cells in the electron microscope reveals the brush border as a very large number of very minute fingerlike projections (fig. 12.7). On a very much smaller scale these projections resemble the villi of the small intestine themselves. Consequently they are called microvilli.

It has been calculated that some 200,000,000 microvilli are developed on one square millimetre of intestinal wall. Because practically all absorbitive or secretory cells possess microvilli it is reasonable to suppose that they are in some way connected with the large-scale movement of materials into and out of the cell.

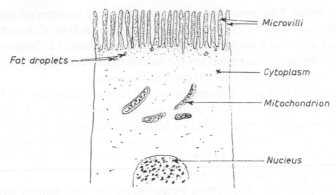

Microvilli

Fat droplets

Cytoplasm

Mitochondrion

Nucleus

Fig. 12.7 The electron microscope shows that the brush border of epithelial cells in fact consists of a mass of microvilli.

Passing inward, now, from the periphery of the cell we find that its interior contains many membraneous structures (fig. 12.5). The major membraneous system of the cytoplasm is said to constitute the endoplasmic reticulum. This seems to consist of a large number of anastomosing sacs and flattened tubes. It has been suggested by Robertson[1] and others that the membranes of the endoplasmic reticulum are continuous with the boundary membrane of the cell. This idea, however, still remains very debatable.

The endoplasmic reticulum is particularly well developed in gland cells. A reason for this fact will be advanced later in this chapter. Plate IX(*b*) is an electron micrograph of a cell in one of the glands of the mouse's small intestine. The well developed endoplasmic reticulum is clearly visible. In addition to gland cells the endoplasmic reticulum is also well developed in some muscle cells.

In Chapter 8 the molecular architecture of striped muscle was discussed. We noticed that this type of muscle develops where rapidity of movement and reaction are at a premium. It was mentioned in Chapter 9 that some muscle fibre membranes are capable of carrying a propagated action potential. This, in fact, is the case with most vertebrate striped muscle fibres.[2] It can be shown without too much difficulty that when an impulse on a motor axon reaches a striped muscle fibre an action potential is initiated on the membrane

[1] Robertson, J. D. (April, 1962), *Sci. Amer.*, p. 72.
[2] Some vertebrate striped muscle fibres are incapable of conducting an action potential. In this respect these so-called slow fibres resemble the majority of invertebrate striped muscles.

of the latter. This spreads rapidly over the fibre membrane (sarco-lemma) preceding by a few milliseconds the contraction of the actino-myosin machinery within. A cause-effect relationship is believed to obtain: the action potential on the sarcolemma is thought to trigger the contraction of the internal protein filaments.

It is plain that in a fast-acting muscle it is advantageous to have the whole muscle fibre contracting as a unit. Indeed in such muscles an 'all-or-nothing' situation exists. If the incoming nerve impulse does not initiate an action potential on the sarcolemma then no contraction occurs; if, on the other hand, an action potential is initiated, then the ensuing contraction is total.

How, then, does the action potential on the sarcolemma trigger the contraction of the internal protein machinery? It is very interesting to find that in these rapidly acting muscles the endoplasmic reticulum, or sarcoplasmic reticulum as it is called in muscle fibres, is especially well developed. Moreover, it appears to be arranged in a very regular manner around the fibre's actinomyosin elements. This regular organisation appears to be associated with the regularly repeated

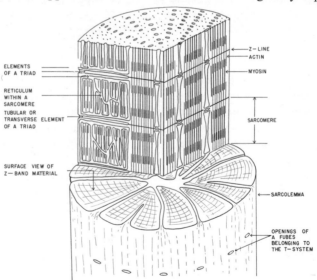

ELEMENTS OF A TRIAD

RETICULUM WITHIN A SARCOMERE

TUBULAR OR TRANSVERSE ELEMENT OF A TRIAD

SURFACE VIEW OF Z — BAND MATERIAL

Z – LINE
ACTIN
MYOSIN

SARCOMERE

SARCOLEMMA

OPENINGS OF A TUBES BELONGING TO THE T–SYSTEM

Fig. 12.8 The sarcoplasmic reticulum of a striped muscle fibre. The diagram shows a single fibre sliced so that its internal structure is made apparent. The tubular elements of the reticulum are shown interspersed among the myosin and actin fibres. In this muscle the triads are shown as recurring adjacent to the Z-lines. From Porter, K. R. and Franzini-Armstrong, C., *Scientific American*, March 1965.

cross striations of the muscle fibre. A typical arrangement is shown in fig. 12.8.

Figure 12.8 shows that interspersed amongst the actin and myosin filaments is a complicated system of membranous tubules and sacs. At regular intervals these cavities coalesce to form a tripartite system. These so-called *triads* may, as in fig. 12.8, be regularly repeated at the level of the fibre's Z-line, or, less frequently, at the level where the A- and I-bands meet. As is shown in fig. 12.8, the central tubular element of a triad is, in fact, an inward extension of the sarcolemma.

The application of very weak electrical stimuli to the sarcolemma shows that the most sensitive regions are at the origins of the triads. A weak stimulus applied in this position causes the two half sarcomeres on either side to contract. A stimulus of similar strength applied else-where on the sarcolemma initiates no contraction at all. Thus it looks as though the tubular invaginations of the sarcolemma or, as they have come to be called, the T-system are instrumental in triggering the internal contractile machinery.

How the T-system achieves this function is still a matter for research. Recent work, however, is beginning to indicate the existence of a mechanism which works on the following lines. It can be shown, first, that myosin loses its ability to hydrolyse ATP if calcium ions are lacking in the immediate vicinity. It follows that the energy source on which muscular contraction depends cannot be tapped. Now it can also be shown that calcium ions are normally removed from the near neighbourhood of the actinomyosin filaments by 'pumps' in the mem-branes of the sarcoplasmic reticulum. It is just as well that this happens else the muscle might remain permanently contracted. It seems, therefore, that the calcium ions in striped muscle are segregated away from the actinomyosin filaments within reservoirs whose walls are formed by the membranes of the sarcoplasmic reticulum.

It is next suggested that the arrival of an action potential either at the origin, or actually along the tubes, of the T-system causes a change in the permeability of the reticular membranes. 'Gates' open and calcium ions are able to flood out on to the protein fibres. Myosin, in consequence, is released from its inability to hydrolyse ATP. The energy liberated in this hydrolysis is used, in some as yet unknown way (see Chapter 8), to bring about the contraction of the sarcomere.

As soon as the action potential has passed from the T-system, the sarcoplasmic reticulum is able to return to its usual task of removing calcium ions from the near neighbourhood of the actinomyosin filaments. It follows that, unable to hydrolyse ATP, the contractile machinery can do nothing but relax.

This brief account of the part played by the sarcoplasmic reticulum of striped muscle fibres emphasises that the membrane systems visible within eukaryotic cells are probably very far from being mere structural scaffolding. It is likely, as has been mentioned in other parts of this book, that they are deeply implicated in the network of interlocking reactions basic to the life of the cell.

Let us now turn our attention away from the muscle fibre and back to the generalised cell of fig. 12.5. In addition to the membranes of the endoplasmic reticulum we can see, in this figure, that, near to the nucleus, there exists another system of membranes labelled the Golgi body. This structure is named after the famous histologist Golgi who first observed it in 1898. For many years after its discovery it was a centre of controversy. Many doubted its very existence. The electron microscope has, however, confirmed that the Golgi body does have real existence in many cells. It appears that the membranes in this region are rather thinner than those of the endoplasmic reticulum, and that they are often associated with a number of vacuoles. The probable function of this complex of membranes will be discussed later in this chapter.

There remains one other membrane within the generalised cell. This is the nuclear membrane. It is closely similar in appearance and dimensions to the membranes of the endoplasmic reticulum. Indeed, as fig. 12.5 shows, it is possible, in some cells, to observe connections between it and the endoplasmic reticulum. Furthermore in very rapidly dividing cells it is sometimes possible to see ribosomes attached to its cytoplasmic edge. The nuclear membrane appears to be interrupted at intervals by pores ranging from 600A to 1,000A in diameter. That these pores are not artefacts and that they allow the passage of materials between nucleus and cytoplasm is suggested by the observation that the electrical resistance of the nuclear membrane is considerably less than that of a comparable cell membrane. This technically very difficult experiment has been carried out on the nuclear membranes of certain amphibian oocytes, and on the nuclear membranes of cells in *Drosophila*'s salivary gland.[1]

In addition to the membrane systems described in the above

[1] Loewenstein, W. R. and Kanno, Y. (1963), *J. Gen. Physiol.*, *46*, 1123.

paragraphs, the electron microscope shows that several types of cell organelle are also built of membranes. The membranous ultra-structure of mitochondria has been discussed already in Chapter 11. However, fig. 12.5 shows that organelles of approximately the same size as mitochondria, but lacking the latter's intricately interweaving cristae, also occur in the cytoplasm. These organelles are called lysosomes.

The discovery of lysosomes is a fairly recent event. It was not until 1955 that de Duve[1] was able to show that mitochondria and lyso-somes were biochemically distinct entities. Instead of containing respiratory enzymes and co-enzymes, it transpired that lysosomes contained a number of digestive enzymes. Indeed if the boundary membrane of a lysosome is ruptured the escaping enzymes are well able to digest away the cell itself. What, then, can be the purpose of such a lethal package within the cell's cytoplasm?

Whilst lysosomes are present in most animal cells it is noticeable that there are more of them in cells which, like some of the white blood cells, are able to ingest and digest particulate matter. In cells of this type, known as phagocytic cells, the ingested particle is first of all enclosed in a small vacuole. The wall of this vacuole seems to be derived from a portion of the phagocyte's cell membrane which becomes 'nipped' off during the ingestion of the particle. When a food-containing vacuole encounters a lysosome the membranes of the two sacs fuse. The contents of the lysosome are then able to pass across into the vacuole and bring about the digestion of its contents.

Intracellular digestion is not the only function which has been ascribed to lysosomes. It has been suggested that the lethal enzymic content of these organelles is employed in the bone-shaping activities of osteoclasts, in the atrophy and resorption of embryonic and larval structures such as the tadpole's tail, and in some disease processes.[2] It is clear that control of the release of so powerful a digestive ferment could prove a very valuable medical technique. In order to achieve such control more must be discovered about the lysosomal membrane. It is evident that this membrane must possess some rather remarkable features to withstand, as it does, the attack of the contained pool of digestive enzymes.

With the lysosome we reach the end of our brief survey of the membranous structures to be found within the cell's cytoplasm.

[1] de Duve, C., *et al.* (1955), *Biochem. J.*, *60*, 604.
[2] de Duve, C. (May 1965), *Sci. Amer.*, *209*, 65.

There are, however, several other important cytoplasmic structures which require a similarly brief discussion. First let us take the centrioles.

Figure 12.5 shows that it is possible to distinguish two centrioles in the animal cell. Together they make up a region of cytoplasm, close to the nucleus, which the classical microscopists called the centrosome. The electron microscope shows that the two centrioles appear remarkably similar to the basal granules of flagella and cilia. Each consists of a ring of nine paired filaments. The minute bundle so formed ranges from about 3,000A to about 6,000A in length, and is about 2,000A in diameter. The two centrioles, as in fig. 12.5, are usually disposed at right angles to each other.

One of the functions of the centrioles is to determine the plane in which the cell is to divide. At the onset of cell division each centriole begins to lay down a daughter centriole alongside itself. The two duplicating centrioles then move apart and travel to opposite poles of the cell. Between them and the chromosomes, which have now become visible, tubular spindle fibres develop. These are about 250A in diameter and thus have very similar dimensions to entire bacterial flagella, and to the fibrils within eukaryotic cilia. The chromosomes, which can now be seen to be composed of two chromatids, arrange themselves at the equator of the cell. Each chromatid becomes attached to a spindle fibre (fig. 13.3), and, during the process of cell division, moves apart from its duplicate towards the centriole to which it is attached. Whether the spindle fibres by, perhaps, contracting cause this movement is not as yet certain. The various stages of cell division are shown in figs. 13.3 and 13.4.

It is clear from the preceding account that centrioles play a very important part in organising the division of animal cells.[1] It is also fascinating to notice that there is a close similarity between centrioles and the basal granules of eukaryotic cilia and flagella. This similarity, already alluded to in Chapter 8, suggests that these minute self-replicating granules represent an important structural and functional level in the architecture of living matter. For not only do these organelles all share an ability to reproduce themselves but also they are all apparently capable of producing the fibres which form either the spindle of a dividing cell, or the ultrastructure of cilia and flagella.

[1] Centrioles appear to be absent from plant cells which otherwise divide in a manner exactly similar to that of animal cells.

Next let us turn our attention to another extremely important granular element: the ribosome. These minute particles have already been mentioned several times in this chapter. They exist in both PPLOs and bacteria. In metazoan cells they are frequently observed to be attached, as is shown in fig. 12.5, to membranes of the endoplasmic reticulum. It is nowadays realised that their ubiquity is due to the fact that they are essential to the processes of protein synthesis. Their rôle in this all-important biochemical activity will be described in Chapter 14.

In fact rather more is known about their biological function than about their structure. They vary, in different cells, from about 100A to 250A in diameter. They consist of protein and ribonucleic acid (RNA) in the proportion of about 3 : 2. Their name arises from the fact that most of a cell's RNA is concentrated within them.

It can be shown that ribosomes consist of subunits. If the concentration of magnesium ions is lowered the ribosome splits into two fragments. The larger of these two fragments is about two thirds the size of the original particle, the smaller about one third the size. Both still consist of a complex of RNA and protein. The fact that ribosomes consist of subunits can also be demonstrated by the electron microscope: negatively stained ribosomes can be seen to be composed of two unequal parts (fig. 12.9).

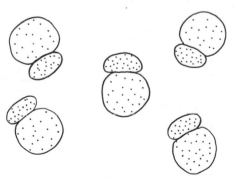

Fig. 12.9 Ribosomes consist of two unequal parts.

Further 'dissection' of ribosomes into yet smaller subunits can be achieved if the concentrations of magnesium and other ions is carefully manipulated.[1]

[1] Gavrilova, L. P., Ivanov, D. A., and Spirin, A. S. (1966), *J. Mol. Biol.*, *23*, 281.

If ribosomes are extracted from cells actively engaged in protein synthesis it is often possible to see, in the electron microscope, that they are connected together into small groups by a thread (fig. 12.10). This thread is believed to be a strand of messenger-RNA. The significance of this observation will emerge in Chapter 14. It can be shown that it is the smaller of the two subunits which becomes attached to the messenger-RNA strand.

Ribosome   mRNA

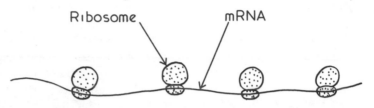

Fig. 12.10 Ribosomes are frequently found to be strung together on a strand of messenger-RNA like beads on a thread.

It was mentioned above that in metazoan cells ribosomes are frequently found attached to the membranes of the endoplasmic reticulum. This is particularly the case in the cells of glandular tissue. Elegant studies involving the radioisotopic labelling of the proteins being synthesised in pancreatic cells have established the functional significance of this morphology.[1] It has been shown, first, that the proteins manufactured by the ribosomes are passed directly into the channels of the endoplasmic reticulum. Next it is possible to demonstrate that the proteins are moved along the channels of the reticulum until they reach the region of the Golgi complex. In the cavities of the latter organelle the secretory proteins are concentrated into packages which grow in size and density until, ultimately, they become visible in the optical microscope. Microscopists have long known these granules as zymogen granules and have recognised that they are the precursors of the pancreatic enzymes. This functional analysis thus explains the strong development of endoplasmic reticulum and Golgi body in glandular cells (Plates IX(b) and (c)).

The last structural elements to be discerned in the cytoplasm of animal cells are the so-called microtubules. In fact these tubules have now been observed in all types of cell: bacterial, plant and animal.[2] They are filaments about 120A to 270A in diameter with a

[1] Jamieson, J. D. and Palade, G. E. (1967) *J. Cell Biol.*, *34*, 577 and 597.
[2] van Iterson, W., Hoeniger, J. F., and Zanten, E. N. (1967), *J. Cell. Biol.*, *32*, 1.

core of relatively translucent material. High resolution electron microscopy shows that they are composed of globular subunits with a lateral spacing of about 50A. It emerges, therefore, that their dimensions and fine structure are very similar to those of bacterial flagella, the fibrils within eukaryocytic cilia and flagella and, lastly, the fibres which form the mitotic spindle. Whether microtubules are involved in cell movement, cytoplasmic streaming, or the transport of materials around the cell is, at present, uncertain.

7

To conclude this bird's-eye survey we may note that there is a considerable uniformity underlying the, at first sight, bewildering diversity of cells. This perception justifies the lumping together of all these disparate forms under one heading: cells.

It is true that there is a fairly sharp discontinuity between the prokaryotic cells of bacteria and their allies, and the eukaryotic cells of animals and plants. This discontinuity is probably, at root, a discontinuity of size. The volume of the average bacterial cell is some five hundred times less than that of the average eukaryotic cell. Nevertheless, it is very interesting to find that at what might be called the 'sub-organellar' or 'macromolecular assembly' level there are striking similarities between the two types of cell.

For example, all the cells we have discussed possess the lipoprotein assemblies which we recognise as membranes. All the cells, too, possess the less well-understood nucleoprotein assemblies called ribosomes. Only in eukaryotic cells, however, do the two types of assembly come together to form the familiar ribosome-studded endoplasmic reticulum.

Eukaryotic cells possess well-defined and highly intricate respiratory organelles in the form of mitochondria. These are not to be discovered in prokaryotic cells. Instead, for the most part, the enzymes and co-enzymes involved in oxidative metabolism are believed to be attached to the cell membrane. In some bacteria, however, as was mentioned on p. 295, the cell membrane appears to invaginate to form mesosomes. Perhaps these membranous whorls may be regarded as the modest primordia of eukarocytic mitochondria. It will be very interesting to learn whether any evidence can be found to show that ETPs, or oxisomes, exist in these archetypal respiratory organelles.

CELLS

The greatest structural difference between eukaryotic and prokaryotic cells lies, of course, in the latter's lack of a well-defined nucleus. Both cells possess DNA, but whereas this is free and relatively uncomplicated in the prokaryotic cell, it is elaborated in conjunction with protein to form the, as yet unknown, macromolecular architecture of the chromosome in the cells of higher organisms. It has been suggested[1] that this increased complexity is a prerequisite for the specialisation which is so marked a feature of eukaryotic cells (see Chapter 15).

In general, it is beginning to look as though cells may be constructed from a certain rather limited number of 'standard parts' which can be found, uncomplicated, in prokaryocytes, but are elaborated into higher structures in eukaryocytes. This conclusion also seemed to emerge from our discussion in Chapter 8 of prokaryocytic flagella, eukaryocytic cilia and animal muscles.

It is also interesting to note in this context the accumulating evidence which shows that macromolecular assemblies like ribosomes and viruses can not only be dis-assembled in certain physico-chemical conditions, but can also be re-assembled if the conditions are reversed. This is reminiscent of the reversible aggregation and disaggregation of globular proteins which we also discussed in Chapter 8. It is conceivable that the day is not too far distant when the assembly of the intricate organelles of eukaryotic cells will also be understood as the outcome of certain thermodynamic forces.

In addition to these sub-organellar structures all cells share in common a multitude of enzymes and co-enzymes which ensure the extraction of energy from the environment and the replication and expression of the hereditary information.

Lastly it is clear that the boundary membrane of the cell plays a very vital role in holding together, in a narrow space, the dynamically interacting entities of the cytoplasm and nucleus. It is probably the possession of this 'skin' which, more than anything else, ensures that a cell *lives*. It is interesting to speculate that the cell's cytoplasm may resemble in some of its important characteristics the physico-chemical constitution of the biopoietic seas of three or so billion years ago. This extension of MacCallum's hypothesis[2] suggests that

---

[1] Palade, G. E. (1964), *Nat. Acad. Sci. Proc.*, *52*, 632.
[2] MacCallum, A. B. (1910), *Proc. Roy. Soc. B.*, *82*, 602. MacCallum concluded that it is '. . . extremely probable that the inorganic composition of the blood plasma of Vertebrates is an heirloom of life in the primeval ocean'.

what we are looking at when we observe the streaming cytoplasm of today's cell is an enclosed and conserved fragment of the environment which existed when life first developed. Like astronomers contemplating receding galaxies we are, in a sense, observing the forms of things long past.

13

DNA

1

I t is generally not possible to point to one particular date and say that at this moment in history such-and-such a science was born. Molecular biology forms no exception to this rule. As mentioned earlier in this book, it can be said to have emerged from the confluence of currents springing from physics, chemistry and biology. Nevertheless, a number of very central and fruitful discoveries were made in the early nineteen-fifties.

In 1951, it will be remembered, the Caltech group under Pauling proposed secondary structures for a number of proteins. In 1955 Sanger established the primary sequence of insulin. In 1954 Perutz demonstrated that the multiple isomorphous replacement method could be used to solve the three-dimensional structure of globular proteins. In the early nineteen-fifties, too, the electron microscope finally became an effective tool for the study of biological ultrastructure and at this time also Hodgkin, Huxley and others made great advances in understanding the ionic bases of the action potential.

However, perhaps the most germinal of all these advances came in 1953 when Watson and Crick proposed a structure for DNA (deoxyribose nucleic acid).[1] Fifteen years later, we find that based on their double helical model is a vast and rapidly developing field of scientific knowledge generally referred to as molecular genetics. It is perhaps here, more than anywhere else in molecular biology, that the generalisation 'Function arises from structure' is validated.

Molecular genetics, too, fills the last gap in our account of the molecular architecture of the body. It will be remembered that at the end of the last chapter we suggested that eukaryocytic organelles, like the protein assemblies of Chapter 8, might well form or 'crystallise' automatically given both the correct physico-chemical

[1] Watson, J. D. and Crick, F. H. C. (1953), *Nature*, *171*, 737, 964.

conditions and the appropriate raw materials. Molecular genetics shows how the appropriate raw materials happen to be present within the confines of a cell.

Before, however, we turn our attention to DNA—how it stores genetic information, and how this information controls the primary structure of proteins—we must familiarise ourselves with the branch of biology which it has revolutionised. This branch of biology is, of course, the study of heredity.

2

That offspring resemble their progenitors is a truth too obvious to be laboured. That the resemblance is not exact is also a truism. Like the observations summarised by the first two laws of thermodynamics both perceptions are commonplace, yet their implications are profound and far-reaching.

The inexact copying of parents by their offspring has provided the grist from which the mills of natural selection have ground out the myriad organic forms inhabiting the planet today. It is the Darwinian credo that the slightly-varying hereditary constitution will fit some individuals rather better than others for the conditions in which they find themselves. The better fitted have a fractionally better chance of surviving to maturity and passing on their advantageous characteristics to their progeny.

Over the vast lengths of time habitually assumed by Darwinists these fractional advantages inevitably establish themselves. As the environment changes, as new conditions for life appear and old conditions disappear, the population of living organisms changes also. Today we observe a cross-section of this vast evolutionary movement. Organisms are to be found populating all the likely habitats and some very unlikely ones as well. In short, the faulty copying of parents by their offspring is a *sine qua non* of the evolutionary process. Without it, organisms, unable to adapt, inflexible, would long since have disappeared from the face of the unheeding planet.

3

How does this vital variability arise? There are two sources: mutation and reassortment. Mutation is said to occur when a completely fresh character makes its appearance in an organism's make-up;

reassortment is said to occur when some of the characters of both parents appear juxtaposed in the offspring.

Mutation is a rare event. Reassortment, however, occurs every time sexual reproduction takes place. Hence we may conclude that the latter process is the principal means by which genetic variability is produced and maintained. So important, indeed, is variation in a population of organisms that we may see in it the reason for the development of sexual reproduction.

The essential feature of sexual reproduction is, of course, the production by each parent of gametes which meet and fuse in the process of fertilisation. The resulting zygote develops via embryo, infant and juvenile into the next generation of adults.

The gametes contributed by male and female parents must clearly carry in some way factors determining the hereditary characters of the offspring. Anticipating matters a little, let us suppose that each hereditary character is determined by one material factor. Now let us remember that these factors are carried by gametes which fuse to produce the zygote. It is clear that the zygote will contain more factors than either gamete alone. Imagine this process continuing over a number of generations. On the face of it, the number of factors would seem to increase indefinitely. This is obviously impossible.

It is thus essential that the number of factors is reduced either in the formation of the gametes or before the next set of gametes is formed. In higher plants and animals, reduction in the number of factors is found to occur in the formation of the gametes. On fertilisation, when gametes from the male and female parent fuse, the factors summate to give the full number characteristic of the adult. This summation allows the reassortment which, as has already been emphasised, is a very central biological phenomenon.

4

The first scientist to study the nature of reassortment rigorously was the nineteenth-century Austrian monk, Mendel. Mendel's approach was to concentrate his attention on the inheritance of certain well-defined characteristics: the height, seed colour, seed shape, etc. of the pea, *Pisum sativum*. He was able to show that a number of these easily recognisable characters behaved as if they were determined by discrete factors. These factors later became known as genes. To illustrate Mendel's work, let us take two examples.

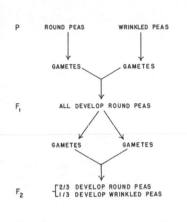

OBSERVATIONS

MENDEL'S INTERPRETATION

P = PARENTAL GENERATION F_1 = FIRST FILIAL GENERATION

F_2 = SECOND FILIAL GENERATION

Fig. 13.1 The result of crossing two plants, one breeding true for round peas and the other for wrinkled peas. On the left-hand side of the figure are the observations and on the right-hand side the Mendelian interpretation. The factors determining roundness or wrinkledness are symbolised by upper and lower case r's respectively. The upper case letter indicates that the factor is dominant—see text.

First, let us consider the result of crossing a pea plant which breeds true for round peas with one breeding true for wrinkled peas. Mendel found that the first generation offspring of this cross all displayed round peas. If, however, the members of this first generation were interbred amongst themselves, their offspring showed a characteristic 3 : 1 distribution between those bearing round peas and those bearing wrinkled peas.

Mendel's theoretical interpretation of this and other similar experiments is shown in fig. 13.1. It involves the notion of dominance and recessiveness. Mendel supposed that the factor determining roundness would always override the influence of the factor determining wrinkledness. Dominance and recessiveness are not of great general importance; what is of importance in Mendel's experiments, however, is the demonstration that the genetic factors contributed by both parents are randomly reassorted and appear in all possible combinations in their offspring. It is also important to notice that Mendel conceived of the genetic factors as discrete

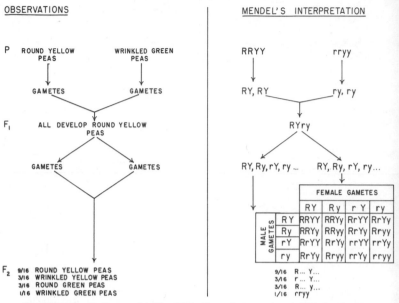

OBSERVATIONS | MENDEL'S INTERPRETATION

P   ROUND YELLOW   WRINKLED GREEN   RRYY   rryy
        PEAS   PEAS

     GAMETES   GAMETES   RY, RY   ry, ry

F₁   ALL DEVELOP ROUND YELLOW   RYry
            PEAS

     GAMETES   GAMETES   RY, Ry, rY, ry ...   RY, Ry, rY, ry...

                                                    FEMALE GAMETES

                                              RY   Ry   rY   ry
                                         RY RRYY RRYy RrYY RrYy
                                         Ry RRYy RRyy RrYy Rryy
                                         rY RrYY RrYy rrYY rrYy
                                         ry RrYy Rryy rrYy rryy

F₂ 9/16 ROUND YELLOW PEAS   9/16 R... Y...
    3/16 WRINKLED YELLOW PEAS   3/16 r... Y...
    3/16 ROUND GREEN PEAS   3/16 R... y...
    1/16 WRINKLED GREEN PEAS   1/16 rryy

Fig. 13.2 Symbolism as in Fig. 13.1. Cross between peas differing in two characters: seed shape and seed colour. The experiment shows that these characters are inherited quite independently of each other.

'hard' units passed on indefinitely from one generation to the next. Their influence might be masked but their existence is not undermined.

The second example of Mendel's work which we may consider, extends and confirms the conclusions to be derived from the first example. Suppose we follow the fates of two characters instead of one. Let us take roundness and wrinkledness again, but let us also take into account the colour of the pea—whether yellow or green.

Suppose, then, we have two true-breeding pea plants, one with a round, yellow pea and the other with a wrinkled, green pea. It is found that the first generation offspring of this cross all display round yellow peas. If this first generation is then interbred, the second generation peas show four different characters. These four characters are found approximately in the ratio of 9:3:3:1. Mendel's interpretation of this result is shown in fig. 13.2. It is clear that the two characters are assorted quite independently of each other.

316

Mendel published the results of his experiments in 1865. Their significance was not, however, realised until the very end of the nineteenth and the beginning of the twentieth century.

5

The science of genetics was inaugurated by the rediscovery of Mendel's work at the beginning of the twentieth century. The organism used for genetic analysis changed from *Pisum sativum* to the fruit-fly *Drosophila melanogaster*.

The advantage of using *Drosophila* lies in its very much shorter generation time. Instead of having to wait months or years, the result of a genetic experiment on *Drosophila* can be observed in a couple of weeks. Consequently, because experiments could be more rapid, there could be more of them. This is of great importance. The elementary experiments in Mendelism mentioned in the preceding section show that genetics is essentially a statistical science. Statistics works best with large numbers.

One of the first findings of *Drosophila* genetics was an apparent breach of Mendel's law of independent assortment. Several hereditary characters were discovered which did not appear in all possible combinations. Such characters appeared to be linked to each other in groups. Two such characters are cream eye colour and curved wing. The insects' offspring inherited either both these characters or neither. Initially no cases were found in which the progeny of such a parent fly inherited one character and not the other.

6

An explanation of this apparent breach of Mendel's laws was soon forthcoming. At the turn of the century the first descriptions of the chromosome movements attending cell division were published. It was soon realised that these colourful threads might well provide a physical basis for the Mendelian theory.

It was shown that two different types of cell division occurred. The type of cell division underlying such processes as wound-healing, growth and embryological development is called mitosis (fig. 13.3). The nucleus of each of the two cells produced by this type of division contains the same number of chromosomes as the parent nucleus. The second type of division occurs during the production of gametes by higher organisms. In this type the number of chromosomes in the daughter nuclei is half that observed in the parental nucleus (fig. 13.4). This type of cell division is called meiosis. It is clear that if Mendel's factors are located in or on the chromosomes a material basis for the theoretical schemes of figs. 13.1 and 13.2 is provided.

Plant and animal nuclei contain a fairly small number of chromosomes. For example, the gametes of man contain twenty-three

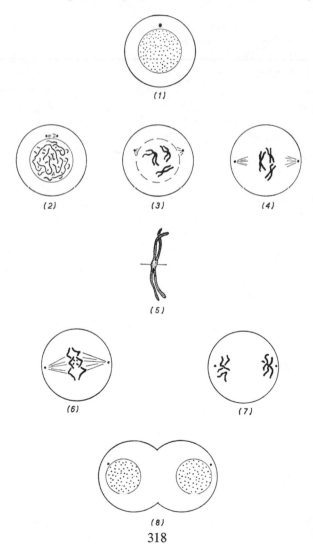

(1)

(2)   (3)   (4)

(5)

(6)   (7)

(8)

318

chromosomes and those of *Drosophila* four chromosomes. It follows that, particularly in the case of *Drosophila*, it is likely that any two Mendelian factors will find themselves on the same chromosome. If this situation obtains then the two factors would be carried together to the same daughter nucleus. In this way microscopists were able to explain the genetical observation that certain characters were nearly always associated together.

It soon became apparent that the hereditary characteristics of *Drosophila* could be classified into four linkage groups. It is clear that these four linkage groups correspond to the four gametic chromosomes.

7

The next step in the story shows how study of exceptions to the rule of linkage provided a yet deeper understanding of the genetic mechanism. First, let us give Mendel's factors their more modern name: genes. Second, let us note that congenital deformities, for example,

---

Fig. 13.3 (*opposite*) The essential features of a mitotic division.

(1) The cell has not yet begun to divide. The nucleus (stippled) appears homogeneous. The two centrioles (at this magnification observed as a single dark spot) are close together in the vicinity of the nuclear membrane.

(2) The centrioles begin to move apart. Long thread-like objects, the chromosomes, appear in the nucleus.

(3) The centrioles move to opposite poles of the cell. The chromosomes shorten and thicken and it can be seen that they are paired structures stuck together near their middles by a region known as a centromere. The nuclear membrane begins to disintegrate.

(4) The chromosomes arrange themselves on the 'equator' of the cell. The nuclear membrane disappears. Bundles of fibres, called 'spindle' fibres, develop to connect the chromosomes to the centrioles.

(5) A single chromosome at this stage can be seen to be divided longitudinally. The two halves are called chromatids. They are held together by the centromere to which the spindle fibres become attached.

(6) The centromeres holding the chromatids together themselves divide. Each chromatid now moves away from its partner to the opposite pole of the cell.

(7) The chromatids gather at opposite poles of the cell.

(8) Nuclear membranes appear around each collection of chromatids. The cytoplasm begins to divide. Soon two 'daughter' cells have been produced.

The sequence of events shown in the diagrams occurs in most animal cells. Plant cells, however, differ in having no distinguishable centriole.

cream eye or curved wing in *Drosophila*, are said to be due to gene mutations. Third, let us note that mutated genes act as tags, or markers, for particular chromosomes. Now let us turn our attention to the study of the exceptions which prove the rule.

It is found that genes which normally belong to one linkage group occasionally appear in another. This is very strange. To explain it, we have to suppose that chromosomes are capable of interchanging

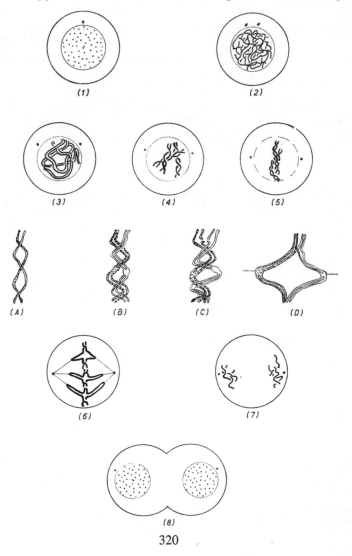

segments. This exchange of segments is called 'crossing-over'; it is of the greatest importance both to the geneticist and to the processes of organic evolution.

The phenomenon of crossing-over occurs before or during meiotic division. Exactly when and how it occurs is still debated. Fig. 13.5 illustrates its basic features.

Fig. 13.5 should be compared with fig. 13.4. In fig. 13.5 we suppose

---

Fig. 13.4 (opposite) The essential features of a meiotic division.

(1) The cell has not yet begun to divide.

(2) The two centrioles separate. Chromosomes become visible in the nucleus.

(3) The chromosomes shorten, thicken, and become more distinct. They can be seen to be grouped in pairs.

(4) The chromosomes continue to shorten and thicken, and twist around their partners. At this stage also the chromosomes can be seen to be composed of two chromatids. Breakages occur and segments of chromatid are exchanged.

(5) The chromosomes arrange themselves on the equator of the cell. The nuclear membrane begins to disintegrate.

(A) A pair of chromosomes at stage 3.

(B) A pair of chromosomes at stage 4. The twisting has increased, and they can be seen to be divided into chromatids.

(C) A little later breakages in the chromatids occur. One such breakage is shown at the top of the diagram. The segments released in these breakages tend to connect up with partner chromatids. This is called 'crossing over'.

(D) A pair of chromosomes at stage 6. They are moving to opposite poles of the cell. They are held together at their cross-over points.

(6) Spindle fibres, as in mitosis, connect the centromeres to the centrioles. The centromeres at this stage have divided, and the chromosomes are moving to opposite poles of the cell.

(7) The chromosomes gather at opposite poles of the cell.

(8) Nuclear membranes appear around each collection of chromosomes. The cytoplasm begins to divide. Soon two 'daughter' cells have been produced.

It will have been observed that whereas in mitosis the two 'daughter' nuclei are constituted from *chromatids*, in meiosis the 'daughter' nuclei are formed from *chromosomes*. This is an essential difference. It means that the number of chromosomes in the 'daughter' nuclei is halved. Thus the nuclei of the reproductive cells which develop from these 'daughter' nuclei have only half the number of chromosomes to be found in the other cells of the body. Now the central feature of fertilisation is the fusion of two reproductive cells: the spermatozoon and the ovum. In this way the number of chromosomes is brought back to normal again, so that the embryo starts off with a full complement, half derived from the father and half from the mother.

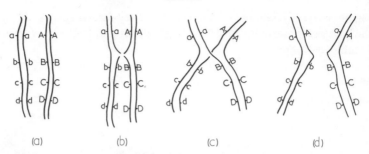

Fig. 13.5 As a result of the process of crossing over in meiotic division, new combinations of characters develop. This is of great importance both for the evolution of species and for the analysis of genetic material.

that one of the two chromosomes carries mutated genes—a, b, c, d—whereas the other chromosome carries the normal or, as they are called, wild-type genes—A, B, C, D. Thus, adverting to our *Drosophila* example, 'a' might stand for 'cream eye' and 'A' for red eye'—the wild-type condition; 'b' might stand for 'curved wing' and 'B' for the normal straight wing. Now as fig. 13.4 shows, the chromosomes involved in the gyrations of meiotic division have already split longitudinally into chromatids. It is, in fact, as figs. 13.4 and 13.5 show, the chromatids which break and exchange segments. The result, as fig. 13.5(*d*) shows, is that each daughter nucleus contains one chromatid in which the genes are linked in a new sequence. This process of forming new combinations or groups of genes is called recombination.

The daughter nuclei to which the chromosomes in fig. 13.5(*d*) are contributed undergo a mitotic division before the gametes are formed. Thus the nuclei of two of the gametes formed will contain the new linkage groups 'Abcd' and 'aBCD'. This ability to recombine genes into new linkage groups is of paramount biological importance. The Mendelian reassortment of characters which we discussed earlier in this chapter is not permanent. The new genetic constellations produced by reassortment are dissolved and remade with each succeeding generation. The special type of reassortment we are discussing here—recombination—is more permanent. Because genes are spaced so closely together along a chromosome it is unlikely that breakage and crossing-over will occur twice running in precisely the same place. Consequently the new genetic make-up, the fresh gene combination, will be transmitted from generation to generation. If its possessor finds his altered hereditary constitution an advantage, he and his progeny will survive in ever-increasing numbers.

Recombination is not only basic to evolutionary change but it also provides a basic tool in genetic analysis. For 'crossing-over' enables the geneticist to map the position of genes along the chromosome.

The principles of genetic mapping are not difficult to understand. Two assumptions are made. First, that the genes are distributed linearly along the chromosome; second, that 'crossing-over' has an equal chance of occurring at any point along the chromosome's length. The truth of the first assumption is nowadays well established and there is much evidence to support the second. If these two assumptions are made, it follows that the further apart a pair of genes are, the more likely it is for a 'cross-over' to occur between them. Thus by examining the recombinant frequencies of genes belonging to the same linkage group it is possible to construct a map showing their relative distances from one another along the chromosome. Those with the highest frequencies will be furthest apart, and vice versa.

By 1920 the American geneticist T. H. Morgan and his collaborators had been able to build up linkage maps for each of the four chromosomes of *Drosophila*. The business of compiling linkage maps is, however, laborious. Numerous mutations have to be discovered or induced. The fate of these mutant genes has to be followed in many breeding experiments. In order to map genes which are close together on a chromosome and hence recombine very infrequently, very large numbers of matings have to be made and their offspring examined. Although *Drosophila* is a more rapidly breeding and more easily handled organism than *Pisum sativum* it is clear that to construct very detailed maps recourse must be made to even more convenient organisms. Thus in the past three decades geneticists have shifted their attention from plants and animals to micro-organisms.

8

Bacteria and, in particular, viruses multiply very rapidly indeed in the correct conditions and hence provide the geneticist with powerful systems for investigating the fine structure of chromosomes. Instead of a generation time of a few weeks, micro-organisms frequently reproduce every few hours; instead of laboriously examining a few hundred *Drosophila* for cream eyes or curved wings it is possible to examine with ease the results of several million microbial crosses.

The favourite organisms of microbial geneticists have been *Escherichia coli* and its parasitic viruses. *E. coli*, as was mentioned in Chapter 12, is a harmless bacterium easily isolated from the human colon. Viruses which attack bacteria are called bacteriophages or, more shortly, phages. Many bacteriophages parasitise *E. coli* but the best known have been designated T2, T4 and T6 or, collectively, the T-even phages.

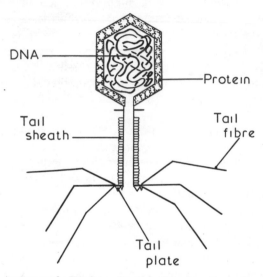

Fig. 13.6 Anatomy of a T4 phage. Bacteriophages are the most complicated of all viruses. The head is composed of a wall built of globular proteins enclosing a mass of DNA. The phage is able to attach itself to an appropriate bacterium by means of the tail plate and fibres; the tail sheath then contracts so that the hollow core is driven into the bacterial cell like a hypodermic syringe into the bacterium.

The structure of the *E. coli* cell was briefly described in Chapter 12 (fig. 12.3). Fig. 13.6 shows the structure of a T-even phage; Plate X(*b*) shows a negatively-stained T4 phage.

Phages, like all viruses, are obliged to parasitise cells, in this case bacterial cells. Viruses, in fact, are unable to reproduce themselves on their own. They depend on the genetic apparatus to be found in cells to achieve this fundamental process.

Fig. 13.6 shows that a T-even phage consists of a central 'chromosome' surrounded by a protective protein coat. The phage's tail is specifically adapted to stick to the surface of a particular type of bacterium. This specificity is, as we shall see, sometimes very precise.

When a T-even phage 'bumps' into an appropriate *E. coli* cell the tail sticks to the cell's surface and the viral chromosome is injected into the bacterium. Once within *E. coli* the phage chromosome commandeers the cell's genetic machinery. The phage chromosome rapidly replicates itself and the bacterium's ribosomal protein manufactory is caused to synthesise new phage coat protein. The new chromosomes and the new coats come together to constitute new T-even phages. Within half an hour the *E. coli* cell contains up to one thousand T-even phages. Each parvenu phage breaks its way out of the bacterial cell into the surrounding medium where it is immediately ready to infect another *E. coli*. It is not difficult to imagine that the egress of a couple of hundred phage particles through the cell wall is catastrophic in its effects on the bacterium. This process, called lysis, in fact destroys the bacterium.

We have seen in the previous section that the technique used by geneticists to map chromosomes depends upon the observation of recombinant genes. Does recombination occur in phage particles? The answer to this question is: yes. Each bacteriophage, it is true, has but one chromosome but when a bacterium, as is frequently the case, is attacked simultaneously by more than one phage, the injected chromosomes are able to 'cross-over' (fig. 13.7).

The genes of bacteriophages are, as in the case of other genes, subject to mutation. Thus positions, or loci, on the chromosome may, as usual, be marked. The mutations which have proved of greatest use to the phage geneticist have been those which affect the phage's parasitic ability.

When a few T-even phage particles are injected into a culture of *E. coli* growing in a petri dish, characteristic 'holes' appear in the formerly continuous culture. The reason for the appearance of these holes is plain. The *E. coli* cells in the infected area have all been attacked and lysed by the phages; the liberated phages have been infected and lysed all their neighbours. The devastated area appears, to the naked eye, as a hole in the bacterial 'lawn'. These holes have been called *plaques*. A plaque will appear within a few hours of introducing a phage to an appropriate bacterial culture.

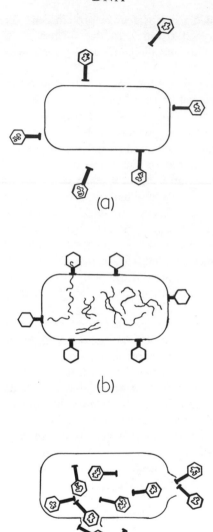

Fig. 13.7 E. coli may be infected simultaneously by several bacterio-phages (*a*). The injected DNA strands, when replicating, may 'cross over' (*b*). Some of the bacteriophages bursting out of the bacterium (*c*) may, in consequence, possess recombinant genes.

Mutations which affect a phage's parasitic ability reveal themselves either as alterations in the appearance of the plaque, or as restriction of plaque-formation to certain strains of the bacterium or, perhaps, in the complete absence of plaque-formation at higher temperatures.

It is clear that plaque-formation provides an excellent technique for detecting mutations. Very large numbers of bacteriophages can be tested in an experiment lasting only a few hours. This fact, in conjunction with the 'cross-over' ability mentioned above, implies that phage genetics is an exceedingly powerful tool with which to analyse the fine structure of a chromosome.

9

As an example of the use of the powerful tool of phage genetics, let us consider Benzer's well known work on a section of the chromosome of the T4 phage.

It was shown that certain mutations on the T4 chromosome increased the size of the plaque produced in cultures of *E. coli* (strain B). This observation can be explained if we suppose that the mutated gene accelerates the life-cycle of T4. If this occurs the time from infection to lysis of the *E. coli* cell is diminished. Hence more *E. coli* can be infected and lysed in a given time: hence the plaques will be larger than those produced by the unmutated phage. It can be shown that the accelerated life-cycle is due to a mutation in any one of at least three genes. These mutated genes, because they make the life-cycle more *rapid*, are designated rI, rII and rIII. Benzer chose to work with the rII mutants.

Careful work on these rII mutants showed that the gene consisted of two distinct regions. This fact was demonstrated by a technique known as complementation. First it was shown that although rII mutants multiplied rapidly in *E. coli* (strain B) there existed another strain, the K-strain, in which they would not grow at all. Normal, wild-type, unmutated phages, however, grew well in *E. coli* (strain K). Benzer then noticed a rather odd phenomenon. If two or more pure-breeding rII mutants infected *E. coli* (strain K) simultaneously then, in some cases, a plaque was formed. The two mutated T4 phages appeared to complement each other.

This was strange indeed. Each pure-breeding rII mutant was, on its own, incapable of forming a plaque on the K-strain of *E. coli*;

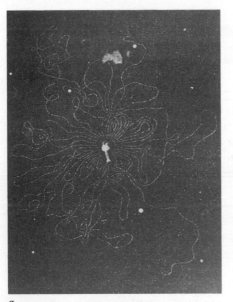

a

b

0.1μ

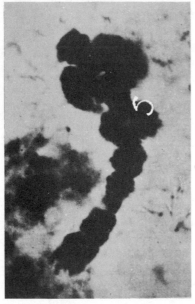

c

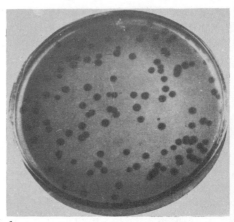

d

328

together, however, infection and thus plaque-formation was possible. Benzer suggested an ingenious solution. He proposed that the rII gene in fact consisted of two regions. For reasons which will appear below he coined the term *cistron* to describe these two regions. Benzer then suggested that each of these two cistrons, called by him the rIIa and the rIIb cistrons, controlled the formation of a product—possibly a polypeptide. The two polypeptides so formed might then combine to form a protein with, perhaps, an enzymic function.

How do these hypotheses explain the anomalous observations described above? The answer to this question is shown in fig. 13.8. The enzymic protein produced by the union of the two polypeptides enables the T4 phage to survive and multiply within the otherwise hostile environment of the *E. coli* (strain K) cell. If a T4 phage with an rIIa mutation or an rIIb mutation, or both, infects *E. coli* (strain K) then for lack of the enzyme the battle for survival is lost. Consequently no plaques form. If, however, two T4 phages, one with an rIIa mutation and the other with an rIIb mutation, infect the K-strain, survival is possible. The intact rIIb cistron of the first phage complements the intact rIIa cistron of the second. Both 'a' and 'b' polypeptides are made, albeit by different chromosomes. The construction of the vital enzymic protein is thus possible. Plaque-formation is observed.

Benzer's complementation technique thus allows the detection of the smallest segment of a chromosome capable of controlling the synthesis of a product. By analogy with the terminology used by

ate X Some aspects of molecular genetics.

(*a*) at the centre of this electron micrograph (magnification 56,000 ×) lie the remains of a T2 bacteriophage. Surrounding the phage lies a tangle of DNA threads which have burst from its head under osmotic shock. A T2 phage will contain a length of DNA approaching 50μ.

(*b*) T4 bacteriophage prepared for electron microscopy by the technique of negative staining.

(*c*) a 'puffed' giant chromosome from the salivary gland of a midge (*Chironomus*). Magnification 1,100 ×.

(*d*) the dark spots are regions where the lawn of *E. coli* growing in the petri dish has been destroyed by an infecting phage.

(a) *courtesy of A. K. Kleinschmidt, D. Lang, D. Jacherts and R. K. Zahn* (*1962*), Biochem. Biophys. Acta, 61, *857;* (b) *courtesy of T. F. Anderson:* Molecular Organisation and Biological Function, *Harper & Row, 1967;* (c) *courtesy of W. Beermann;* (d) *courtesy of G. S. Stent:* Molecular Biology of Bacterial Viruses, *W. H. Freeman & Co., 1963.*

organic chemists, Benzer used the words *cis* and *trans* to describe the complementation situations depicted in fig. 13.8. From this terminology the term cistron is derived.

It has been implicit in the above account and in fig. 13.8 that phage

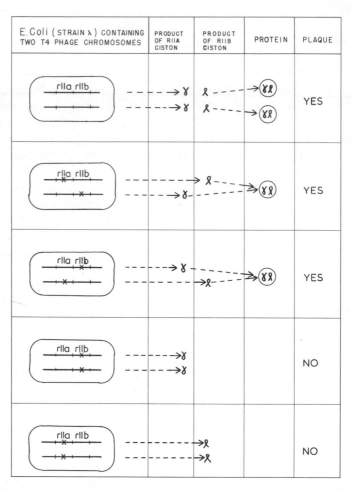

Fig. 13.8 Scheme to show the essence of Benzer's interpretation of the phenomenon of complementation. In each case the *E. coli* cell is shown as containing two T4 phage chromosomes. The products of the rII regions of these chromosomes are shown on the right-hand side of the figure. It is supposed that the biologically-active protein manufactured by the rII gene consists of two polypeptides. For further explanation see text.

330

genetics allows us to detect and map mutations within a single gene and, indeed, within a single cistron. An alteration at any point in the segment of the phage chromosome constituting a cistron will interfere with the cistron's ability to control the production of its characteristic product. Bearing in mind the vast number of crosses possible in an experiment involving phages, the very rare event of a 'cross-over' occurring within a gene or within a cistron becomes detectable. Hence by analysing recombinant frequencies in the classical manner genes and cistrons may be mapped.

The rIIa and rIIb cistrons of the T4 bacteriophage chromosome are probably the most thoroughly understood regions of any chromosome. Several hundred mutable sites have been detected in both cistrons. A few other phage and bacterial cistrons have been mapped and the results show that the rII gene of T4 is in no way unique. Although, as we have seen, the rIIa and rIIb cistrons can be mapped—in other words, the potentially mutable sites can be arranged in a linear array—the *physical* dimensions of these sequences remain unknown. The technique of recombination analysis, as the careful reader will have realised, allows the geneticist to state the sequence in which mutable sites are arranged along a chromosome; it, however, says nothing about the physical distance of these mutable sites from each other.

In order, to borrow Max Delbruck's phrase, 'to run the map into the ground', it is necessary to determine the physico-chemical nature of that ground. We have to leave the realm of the geneticist and enter once more the realm of physics and chemistry. We have to examine in terms of physics and chemistry the nature of the chromosome.

10

For many years it has been known that chromosomes are composed of nucleoprotein. For many years, too, it was debated which of the two moieties—nucleic acid or protein—was responsible for carrying and transmitting the genetic information. As knowledge accumulated it became apparent that the type of nucleic acid present in the chromosomes was deoxyribonucleic acid (DNA),[1] and that the proteins with which it was associated had fairly small molecular weights. These proteins are known as histones.

[1] It is nowadays known that the chromosomes of a few viruses are composed of RNA.

The structure of DNA is far less complex, as we shall see, than that of even a small protein like a histone. In consequence it was for long· believed that DNA was too simple a molecule to carry and transmit the cell's genetic information. Thus when the first real evidence that DNA was deeply implicated in this genetic function was discovered, many biochemists remained sceptical.

The initial pointer to DNA's role in the cell was provided by an experiment which Avery and McLeod carried out in 1943. These investigators first extracted DNA from the dead bodies of a once virulent strain of pneumococci. Next they added this DNA to a suspension of non-virulent pneumococci. They observed that the non-virulent strain was transformed into virulent pneumococci. Their interpretation was that the DNA carried information from the virulent to the non-virulent strain. This information specified an enzyme, or some other factor, which conferred the property of virulence on pneumococci.

After this first break-through many other lines of evidence began to accumulate, all supporting the idea that DNA is the molecule in or on which the hereditary information is inscribed. For example, the amount of DNA in the nuclei of different cells of the same organism is constant and double that found in the nuclei of the gametes; the DNA molecules are remarkably static structures and are not usually involved in the hurly-burly of anabolism and catabolism which is the fate of other biomolecules; elegant experiments involving the isotopic labelling of the protein and DNA components of bacteriophages showed that DNA alone was transmitted from one generation to the next.

From all this it follows that there is little doubt today that DNA is 'the ground' into which the genetic map must be run. Our next task, therefore, is to discuss the structure of DNA and to consider whether this structure gives us any inkling as to how DNA's vital biological rôle might be carried out.

11

The structure of DNA resembles, in general, the structure of those other important biomolecules—the proteins and polysaccharides. In all three cases the molecule is built of a long chain of repeating units. In the case of proteins we have seen that these units are amino-acids; in the case of DNA the units are called nucleotides. We noted

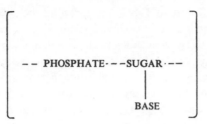

Fig. 13.9 General structure of a nucleotide.

in Chapter 4 that there are twenty different amino-acids; the situation with nucleotides is simpler—only four different types exist in DNA. Hence the structure of DNA, as we have already mentioned, is less complicated than that of the average protein.

A nucleotide consists of a phosphate group joined to a sugar which in turn is joined to a base (fig. 13.9).

Now we have mentioned that there are four different nucleotides. It is found that the difference is solely a matter of the base. The four

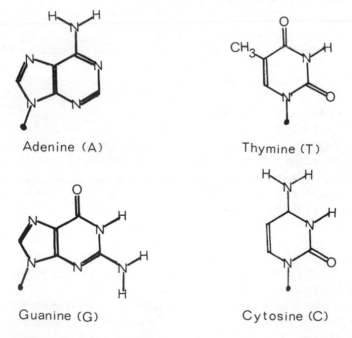

Fig. 13.10 Structure of the four common nucleotide bases. Adenine and guanine are purines; thymine and cytosine are pyrimidines.

333

different bases found in DNA are adenine, cytosine, guanine and thymine. Their structures are shown in fig. 13.10.

The sugar moiety of a nucleotide derived from DNA is called deoxyribose; this contrasts with the sugar obtainable from RNA which, as we shall see in the next chapter, is ribose. In fact the difference between the two sugars, as the following formulae show, is slight. As its name suggests, deoxyribose lacks one of ribose's oxygen atoms:

ribose   deoxyribose

It is worth noting at this point that the structure left behind when a nucleotide is stripped of its phosphate group is called a *nucleoside*. Thus, adenosine, for example, consists of the base adenine joined to either ribose or deoxyribose. It does not possess a phosphate group. If adenine is joined to ribose, as it is in the by now familiar ATP, it is sometimes referred to as a *ribonucleoside*; if it is joined to deoxyribose it is a member of the class of *deoxyribonucleosides*.

After this brief terminological digression let us now return to our account of the structure of DNA. It is found that the nucleotides are joined together to form a polynucleotide chain by linkages between the phosphate and sugar moieties (fig. 13.11). This structure was well understood at the beginning of the nineteen-fifties. The various bond lengths and angles had been established by subjecting small nucleotides to X-ray crystallography. The fact that the planar bases were arranged with their planes at right angles to the long axis of the molecule had been established as far back as 1938 by Astbury and Bell. Finally it was known that the ratio of purine to pyrimidine bases in the DNA molecule was 1 : 1.

The stage was thus set for the seminal advance made by Watson and Crick in 1953. This advance depended on the interpretation of good quality X-ray diffraction patterns obtained by a group of crystallographers at King's College, London. This group, under the

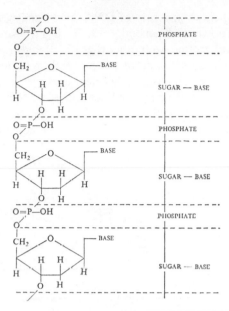

Fig. 13.11 Section of one of DNA's polynucleotide chains.

leadership of Wilkins, obtained DNA from various sources which, after purification, was drawn out into long threads. These fibres were subjected to X-ray analysis.

The method for interpreting these X-ray pictures was similar to that used by the Caltech group under Pauling which had proposed structures for protein fibres (Chapter 5). Thus Crick and Watson reasoned first from the density of the DNA fibres that only two or three polynucleotide strands could be present in the nucleic acid molecule. Then proceeding by careful model building, taking especial notice of van der Waals radii and covalent bond distances, they eventually arrived at a structure which could be responsible for the observed diffraction pattern. The result of this work was published in 1953 and, as Watson writes, 'initiated a profound revolution in the way in which many geneticists analysed their data. The gene was no longer a mysterious entity whose behavior could be investigated only by breeding experiments. Instead it quickly became a real molecular object. . . .'[1]

[1] Watson, J. D. in *Molecular Biology of the Gene*, Benjamin, New York, 1965, p. 66.

The double-helical structure of DNA is nowadays, of course, extremely well known and generally accepted. Two sugar-phosphate backbones spiral around each other (fig. 13.12) and the bases project inwards towards the mid-line of the molecule resembling the steps of a spiral staircase. This is a rather neat arrangement as it ensures that the large hydrophobic pyrimidines and purines are tucked away inside the molecule whilst the hydrophilic phosphate and, to a lesser extent, sugar residues are left in contact with the aqueous medium.

The X-ray pictures show strong reflections corresponding to a repeat distance of 3·4A and of 34A. This suggests that each base is set

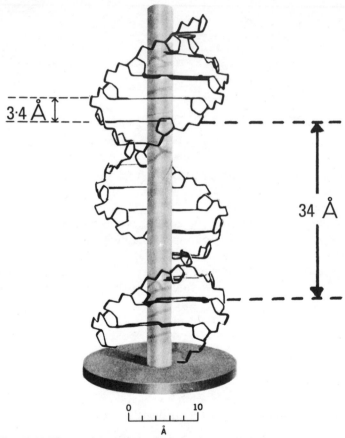

Fig. 13.12 The structure of the DNA molecule. From J. C. Speakman (after F. H. C. Crick and J. B. Watson (1954)) *Molecules* McGraw Hill (1966) p. 117.

336

3·4A above and below its nearest neighbours and that the structure repeats itself every ten nucleotides (fig. 13.12). The diameter of the double helix is 20A.

A very important feature of the molecule becomes apparent if we bear in mind fig. 13.10 when examining fig. 13.12. Fig. 13.10 shows that the bases which form the core of the DNA molecule are of two types: purines and pyrimidines. The purines are considerably larger than the pyrimidines. Yet fig. 13.12 shows that the molecule's diameter does not vary along its length. This suggests that the base pairs in the centre of DNA must consist of a purine partnering a pyrimidine. Purine-purine and pyrimidine-pyrimidine partnerships would be inconsistent with a constant diameter. The necessity of purine-pyrimidine partnership accounts for the 1 : 1 ratio between these two types of base which is, as mentioned above, characteristic of DNA.

What, then, is the physico-chemical nature of this base-pairing? It is very interesting to find that if the hydrogen-bonding potentialities of the bases are to be fully satisfied thymine (T) will partner adenine (A) and cytosine (C) will partner guanine (G). The structural reasons for these unions are shown in fig. 13.13.

The hydrogen bonds shown in fig. 13.13 unite the formerly separate conjugated structures of each base into one large conjugated unit. As the base pairs lie in a single plane, molecular orbitals containing 24 π electrons are believed[1] to extend over the surfaces of both bases. The resonance energy associated with such a large conjugated unit, when repeated, perhaps many million times, along the length of the double helix helps to stabilise the molecule. Thus resonance energy, hydrogen bonding and hydrophobic forces all summate to keep the two polynucleotide chains paired to each other in a stable and lasting structure.

12

The second part of our task is to consider whether the structure of DNA throws any light on how it carries out its biological function. It is not difficult to see that the biological function of the molecule in fact lies implicit in its structure. This is the reason why the Watson-Crick model has proved so seminal. Not only is it a beautiful and satisfying solution to the crystallographic problem but it also

[1] Pullman, A. and Pullman, B., *Quantum Biochemistry*, Interscience, New York and London, 1963.

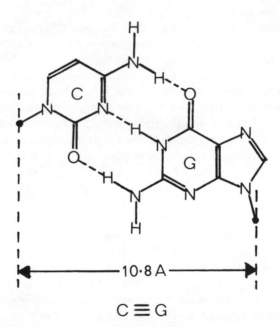

Fig. 13.13 Adenine and thymine, guanine and cytosine form very specific hydrogen bonds between each other.

provides a molecular mechanism for storing and transmitting hereditary information.

We have seen that, for physico-chemical reasons, 'A' and 'T' partner each other as do 'C' and 'G'. Thus one polynucleotide strand specifies the nature of its partner. In other words, if we were informed of the sequence of bases on one polynucleotide strand in a DNA molecule, we could easily predict the sequence of bases in the other strand. Furthermore if, in the cell, the two polynucleotide strands should unwind, each would form a template for the laying-down of a new strand. It is clear that the result of this process would be two identical DNA molecules, each exactly similar to the original DNA.

Let us suppose that the hereditary information is, in some way, coded in the base sequences of the polynucleotide strands. It follows from our account of the DNA molecule's stability that the code would remain safe and unscrambled. It also follows, from the account in the previous paragraph, that the code could be readily replicated. Evidently the Watson-Crick structure for DNA admirably fits the molecule for storing and transmitting hereditary information. Our next question must be: *does* it act in this way?

13

There is, nowadays, much evidence to show that DNA does indeed function in the way suggested in the previous section. In this section two of these pieces of evidence will be described. First, some evidence to show that DNA replicates itself in the way we have suggested; second, some evidence to show that the DNA resulting from the process of replication does in fact have the same base sequence as the original.

In order to show that DNA replicates itself in the way suggested, Meselson and Stahl carried out an elegant and ingenious experiment.[1] The essential steps in this experiment are shown in fig. 13.14. The fundamental technique used is called density gradient centrifugation. In this technique a caesium chloride density gradient is developed by prolonged centrifugation. After this centrifugation the caesium chloride ($CsCl_2$) solution is found to be more concentrated (denser) at the bottom of the tube than at the top. If DNA, or any other molecule, is placed in, or on top of, the $CsCl_2$ solution before

[1] Meselson, M. and Stahl, F. W. (1958), *Proc. Nat. Acad. Sci. U.S.*, *44*, 671.

DNA

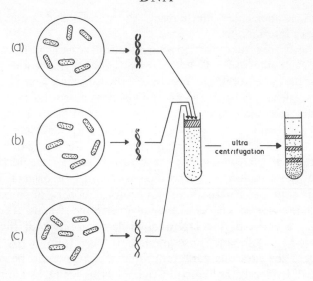

Fig. 13.14 Main steps in the Meselson-Stahl experiment. On the left-hand side of the figure, cultures of *E. coli* growing on (*a*) ^{15}N medium, (*b*) first generation on ^{14}N medium and (*c*) after many generations on ^{14}N medium. The DNA extracted from (*a*) contains ^{15}N and is represented by a thick line; that extracted from (*c*) contains ^{14}N and is represented by a thin line. After centrifugation three distinct layers may be detected in the centrifuge tube: ^{15}N DNA at the bottom, $^{15}N/^{14}N$ hybrid DNA halfway down and ^{14}N DNA at the top of the tube. For further explanation see text.

centrifugation is commenced it will, on centrifugation, move up or down the forming density gradient until it comes to rest at a point where its density equals that of the surrounding $CsCl_2$ solution.

Meselson and Stahl made use of this technique in the following way. First they grew a culture of *E. coli* on a medium whose sole source of nitrogen consisted of the stable heavy isotope ^{15}N. After a number of generations practically all the nitrogen in the bacterial cell, including that in its DNA, was ^{15}N instead of the usual, lighter, ^{14}N. It can be calculated that such DNA should be 0·8 per cent denser than normal DNA. Next a portion of the bacterial culture was removed from the heavy nitrogen medium and placed back on to a normal ^{14}N medium. After one generation, it was reasoned, the bacterial DNA, if it replicated in a Watson-Crick manner, should be a hybrid of ^{15}N and ^{14}N and consequently have a density halfway between the ^{15}N and ^{14}N DNA.

The density gradient technique described above provides a means

340

for confirming these different densities. Thus Meselson and Stahl extracted DNA from ^{15}N bacteria, hybrid $^{15}N/^{14}N$ bacteria and from normal ^{14}N bacteria, and subjected it to density gradient centrifugation. If the Watson-Crick theory is correct, three distinct bands of DNA should be observable in the centrifuge tube. Meselson and Stahl observed three such bands. This, then, constitutes strong evidence in favour of the Watson-Crick hypothesis.

The Meselson-Stahl experiment shows that DNA replicates in the way which Watson and Crick suggested. It follows that the base sequences of the newly synthesised DNA are identical with those of the original molecule. This conclusion was confirmed by Kornberg and his co-workers using an entirely different approach. In fact the Kornberg and Meselson-Stahl experiments approach the problem from opposite ends. They both establish the truth of the same hypothesis: that the Watson-Crick theory is correct. Kornberg's approach was to establish that the base sequences of the newly synthesised DNA were identical with those of the original molecule.

Kornberg proceeded by showing first that an enzyme—DNA-polymerase—is extractable from E. coli cells. This enzyme, in the presence of a length of DNA which acts as a 'primer', and the four bases, present in the form of their nucleoside triphosphates—ATP, GTP, etc.—is able to synthesise DNA in vitro.[1] If any one of the four bases is absent the enzyme is unable to effect the synthesis of new DNA. This, in itself, is a strong pointer to a base-pairing synthetic mechanism of the Watson-Crick type. For it would seem to imply that normally the four bases are lined up against a strand of the DNA primer and then joined to form a new polynucleotide strand. It would follow that if one type of base is missing, gaps would occur in the lined-up bases and complete new polynucleotide chains could

[1] Recently Kornberg's group (*Proc. Nat. Acad. Sci. Wash.*, 58, 2321, (1967)) have carried their work a stage further. After considerable tribulation they have been able to prepare a highly purified sample of DNA-polymerase and use it to replicate the entire isolated DNA strand of a small virus. The DNA synthesised in this way proved to be biologically active and was, in fact, capable of directing the synthesis of fresh virus when injected into *E. coli*. Furthermore it proved possible to use this synthetic strand of DNA as a primer, or template, for the *in vitro* synthesis of another, similarly infective, strand of DNA. This work was hailed by the President of the United States as an 'awesome achievement' and the first artificial synthesis of life. However as Perutz and others have pointed out, outstanding though the achievement undoubtedly is, it falls somewhat short of President Johnson's eulogy. A genuine synthesis of 'life' would have, at the least, to have included the synthesis of the original strand of DNA. And even then, as we noted in Chapter 12, is it justifiable to regard a virus as 'alive'?

not be formed. Kornberg and his co-workers, however, were able to produce stronger evidence for base-pairing than this. They were able to develop a technique which could pick out one faulty pairing in 100,000.

Their technique depended on the synthesis of an artificial DNA consisting of a monotonous sequence of adenine and thymine residues: ATATAT. . . . If this synthetic DNA is added to the usual synthetic system consisting of DNA-polymerase and the four nucleoside triphosphates, replication is found to occur. It is clear, however, that neither cytosine nor guanosine should be incorporated into the new DNA. To demonstrate that guanosine is not in point of fact incorporated, Kornberg's group labelled this nucleoside with the radioactive isotope of phosphorus—32P. They found that it was impossible to detect any radioactivity in the newly synthesised DNA.

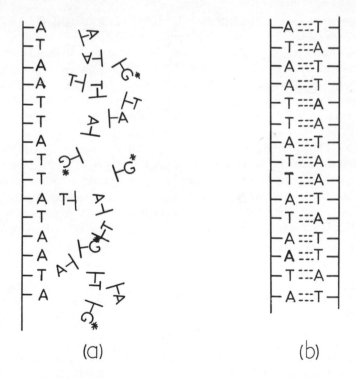

(a)   (b)

Fig. 13.15 Kornberg's experiment. The capital letters represent the nucleotide bases. Radioactivity is represented by an asterisk. For further explanation see text.

As mentioned above, the technique was sufficiently sensitive to detect one radioactive residue in 100,000. The principle of the method is illustrated in fig. 13.15.

14

The two experimental approaches described in the above section thus support the biological function assigned by Watson and Crick to the double-helical structure of DNA. Many other lines of evidence support the essential correctness of the Crick-Watson DNA model and its genetical significance. Thus there is little doubt that the physical basis of the gene is none other than DNA.

15

To conclude this chapter, let us see if we can bring together the two sub-plots of our story. Let us see whether we can unify the genetical and the physico-chemical approaches. In short, can we now define a gene in physico-chemical terms?

We saw, in the earlier part of this chapter, that probably the gene best known to geneticists is the rII gene of the T4 bacteriophage. Now phage chromosomes, in common with that of $E.\ coli$, but unlike those of higher organisms, consist entirely of DNA. Thus one way of investigating the physical nature of the gene would be to discover how much DNA is present in the rII region of T4's chromosome.

The DNA from the T4 phage can be extracted and its molecular weight determined. It turns out to have a molecular weight of about $1\cdot2\times10^8$. Now the molecular weight of a pair of nucleotides is about 650. It follows that there are about $1\cdot2\times10^8/6\cdot5\times10^2=1\cdot8\times10^5$ nucleotide pairs in the T4 phage chromosome. Now it is estimated that the rII region constitutes about 1 per cent of the entire T4 chromosome.[1] Hence this gene consists of $1\cdot8\times10^5/1\times10^2=1\cdot8\times10^3$ nucleotide pairs.

It will be remembered (p. 337) that the results of X-ray analysis indicated that each base in the DNA molecule was stacked 3·4A above and below its nearest neighbour. Hence, knowing the number of bases in the rII gene we can calculate its length: $(1\cdot8\times10^3)\times3\cdot4A=6\cdot12\times10^3A$, or $0\cdot612\mu$.

[1] Nomura, M. and Benzer, S. (1961), *J. Mol. Biol.*, *3*, 684.

Finally let us consider the molecular bases of mutations in this gene. Five hundred different mutations have already been detected in the rIIa cistron alone. If this cistron makes up about half the rII gene it can be composed of no more than about nine hundred nucleotide pairs. It is clear, therefore, that the mutable sites of the geneticist are in all probability single nucleotide pairs.

We are thus, in the rII gene of the T4 phage, within sight of the molecular geneticists' goal. We are in sight of a total description, in molecular terms, of a gene.

14

Deciphering the Code

1

The eminent geneticist Seymour Benzer has suggested[1] that the T4 bacteriophage carries in its head a quantity of information equivalent to that printed in several pages of the *New York Times*. This information, we have seen, specifies the hereditary make-up of an organism. It is the blueprint which ensures that mountains do not, in fact, bring forth mice, nor lions bees.

In Chapter 13 we saw that this information is, in some way, encoded by DNA. In this chapter it is intended to consider two closely related questions—the nature of the code, and how the code is deciphered by the cell.

2

Let us make a start by considering what it is that is coded for. We have alluded to hereditary information, to an hereditary blueprint, and, of course, it is clear enough that members of a species all share many characteristics in common; but, in molecular terms, what does the blueprint specify?

The answer to this question is, of course, implicit in many of the foregoing pages of this book. In general the hereditary information specifies the design of protein molecules. We saw that this was the case in the *E. coli*-T4 phage system discussed in the last chapter. We met another clear instance when we considered, in Chapter 6, the congenital abnormalities of haemoglobin. The hereditary code thus works at one remove. It specifies the structure of certain crucial protein molecules and these, in their turn, determine the in-built characteristics of the individual.

One of the most striking demonstrations of an individual's

[1] Benzer, S. (1960), *Harvey Lectures*, **56**, 1.

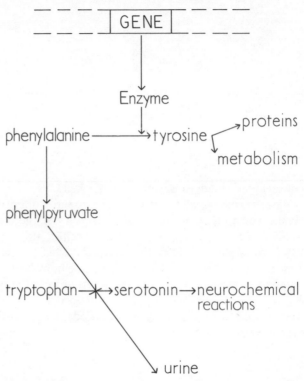

Fig. 14.1 Phenylalanine is normally converted to tyrosine. If a certain enzyme is not present this conversion does not occur—with disastrous results. See text.

dependence on his proteins, in this case his enzymes, is provided by the work of Garrod, in the nineteen-thirties, on the inheritance of phenylketonuria.

It was observed, initially, that about one in every hundred individuals suffering severe mental retardation excreted phenylpyruvic acid in his urine. It was shown that this character was inherited in a straightforward Mendelian fashion. Its expression resembled that of one of the recessive genes discussed in Chapter 13. It turned out that the presence of phenylpyruvic acid in the urine was due to the inactivity of a single enzyme. In normal individuals this enzyme catalyses the conversion of phenylalanine to tyrosine. Because the enzyme is inactive in individuals suffering from phenylketonuria the conversion, in consequence, does not occur. Instead phenylalanine mounts up in the body and is eventually oxidised to phenylpyruvic acid which is excreted in the urine. These relationships are shown in fig. 14.1.

So far no great tragedy has occurred. Tyrosine can be obtained in other ways. Unfortunately, however, if phenylpyruvic acid begins to accumulate in the nervous system an important neurochemical reaction is inhibited. This is the transformation of tryptophan into serotonin. Serotonin appears to be essential for normal mental development and functioning. Thus we see that inactivation of the enzyme has calamitous side-effects.

It is clear, therefore, that 'the commanding heights' of the body's economy are the protein molecules. If these are specified then not only the form but also the functioning of the body is specified.

In the earlier chapters of this book it was shown that the primary structure of a protein determines its higher structure and thus its biological function. If the hereditary information is largely to do with the structure of proteins then it is most likely to specify the order of amino-acids in the protein's primary structure.

It will be recalled from Chapter 4 that there are twenty commonly occurring amino-acids. There are, however, as we saw in Chapter 13, only four different nucleotides in DNA. In the last chapter, also, we saw that it is probably the sequence of nucleotide bases which constitutes the genetic code. In consequence the major problem facing the molecular geneticists in the late nineteen-fifties was: how do sequences of four different bases code for twenty different amino-acids?

3

A start can be made on this problem by determining the *minimum* length a sequence must be to enable coding for all twenty amino-acids. The shortest possible sequence is, of course, a sequence of two. Unfortunately the number of sequences it is possible to construct from four different bases taken two at a time is $4^2 = 16$. Clearly this is not quite enough. The next possibility, a sequence of three bases, gives too many code words. There are $4^3 = 64$ different ways of arranging four different bases in groups of three. At first sight it would seem that many of these sequences would be unnecessary. In consequence triplet codes are said to be degenerate. Lengthier sequences are correspondingly more inefficient. Codes involving quadruplets and quintuplets of bases could carry sufficient information to code for molecules made up of 256 and 1,024 different monomers.

The mathematical reasoning set out in the previous paragraph indicates that the smallest sequence capable of coding for each of the twenty different amino-acids is a sequence of three. However, there are many other questions which require answers. Perhaps some amino-acids are coded by a sequence of two whilst others are coded by a sequence of three bases. Do the sequences overlap? Are there 'punctuation marks' between one triplet and the next? *A priori* reasoning cannot answer these and similar questions.

At the end of 1961 Crick and his colleagues published an important paper[1] giving some experimental answers to these pressing questions. They were able to show that, at least in the T4 bacteriophage, the code words did indeed consist of base triplets. Moreover, they were able to demonstrate that the triplet sequences did not overlap, and that there were no punctuation marks between them.

In essence Crick's approach was to apply certain well-studied chemical mutagens[2] to one of the cistrons of the rII gene of the T4 phage. The mutagen used was proflavin which is believed to either insert or delete a base pair of DNA. It will be recalled from Chapter 13 that the alteration of a single base pair is probably the physical basis of a mutation. It follows that, in principle, insertion or deletion of a base pair can be detected in the same way that a mutation can be detected. It will be recalled that the rII gene enables the bacteriophage to form plaques on a culture of *E. coli* (strain K). Any mutation of this gene will affect this ability: plaque formation may be prevented altogether, or the form and/or size of the plaque may be altered.

The break-through for which Crick's group was responsible was the demonstration that although one, or two, insertions or deletions in a cistron showed up as a detectable mutation, three insertions or deletions resulted in little or no malfunction. Crick pointed out that the only way to explain these findings was to suggest that in the T4 bacteriophage a triplet code was operating.[3]

Crick and his colleagues reasoned in the following way. Suppose,

[1] Crick, F. H. C., Barnett, L., Brenner, S. and Watts-Tobin, R. J. (1961), *Nature, 192,* 1222.

[2] A mutagen is a factor capable of producing a mutation.

[3] In fact a code consisting of a small multiple of three bases would also fit the observations. Subsequent work, however, has confirmed that amino-acids are specified by nucleotide triplets.

first, that one polynucleotide strand of an rII cistron consists of the following sequence of bases:

C-A-T-C-A-T-C-A-T-C-A-T-C-A-T-C-A-T-C-A-T-C-A-T-C-A-T

Suppose that the triplet CAT (where the capital letters have the significance assigned to them in Chapter 13) codes for a particular amino-acid, say, histidine.

Now let us insert into the sequence an additional base, for example, guanine (G):

C-A-T-C-G-A-T-C-A-T-C-A-T-C-A-T-C-A-T C-A T C A T C A T-C-A-T

To understand the effect of this insertion we have to make a further assumption. This is that the code is read, rather like a classical inscription, continuously from left to right. There are no punctuation marks: each letter follows directly on from its predecessor. If this assumption is made we can see that the insertion of G into the second triplet from the left completely alters the 'meaning' of all the triplets to the right of it. Instead of reading CAT which translates, we have suggested, into histidine, the triplets read TCA which may specify some other amino-acid, or something quite different.

A similar destruction, or alteration, of meaning occurs if two strange bases are inserted, or if two bases normally present are deleted:

C-A-T-C-G-A-T-C-A-T-C-G-A-T-C-A-T-C-A-T-C-A-T-C-A-T

Once again the amino-acids specified by this fragment of the polynucleotide chain have been radically altered. Moreover, as in the previous case, *all* the amino-acids specified by the cistron to the right of the first insertion are altered. In consequence it is highly unlikely that an appropriate polypeptide or protein could result.

However, if we proceed a step further, and add a third strange base or, alternatively, delete three bases at once, then the correct sequence is re-established in the region to the right of the last insertion or deletion. This, of course, provides the explanation for Crick's observations.

C-A-T-C-G-A-T-C-A-T-C-G-A-T-C-A-T-C-A-G-T-C-A-T-C-A-T

In the formulation above six triplets have been altered. The triplets to the right and left of this region remain unchanged.

It will be recalled from Chapter 13 that the rII cistrons of T4 phage are believed to be composed of about 900 nucleotide pairs.

It follows that the polynucleotide chain of an rII cistron consists of some 300 base triplets. Because these triplets are believed to be the genetic code words they are called *codons*. It is reasonable to suppose that six or so altered codons out of 300 may not make a vital difference to the protein specified by the cistron. The probability that the amino-acids which they specify should occur in an active site or other biologically sensitive region is rather small. Consequently a sequence with three insertions or deletions usually codes for something very like the normal polypeptide or protein.

Crick's experiment shows that not only does the genetic code in the T4 phage consist of nucleotide triplets but also that it is 'comma-less'. There is no molecular equivalent of a punctuation mark separating one codon from the next. The code must be 'read' in a continuous and uninterrupted fashion from the beginning of one cistron to its end. The experiment also shows that the great majority of codons are meaningful. When, as in our last example, three strange bases are inserted, various abnormal codons are perforce produced: CGA,TCA,TCG,ATC,ATC, AGT. If these codons were meaningless then a gap would occur in the primary sequence of the specified protein. The molecule might then fall apart into two useless fragments. One final conclusion may be drawn from Crick's fruitful experiment. Although a cistron is read from beginning to end, in one breath, so to speak, this continuity is broken at the end of the cistron. Crick found that only one cistron at a time was inactivated by the insertion or deletion of one or two base pairs. It looks as though, in spite of being 'comma-less', the code does possess 'full stops' and, perhaps, 'capital letters'. The nature of the macromolecular 'full stop' will be discussed later in this chapter.

To sum up we can say that the Cambridge group had, at the end of 1961, shown that hereditary information was built into the structure of the DNA molecule in the form of nucleotide triplets. Experiments on the *genetics* of the T4 phage-*E. coli* system do not, however, enable us to crack the code. It is not possible, using this technique alone, to specify which codons 'mean' which amino-acids.

4

In order to investigate the so-called 'translation' problem, in other words to determine which of the sixty four different codons specifies which of the twenty different amino-acids, the skills and techniques of the geneticist are supplemented by those of the biochemist. For in order to understand how a nucleic acid codon is translated into an amino-acid, and how a sequence of such codons governs the production of a specific sequence of amino-acids, it is necessary to understand something of the process of protein biosynthesis. How are proteins and polypeptides manufactured from amino-acids? How does the information stored in the structure of DNA control this synthesis?

5

Logically, the first thing we must know about protein biosynthesis is its geography: where, in the cell, does it occur? This, in fact, is not difficult to establish. One can proceed as follows. First, amino-acids are labelled with a radioisotope. Second, these tagged amino-acids are placed in a cell known to be actively engaged in protein synthesis. Third, the cell is homogenised and the homogenate centrifuged into different fractions. Fourth, the different fractions are searched for radioactivity. It is found that the radioactivity is associated with the fraction containing the cell's ribosomes.

This observation reinforces conclusions derived from electron microscopy. It will be remembered from Chapter 12 that cells which are known to be highly active in the synthesis of proteins contain more than the usual complement of ribosomes.

We can thus conclude that the ribosomes are the centres of protein biosynthesis within the cell. Frequently, however, ribosomes are situated at some distance from the cell's DNA. This is especially the case in eukaryotic cells where the DNA is confined (largely) to the nucleus, whereas the ribosomes are cytoplasmic. It is also the case in bacteria where many of the ribosomes are located at some distance from the DNA molecule (fig. 12.3). Thus the geography of protein synthesis, its location in or on the ribosomes, leads us towards a further question. How does the DNA information store, located some distance away, influence the synthetic process?

6

Before, however, we can get to grips with this question we must return to one of the questions posed at the end of the previous section: how are proteins and polypeptides built from amino-acids?

DECIPHERING THE CODE

Before we can consider how the cell manages to string together amino-acids in a specific order, we must ask how the cell sets about stringing them together at all.

We saw in Chapter 4 that mineral acids or enzymes can break the peptide bonds holding amino-acids together into a polypeptide chain, or protein. This reaction, a hydrolysis, occurs spontaneously, or, to use the concepts introduced in Chapter 7, the products of the reaction (amino-acids) possess less energy than the initial reactants (protein and water). It follows that the reverse process, the synthesis of proteins or polypeptides from amino-acids or, in short, the formation of peptide bonds, requires energy. In other words it does not occur spontaneously.

The necessary energy, as in so many other biosynthetic reactions, is obtained from the energy-rich bonds of ATP. The reaction of an amino-acid with ATP is catalysed by an enzyme called an *amino-acyl-synthetase*. We shall have more to say about this very important class of enzymes later in this chapter. At this point, however, it is sufficient to notice that the enzyme catalyses a reaction in which the amino-acid becomes attached, by an energy-rich bond, to AMP (fig. 14.2). Because of the presence of the energy-rich bond the amino-acid is said to be activated. In this high energy state it is able to react with similarly energised amino-acids in such a way that peptide bonds can spontaneously form.

Having seen how the cell is able to synthesise peptide bonds we can now return to our initial concern: how does the cell manufacture a specific sequence of amino-acids? Activation of amino-acids is a *sine qua non* for peptide bond formation and thus for the establishment of any sequence at all; the influence of the information stored in DNA's double helix, however, makes itself felt in the organisation of amino-acids into a particular and biologically significant sequence. We can thus return to the question with which we finished the previous section: how does the DNA information store, located some distance from the ribosomes, influence the synthetic process?

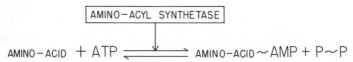

Fig. 14.2 The activation of amino-acids: a preliminary step in protein biosynthesis.

The question we are slowly edging towards is thus the question of how the amino-acids are joined up in a unique and particular order. Moreover, this order is the order specified by the base sequences built into the cell's DNA. The answer to this question seems to be that the amino-acids are lined up in or on a template, or mould, before being joined together by peptide bonds.

We have seen that protein biosynthesis occurs in or on the ribosomes; it follows that the template must exist in or on these particles. What form could a molecular template take? In our discussion of an enzyme's active site in Chapter 7 we became familiar with the idea of complementary surfaces. Enzymes and substrates explored each other's surfaces until appropriate combinations occurred. It seems highly probable that a molecular template would use a similar mechanism. In other words it seems likely that a molecular template would be built in such a way that it exposes a surface complementary to the group of molecules that it is designed to organise (fig. 14.3).

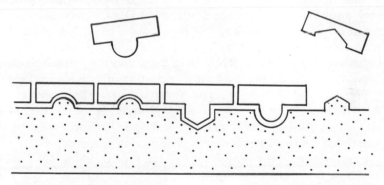

Fig. 14.3 A molecular template.

Our putative molecular template occurs, we have seen, in or on the ribosomes. Ribosomes, we saw in Chapter 12, consist of a complex of ribonucleic acid (RNA) and protein. Could either of these two molecular species act as a template? The answer is that both *could* act in this way. Both are capable of developing complementary surfaces. If, however, protein forms the template we tend to be involved in an infinite regress. For we have to ask how the proteinaceous template is itself manufactured. It, too, must be formed on a template. The lines of argument, like the lines of information transmission, inevitably lead back to the DNA molecule. For it is in the structure of the latter that the hereditary information is inscribed. At some stage this information has to be translated into amino-acid sequences. It is clear that the situation would be considerably complicated if the translation was first into the form of a proteinaceous template and then into the form of a proteinaceous enzyme.

'Essentia non sunt multiplicanda praeter necessitatem' has been a rule of thumb for scientists since at least the time of Occam. Thus it is sensible to suspect the other ribosomal constituent: RNA. Because RNA is also a nucleic acid it is *a priori* reasonable to believe that the information present in the coils of DNA could be transcribed directly into its structure.

8

Before going any further let us briefly consider the structure of RNA. Chemically it is very similar to DNA. Perhaps the most important point of difference between the two nucleic acids is that RNA consists of only one polynucleotide chain. The length of this chain, also, is very much shorter than that of either of DNA's polynucleotides. Another difference between the two molecules is that the sugar residue in RNA is ribose instead of deoxyribose. Finally the base thymine is not present in RNA; in its place another pyrimidine base —uracil—is found.[1] Fig. 14.4 shows a portion of an RNA molecule.

Fig. 14.4 should be compared with fig. 13.11. The similarity of RNA to one of DNA's polynucleotide strands is obvious. Fig. 14.4 also shows the close similarity of uracil and thymine. In fact it is found that the two bases have the same pairing properties.

Examination of the proportions of the four bases in RNA does not show, as a similar examination of DNA's bases showed, that the quantity of adenine is roughly equivalent to that of uracil, and that the quantity of guanine is approximately equal to that of cytosine. It follows that base pairing does not occur to the same extent as it does in DNA. This, of course, is hardly surprising when it is remembered that RNA possesses only one polynucleotide chain. Nevertheless, it is believed that, in some cases, the single chain is bent back on itself, rather like a hairpin, and that the bases in the arms of the hairpin pair with each other.

[1] In one type of RNA—tRNA—a large number of 'unusual' bases are found. The structure of tRNA will be mentioned again later in this chapter.

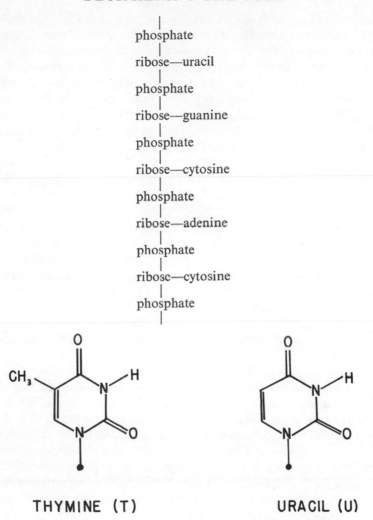

THYMINE (T)   URACIL (U)

Fig. 14.4 The structure of RNA. At the bottom of the figure the structure of uracil is compared with that of thymine.

9

The brief description of the structure of RNA in the previous section indicates that its ability to store genetic information is equal to that of DNA. Four different bases are found in both molecules

355

and, as we have seen, it is the sequence of bases in the DNA molecule which constitutes the hereditary code. It thus seems a tenable hypothesis to suggest that the base sequences in DNA are, in some way, transcribed on to RNA and this, passing in some way, at some time to the ribosomes acts, in some way, as a template for the assembly of amino-acids. Omitting the 'some ways' and 'some times' our hypothesis, more concisely stated, reads: 'DNA makes RNA, and RNA makes protein'. So far our argument has been very *a priori*. Let us now see what experimental evidence there is for these ideas.

10

That DNA makes RNA is not too difficult a concept. We shall return to it later. How RNA 'makes' protein is, however, considerably more obscure. Indeed this forms one of the crucial issues in molecular genetics. How can the base sequences of RNA form a template for the ordering of amino-acids in a protein? The replication of DNA and the consequent transmission of hereditary information was discussed in Chapter 13; the translation of this information into the language of protein structure forms the central matter of this chapter.

It will be recalled that amino-acids differ from each other only in the nature of their side chains. It might thus be supposed that the RNA template must develop specific cavities to fit these side chains— much as the complementary surface of an enzyme fits the peculiar conformation of its substrate. There are, however, a number of powerful objections to this idea. Not the least important of these objections is that the base sequences which form the genetic code depend for their specificity on their hydrogen-bonding potentialities, whereas far from all amino-acid side chains are capable of forming this type of bond. It seems, therefore, that RNA cannot form a direct template for the ordering of amino-acids. It looks as though it must in some way act indirectly. Perhaps the amino-acids are first modified, or 'adapted', to fit the RNA mould. One way of achieving this adaptation could be to attach each amino-acid to a *specific* small molecule of RNA. These small molecules of RNA could then be ordered on the RNA template and would, in consequence, line up their attached amino-acids in a specific sequence (fig. 14.5).

356

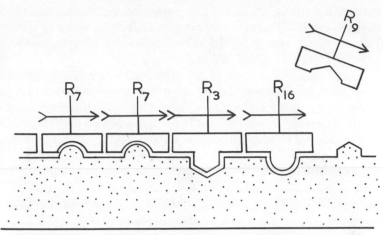

Fig. 14.5 Adaptor molecules may be necessary if the molecules to be orientated are of one type and the template is of another.

11

There is nowadays a great deal of evidence to show that this adaptor hypothesis does indeed reflect the facts. We have already noticed in this chapter that if a protein-synthesising cell is provided with an amino-acid labelled with a radioisotope, the radioactivity shows up in the cell's ribosomes. Now this technique can be extended and developed. Instead of providing a cell with a labelled amino-acid and then fractionating it into its various parts we can try the experiment in reverse. We can fractionate our protein-synthesising cell and then add a labelled amino-acid to each of the various fractions. It can be demonstrated that the labelled amino-acid is incorporated into freshly synthesised protein in only one of the fractions.

It is clear that this technique allows the investigator to analyse the constituents of the cell's protein-synthesising system. It was quickly shown that this *in vitro* system contained ribosomes, as expected; a number of soluble enzymes; energy-rich compounds like ATP and GTP, and, finally, *a low molecular weight RNA*.

Because this RNA was not built into the ribosomes, but was, instead, apparently in solution in the cytoplasm, it was initially called soluble RNA, or more concisely sRNA. In more recent years since its adaptor function has become clear it has come increasingly to be called transfer, or tRNA. Further analyses of the protein synthesising system showed that amongst the soluble enzymes there existed a number whose job it was to attach amino-acids to tRNA. These enzymes were identified as the amino-acyl-synthetases which were mentioned on p. 352 above.

It has emerged that there is *at least one* tRNA molecule for each amino-acid. In other words there are at least twenty different tRNAs in the cytoplasm of any protein-synthesising cell. This feature is, of course, demanded by the adaptor hypothesis outlined in the previous section. Furthermore it is also a requirement of this hypothesis that there be an amino-acyl-synthetase enzyme specific to each amino-acid *and* to its appropriate tRNA.

In recent years much work has been done on the molecular structure of the tRNAs. In addition to the usual four 'Watson-Crick' bases this type of RNA was quickly shown to possess up to 20 per cent of 'unusual' bases. The biological and chemical significance of these unusual bases, for example pseudouridine, ribothymidine, dihydrouridine, etc. is not yet fully understood. It is possible that they break up an otherwise regular secondary structure and thus give to each tRNA a specific shape which can be recognised by the appropriate amino-acyl-synthetase. The possession of these unusual bases has, however, proved a boon to the chemist interested in elucidating the primary structure of these nucleic acids. For the variegated base sequences of the tRNA molecule allows the overlapping sequence approach of the protein chemist (Chapter 4) to be used. Thus the primary structures of a number of tRNAs are nowadays known.

Alanine-tRNA from yeast was the first to have its primary structure solved.[1] It was shown to consist of a chain of 77 nucleotides. More recently the 84-nucleotide sequence of yeast serine-tRNA has been elucidated. It is probable that several other types of tRNA will soon yield their secrets to the chemist's art. It is, however, already clear that tRNA molecules have certain common features. They are all about the same size—approximately 80 nucleotides, giving them a molecular weight of about 25,000. Furthermore, it has been known for some years that the nucleotide chain ends, in each case, with a similar triplet of nucleotides—cytidine, cytidine, adenosine. It is to this end of the chain, moreover, that the amino-acid becomes attached. Some of the features held in common by tRNA molecules are shown in fig. 14.6.

[1] Holley, R. W., Apgar, J., Everett, G. A., Madison, J. T., Marquisee, M., Merril, S. M., Penswick, J. R. and Zamir, A. (1965), *Science, 147*, 1462.

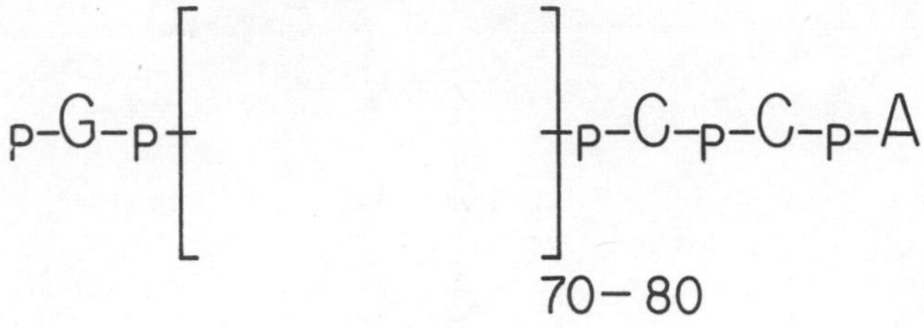

Fig. 14.6 Common features of all known tRNA molecules. p=phosphate, G, C and A have the usual significance; from 70 to 80 nucleotides are within the square brackets.

The secondary structure of tRNAs with known primary structures can be tentatively deduced by building models with maximum Watson-Crick base pairing. To obtain base pairing the single poly-nucleotide strand has, as mentioned previously, to be bent back, on itself. If this is done the two arms of the 'hairpin' are able to spiral around each other in such a way that a DNA-like helix can be con-structed.[1] The helix, however, is by no means as regular as the helix of DNA. This comparative irregularity is due to the presence of the unusual bases which are unable to pair in the classical way. In consequence model building has suggested several possible three-dimensional configurations. A favourite shape, at present, is one in which the polynucleotide strand is twisted into the form of a three-leaved clover (fig. 14.7).

It will be recalled that the function of tRNA is to 'adapt' amino-acids so that they fit an RNA template. It will also be recalled, from the earlier part of this chapter, that an amino-acid is coded in the form of a triplet of bases in the DNA molecule. We have suggested, without so far presenting any evidence, that this codon, or sequence of codons, is transcribed into an RNA template. It is clear, therefore, that in order to act as an adaptor tRNA must possess, somewhere in its structure, a triplet with precisely opposite pairing properties. This triplet, for obvious reasons, is called the *anticodon*.

The position of the anticodon in the tRNA molecule is clearly a problem of considerable interest to the molecular biologist. There is some evidence that it is present halfway along the polynucleotide

[1] There is evidence from X-ray diffraction studies that tRNAs do possess double helical regions. Spencer, M., Fuller, W., Wilkins, M. F. H. and Brown, G. L. (1962), *Nature*, *194*, 1014.

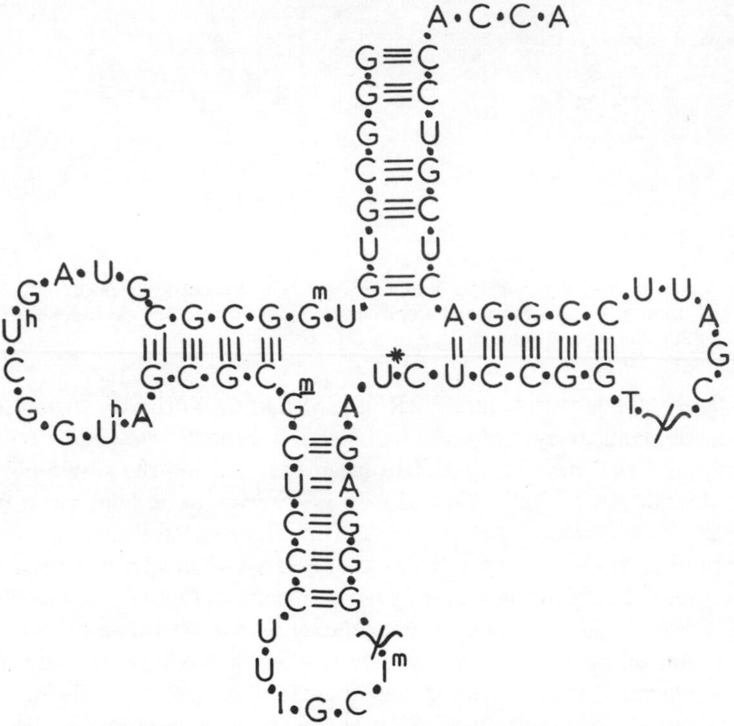

Fig. 14.7 Alanine tRNA. The triplet IGC is believed to be the anticodon. Note the large number of unconventional bases. I=inosine, I^m=methyl inosine, G^m=methyl guanine, G^m=dimethyl guanine, C=cytosine, U=uracil, A=adenine, T=ribothymidine, U^h=dihydrouridine, U*=mixture of uridine and dihydrouridine, ψ=pseudouridine.

Redrawn from Holley, R. W., *Scientific American*, March 1966.

chain.[1] It follows that in a secondary structure like that shown in fig. 14.7 the anticodon will be at the top of the central 'leaf'.

12

The adaptor hypothesis requires an adaptor and there is little doubt, as we have seen, that the tRNAs serve in this capacity. The hypothesis also requires a means of attaching an appropriate amino-acid to the appropriate tRNA. This is believed to be achieved, as has already been mentioned, by a group of enzymes—the amino-acyl-synthetases. These enzymes play a very central rôle in molecular genetics.

[1] Crick, F. H. C. (1966), *J. Mol. Biol.*, *19*, 548.

We have already seen that they are instrumental in activating amino-acids by attaching them via an energy-rich bond to AMP (fig. 14.2). The amino-acid-AMP complex does not, however, immediately fall away from the synthetase enzyme when this reaction is completed. Instead the three-molecule system stays together until contact is made with an appropriate tRNA molecule. The amino-acid then becomes attached through an energy-rich bond to the ribose sugar of the tRNA's terminal adenosine. When this has been accomplished the synthetase enzyme and the AMP drop away and recycle. This intricate set of reactions is schematised in fig. 14.8.

It is clear that the amino-acyl-synthetase enzymes bear great responsibilities. Not only do they activate amino-acids and hence make peptide bond formation thermodynamically possible, but they also attach the correct amino-acid to the correct tRNA. It follows that it is necessary for the synthetase enzymes to have two complementary surfaces. One surface is complementary and specific to a particular amino-acid, and the other is complementary and specific to a particular tRNA. An attempt is made to represent these dual specificities in fig. 14.8.

With the attachment of an activated amino-acid to the correct tRNA molecule the stage has been set for the synthesis of a poly-peptide or protein molecule. The nature of this polypeptide or protein, determined, as we have seen in earlier chapters, by its primary structure, depends on the nature of the RNA template. Our next task, therefore, is to examine the characteristics of this template.

13

We have already emphasised, more than once, that protein synthesis occurs in or on the ribosomes and that, in consequence, the RNA template must be associated with these particles. On p. 307 it was stated that the ribosomes contain large quantities of RNA. It was suggested that this RNA might well function as the looked-for template. However, things turned out to be rather less simple. It seems that the major part of the ribosomal RNA, or rRNA, whatever its functions may be, does not function as a template for ordering amino-acids. This conclusion follows from several lines of reasoning and experiment.

First it can be shown that the base ratios of rRNA are rather unlike those of the cell's DNA. This fact in itself suggests that rRNA cannot function as a template. But worse, not only are the base ratios of a ribosome's rRNA unlike those of the cell's DNA, but they are very similar to the base ratios of rRNA extracted from all the other ribosomes in the cell. Indeed rRNAs derived from a wide variety of organisms can all be shown to possess rather similar base ratios. This is hardly what would be expected if the rRNAs formed

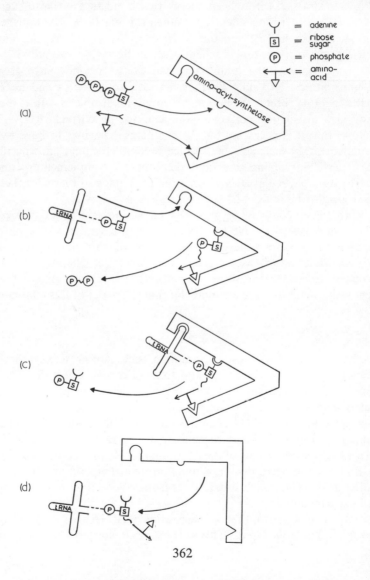

362

templates for the production of many different sorts and sizes of protein.

If rRNA does not form the desired molecular template, what does? The answer to this question is nowadays well established. It has been known for some time that a small fraction (2–3 per cent) of the RNA present in the ribosomes can be very easily separated from these particles. Unlike the bulk of ribosomal RNA it appears to be extremely unstable. Labelling with radioisotopes shows that it is continually synthesised from, and broken down into, free nucleotides. Furthermore there is evidence that the synthesis of this unstable fraction occurs in the vicinity of the cell's DNA. Finally if the base ratios of this small fraction are examined they are found to be very similar to those of the same cell's DNA.

It looks, therefore, as though the unstable fraction of RNA is synthesised alongside the cell's DNA and subsequently carries its imprint to the ribosomes. In short, the emerging hypothesis suggests that the unstable RNA acts as a messenger carrying information from the DNA to the ribosome. The ribosome, according to this way of looking at things, is analogous to a general-purpose machine tool. Similarly, the unstable RNA fraction may be compared to a punched or magnetic tape which programmes the machine tool to

---

Fig. 14.8 (opposite) The action of an amino-acyl-synthetase enzyme.

In (*a*) the enzyme is shown to have three complementary surfaces. One of these surfaces fits a specific amino-acid, represented by an arrow with a triangle symbolising its side chain (R). Another surface fits adenine, which in this figure is represented by a semicircular cup. The third complementary surface of the enzyme is designed to accept a specific tRNA molecule, symbolised by the cross-shaped structure.

In (*b*) adenosine triphosphate has occupied the adenine site and the amino-acid has taken up position in its site. The amino-acid is activated by forming an energy-rich bond with AMP. The other two phosphates of ATP escape as pyrophosphate (P~P). The diagram is drawn to suggest that there is some strain in the link between AMP and the amino-acid.

In (*c*) an appropriate tRNA molecule fits itself into its appropriate site and in so doing displaces the AMP molecule. The adenine, which is always present at the end of tRNA, takes up the position vacated by AMP's adenine and accepts the energy-rich bond from the amino-acid.

In (*d*) the tRNA-amino-acid complex is liberated from the amino-acyl-synthetase enzyme.

Note that tRNA's anticodon is at the opposite end of the molecule to the amino-acid.

Note also that the figure is highly diagrammatic and is only intended as a pictorial aid to understanding a very intricate series of events.

manufacture a particular protein. If this interpretation is correct we can call the unstable fraction of RNA messenger RNA, or mRNA.

We have seen some evidence showing that mRNA exists; what evidence is there, however, that it functions in the way we have suggested? In fact quite a large number of pieces of evidence have accumulated in support of the messenger hypothesis. Space, however, allows only two of these pieces of evidence to be outlined here. The first shows that a messenger exists; the second shows that the messenger is mRNA.

The first experiment makes use of the sexual behaviour of *E. coli*. This is, as might be expected, extremely primitive. Two bacteria come together, side by side, and a tube develops between them so that their respective cytoplasms are in contact. Through this conjugal 'conjugation' tube the chromosome is passed from one cell (defined as the male) to the other (defined as the female). The extrusion of the chromosome is believed to occur at a constant rate. However, any agitation of the medium in which the two bacteria are suspended is found to rupture the delicate conjugation tube. This brings to an abrupt halt the pleasures of sexual reproduction. Next we have to anticipate ourselves a little. In Chapter 15 it will be shown that not all genes are concerned in the production of proteins and other cell structures, but that some are believed to control the activity of other genes. These genes are called regulator genes. The chromosome of *E. coli* possesses a number of such genes. Let us designate one of these regulator genes as G_1, and the gene whose activity it regulates as G_2. Furthermore let us call the enzyme whose production is controlled by G_2, E.[1] Using this symbolism let us now consider an experiment which supports the case for a messenger carrying information from DNA to the ribosomes.

In the normal *E. coli* cell G_1 suppresses the activity of G_2. In consequence the enzyme, E, is not synthesised. However, another strain of *E. coli* exists in which E is not synthesised for another reason. In this second strain the gene, G_2, has mutated and is, in consequence, incapable of programming the production of E. The essence of the experiment is to arrange matters so that the female *E. coli*, receiving the chromosome, is a member of the mutated strain, whilst the chromosome is provided by a male belonging to the normal strain.

The two genes G_1 and G_2 are situated some distance apart on the

---

[1] This case will be considered more explicitly in Chapter 15. There it will be explained that the enzyme, E, is called β-galactosidase.

chromosome and it is found that G_2 passes into the female cytoplasm first. It follows that it is possible, by carefully timing the agitation of the bacterial suspension, to rupture the conjugation tube after G_2 has passed across but before G_1 has left the male. The mutated *E. coli* thus possesses the gene G_1, unmutated, and without its suppressor. What happens? It is found that large quantities of the enzyme, E, are manufactured almost immediately. It is difficult to believe that the female ribosomes have been altered in the very short space of time involved. It seems far more likely that G_2, in the absence of its suppressor, is able to synthesise a messenger which programmes the pre-existing ribosomes to manufacture E.

The second experiment, which indicates that the messenger is the unstable RNA fraction which we have called mRNA, utilises the response of *E. coli* to parasitism by T-even phages. Jacob and Monod describe a very elegant experiment in which the various relevant components of the bacterium and its parasite are labelled so that it is possible to follow the exact sequence of events after the entry of the phage.

In brief, the procedure was to grow *E. coli* on a medium whose sole nitrogen source was the heavy isotope, ^{15}N. After infection by T-even phage the *E. coli* were transferred to a medium containing the normal isotope, ^{14}N. After infection the *E. coli* were also exposed to brief 'pulses' of radioactive phosphorus and sulphur isotopes: ^{32}P, and ^{35}S. The bacteria were then harvested and their ribosomes examined.

By the use of density gradient centrifugation (Chapter 13, p. 339) it could be shown that the ribosomes had been synthesised before infection. By detecting ^{32}P it could be shown that the unstable RNA fraction, the mRNA, was formed *after* infection and had become associated with the pre-existing ribosomes. Finally it could be shown that the ^{35}S had been incorporated into newly-formed phage protein.

The construction put on the above observations runs as follows. It is suggested that the phage DNA is able to use the bacterial ribonucleotides to synthesise a small quantity of mRNA. This mRNA, synthesised alongside the phage DNA, is believed to carry the latter's imprint to the bacterium's ribosomes. These ribosomes will, in consequence, be reprogrammed to manufacture phage protein. In this way a bacteriophage is able to commandeer a bacterium's protein-manufacturing machinery.

These two pieces of evidence, and many others, support the idea that the small unstable fraction of RNA which can be detected in cells acts as a messenger, carrying the hereditary information from the DNA library to the ribosomal protein manufactory. We have assumed all along that the message is in the form of an imprint: that the mRNA is, in fact, also the sought-for template. Some evidence supporting this assumption is presented in the next section.

14

The means by which information built into the structure of DNA controls the type of protein manufactured by the ribosomes is thus becoming clear. We have identified the messenger which carries information from the DNA to the ribosomes. We have established the existence of molecules which adapt amino-acids to fit an RNA template. We have shown that special enzymes are present in the cell which are able to attach appropriate amino-acids to appropriate adaptors. One piece, only, of the jigsaw is missing—how does the information built into the DNA base sequences transcribe itself on to the messenger?

In fact the answer to this question has, to some extent, already been assumed in the previous section. It was stated, for example, that mRNA was synthesised alongside the cell's DNA. It will, moreover, be remembered that the pairing properties of the 'classical' RNA bases are identical to those of the DNA bases. It will come as no surprise, therefore, to learn that mRNA is believed to be synthesised on a DNA template. It is in this sense that the phrase 'synthesised alongside DNA' is used.

If mRNA is synthesised on a DNA template we should expect its base sequences to be closely similar to those of the DNA. That this should be so is, of course, vital to our theory. That it *is* so can be shown by a technique called hybridisation. It is found, first, that if DNA is heated to about 100°C the hydrogen bonds holding the two polynucleotide strands together are ruptured (compare this with the similar case of keratin, Chapter 8, p. 203). On cooling, in the correct conditions, the two strands coalesce, or anneal, once more. Now if another nucleic acid, say RNA, is present when the two strands of DNA have been 'melted' apart, a hybrid of DNA and RNA may form when the mixture is cooled. This, it is clear, can only occur if the base sequences of the two nucleic acid strands are very much alike. Hybridisation thus provides a powerful and precise tool for detecting homologous or heterologous nucleic acids.

Adverting back to the *E. coli*-phage example of the last section it is very interesting and satisfactory to find that the mRNA found on the bacterium's ribosomes is able to hybridise with the phage DNA but not with the *E. coli* DNA. This observation confirms our suggestion that the mRNA carries an imprint of the phage DNA to the bacterial ribosomes.

The fact that mRNA is homologous with the relevant DNA has now been established in many instances. Furthermore it has been possible to extract from many cells an enzyme—RNA-polymerase—which is normally found associated with the cell's DNA. This enzyme is able to form RNA molecules by linking together the appropriate ribonucleotides. Two things are necessary for its activity. First the ribonucleotides must be present in the form of their triphosphates:[1] adenosine triphosphate, guanosine triphosphate, etc. Second, a length of DNA must be present. This acts as a template on which the ribonucleotides can arrange themselves. It will be recalled from Chapter 13, p. 341, that a precisely analogous situation obtains for DNA polymerase. It, too, requires a length of DNA to act as a template.

In the case of RNA polymerase the situation is, however, rather more complicated. It is assumed that either of the two strands of DNA can act as a suitable template for the polymerisation of another strand of DNA. A little thought will show that considerable difficulties would arise if this were the case with RNA polymerase. It follows from the discussion in this chapter and in Chapter 13 that only one DNA strand carries the genetic information. This is sometimes called the *sense* strand. The other strand, clearly, carries the mirror image of this information which, when translated into amino-acid sequences, probably 'means' nothing at all. In consequence only one strand can act as a template for RNA polymerase.

That this is in fact the case seems to be emerging from recent work on microbial systems.[2] How the 'sense' and the 'nonsense' strands are distinguished by RNA polymerase remains, to date, one of the major unsolved problems of molecular genetics.

We can conclude, therefore, by suggesting that the DNA double helix opens at certain points along its length, thus exposing a template surface. How this is brought about remains obscure, although some suggestive observations are discussed in the next chapter. The

---

[1] The energy-rich phosphate bonds provide the energy necessary to drive the synthesis.

[2] Sibatani, A. (1966), *Progr. in Biophys. & Molec. Biol.*, *16*, 41.

RNA-polymerase, selecting the sense from the nonsense strand, is then able to synthesise a complementary strand of mRNA. This, on reaching the ribosomes, can act as a template ensuring that the adapted amino-acids are lined up in the order specified by the genetic code.

15

It will be recalled from Chapter 12 that ribosomes are composed of two unequal subunits, and that they are frequently observed to be connected together into small groups by a thread believed to be composed of mRNA. It can be shown that it is the smaller of the two ribosomal subunits which becomes attached to mRNA. It will be remembered that a group of ribosomes connected by an mRNA thread is called a polysome.

In parenthesis, it is interesting to find that the number of ribosomes constituting a polysome varies with the size of the protein being synthesised. The larger the protein the greater the number of ribosomes connected together by the mRNA. Now it is believed that ribosomes are attached to an mRNA strand at constant intervals. In other words there is evidence to show that any two neighbouring ribosomes on an mRNA strand are separated from each other by about 150 nucleotides. It follows that the larger proteins require a longer strand of mRNA. This is yet another piece of evidence confirming the essential correctness of the modern scheme of protein biosynthesis.

The precise mechanism whereby a ribosome is able to orientate tRNA-amino-acid complexes on the mRNA tape is the subject of intensive research at the present time. It seems probable that there are positions for two tRNA molecules within the larger subunit of the ribosome (fig. 14.9). Let us call these positions A and B. When a tRNA-amino-acid complex occupies both positions (fig. 14.9) the two amino-acids are orientated in such a way that a peptide bond can form. When this has occurred (it will be remembered that the amino-acids are in an activated state) the amino-acid in position A is released from its attachment to tRNA. The ribosome is then believed to move (relative to the mRNA) one codon to the right, so that the tRNA-amino-acid complex occupying position B in fig. 14.9 comes to occupy position A. It is then possible for a third tRNA-amino-acid complex to move into position B.

DECIPHERING THE CODE

As fig. 14.9 shows, the type of tRNA-amino-acid complex capable of occupying either of the ribosomal sites is determined by the codons on the mRNA tape. Thus in the presence of a full selection of tRNA-amino-acid complexes the ribosome is believed to move along the mRNA template adding one amino-acid at a time to a lengthening polypeptide chain. On reaching the end of the tape the ribosome and polypeptide chain are released. It is probable that special codons exist which ensure that this separation occurs. If such codons did not exist it is clear from the foregoing account that the terminal amino-acid of the polypeptide chain might remain permanently fixed in position A of fig. 14.9.

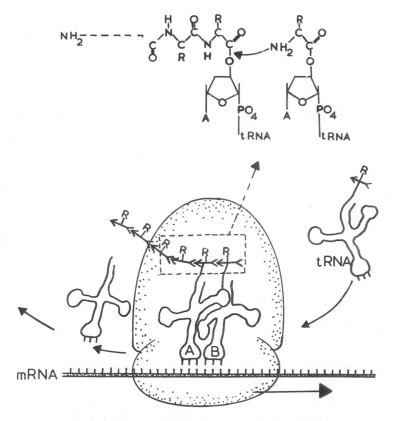

Fig. 14.9 How a ribosome is believed to synthesise a polypeptide chain. At the top of the figure the chemistry of peptide bond formation is shown in more detail. For further explanation see text.

This account of the way in which a ribosome is believed to synthesise a polypeptide chain draws our attention to a further feature of a cell's protein manufactory. If mRNA is synthesised in the way we have described, and if the ribosomes act in the way outlined above, then it follows that there must be colinearity between cistron and polypeptide chain. In other words the amino-acid sequence in the polypeptide chain must be reflected, or mapped, in an exactly similar sequence of codons in the appropriate cistron. For the sequence of codons in the cistron is mapped into a sequence of codons in mRNA and this, in turn, is mapped into a sequence of amino-acids in the polypeptide.

In order to demonstrate that this colinearity does indeed exist it is necessary to be able to correlate the positions of any mutations in a cistron with the positions of any amino-acid substitutions in the corresponding polypeptide. This is no mean requirement. It requires that the skills and techniques of the microbial geneticist be combined with those of the protein biochemist. However, the requirement has been met. The fine structure of the gene controlling the synthesis by *E. coli* of the enzyme tryptophan synthetase has been analysed and so have large fragments of the enzyme's primary structure. It can be shown in this system that colinearity between gene and polypeptide exists.[1] It can be shown that the linear relation between mutations on the genetic map is reflected in a similar linear relation in the amino-acid substitutions detectable in the enzyme. This finding strengthens our belief that the present scheme for protein biosynthesis cannot be greatly mistaken.

16

On p. 356 we stated a hypothesis: that DNA makes RNA, and RNA makes protein. In the following pages some of the evidence for this hypothesis has been sketched in. In fact there is nowadays so much interlocking evidence that the idea can be put forward as something rather more than just a hypothesis. Indeed the phrase has been said to constitute the 'central dogma' of molecular biology. Fig. 14.10 symbolises this dogma and also summarises some of the terms introduced to describe the different phases of the process.

[1] Yanofsky, C., Carlton, B. C., Guest, J. R., Helinski, D. R. and Henning, U. (1964), *Proc. Nat. Acad. Sci. Wash.*, *51*, 266.

DECIPHERING THE CODE

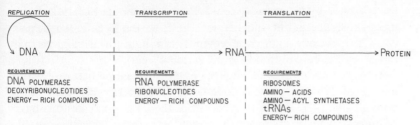

Fig. 14.10 Summary of the means by which the living cell controls protein biosynthesis.

17

In the earlier parts of this chapter we saw how the group of molecular biologists under the leadership of Crick had shown that triplets of nucleotide bases specified particular amino-acids. We noted, however, that in order to determine which triplets coded for which amino-acids it was necessary to add the techniques of the biochemist to those of the microbial geneticist.

In the immediately preceding sections of this chapter modern ideas on the biochemistry of protein biosynthesis have been outlined. In particular we saw on p. 357 that it is quite possible to extract the protein-synthesising system from a cell and study it *in vitro*. Furthermore we have seen that mRNA controls the amino-acid constitution of proteins and polypeptides synthesised by the ribosomes. It follows that one way of seeking to discover which codon specifies which amino-acid is to feed into the *in vitro* protein-synthesising system a known mRNA strand and analyse the polypeptide resulting.

Unfortunately there is a rather big snag to this otherwise simple technique. It is not yet possible either to determine the nucleotide sequences of natural mRNA, nor to synthesise in the laboratory long and intricate sequences of artificial mRNA. However, it is possible to synthesise very simple sequences and, in 1961, Nirenberg and Matthaei[1] carried out an experiment of the type described in the previous paragraph. As a messenger these investigators used a polynucleotide strand consisting of a monotonous sequence of uridine residues. It was found that in response to this polyuridylic acid, or, in the jargon of molecular biology, polyU, a polypeptide consisting of a monotonous chain of phenylalanine residues was synthesised. This result, taken in conjunction with Crick's experiments, suggests that

[1] Nirenberg, M. W. and Matthaei, J. H. (1961), *Proc. Nat. Acad. Sci. U.S.*, **47**, 1588.

371

the triplet, UUU, 'means' phenylalanine. At the end of 1961 when the significance of the biochemical work to the genetic work, and vice versa, became apparent excitement ran high: it was believed that the genetic code would be solved within a year.

The prediction proved slightly optimistic. Nonetheless, by the middle of 1966 an agreed 'code-book' had been established. This book (Table 14.1) shows that 63 out of the 64 possible codons have meanings. The delay in establishing these meanings was caused, mainly, by the inability of biochemists to synthesise mRNA strands with specific and known nucleotide sequences. This difficulty was finally overcome by the development of a new technique.

It was found that if mRNA *triplets* were added to the *in vitro* protein-synthesising system the amino-acid corresponding to the triplet became attached to a ribosome. Indeed from our earlier account of the activity of ribosomes in protein biosynthesis this finding might have been predicted. Now the synthesis of mRNA *triplets* is well within the chemist's art. All that has to be done, therefore, is to add a known mRNA triplet to an *in vitro* protein-synthesising system which contains a single radioisotopically-labelled amino-acid species. When the 'correct' mRNA triplet is added the labelled amino-acid is bound to the ribosomes. Addition of an 'incorrect' mRNA triplet would have no such effect and the tagged amino-acid would, in consequence, remain in solution. There is no difficulty in isolating the ribosomes from the rest of the system and determining whether or not they are radioactive. Radioactivity indicates that the correct nucleotide triplet has been added to the system; lack of radioactivity shows that an incorrect triplet has been added.

Table 14.1 shows the results of these and other experiments. All the triplets with the exception of UGA have now been assigned a meaning. It is also shown that all the amino-acids, with the exception of methionine and tryptophan, are coded by more than one codon. There is some evidence that the first two bases of a triplet are more important than the third: indeed it is suggested that the third base is liable to 'wobble'.[1] This finding is symbolised

---

[1] Crick, F. H. C. (1966), *J. Mol. Biol.*, *19*, 548. The lesser importance of the third base suggests that a doublet code may have preceded the triplet code in the evolution of life. This code, of course, could only have specified a maximum of sixteen primitive amino-acids (p. 347). Jukes has advanced some persuasive arguments for the one-time existence of such an ancestral doublet code in his book *Molecules and Evolution* (Columbia University Press, New York, 1966) and elsewhere.

DECIPHERING THE CODE

TABLE 14.1
The genetic code

1st position (5′ end of mRNA)	U (Middle position)	C	A	G	3rd position (3′ end of mRNA)
U	UUu ⎫ Phe	UCu ⎫	UAu ⎫ Tyr	UGu ⎫ Cys	u
	UUc ⎭	UCc	UAc ⎭	UGc ⎭	c
	UUa ⎫ Leu	UCa ⎬ Ser	UAa ⎫ C/T	UGa *non*	a
	UUg ⎭	UCg ⎭	UAg ⎭	UGg Try	g
C	CUu ⎫	CCu ⎫	CAu ⎫ His	CGu ⎫	u
	CUc	CCc	CAc ⎭	CGc	c
	CUa ⎬ Leu	CCa ⎬ Pro	CAa ⎫ Gln	CGa ⎬ Arg	a
	CUg ⎭	CCg ⎭	CAg ⎭	CGg ⎭	g
A	AUu ⎫	ACu ⎫	AAu ⎫ Asn	AGu ⎫ Ser	u
	AUc ⎬ Ile	ACc	AAc ⎭	AGc ⎭	c
	AUa ⎭	ACa ⎬ Thr	AAa ⎫ Lys	AGa ⎫ Arg	a
	AUg Met	ACg ⎭	AAg ⎭	AGg ⎭	g
G	GUu ⎫	GCu ⎫	GAu ⎫ Asp	GGu ⎫	u
	GUc	GCc	GAc ⎭	GGc	c
	GUa ⎬ Val	GCa ⎬ Ala	GAa ⎫ Glu	GGa ⎬ Gly	a
	GUg ⎭	GCg ⎭	GAg ⎭	GGg ⎭	g

C/T=chain termination   *non*=no known meaning

The Table shows that with one exception each of the 64 possible codons has been assigned a meaning. The nucleotides occupying the first two places in a codon have been symbolised by upper case initials; the nucleotide occupying the third position, because it is believed to be of less importance, has been represented by a lower case initial.

373

in Table 14.1 by assigning upper case initials to the first two nucleotides in a codon and a lower case initial to the third. Finally, two codons—UAA and UAG—are believed to be responsible for terminating the synthesis of a polypetide by a ribosome.[1] The necessity for some form of macromolecular 'full-stop' has been stressed in previous sections of this chapter.

18

Solution of the cryptographic problem marks another major step forward in the molecular analysis of the genetic mechanism. Many problems, of course, remain. One of the most important of these has been to determine in which direction the base sequences of mRNA are read. Is the reading from left to right as we have in this chapter, for reasons of convenience, assumed? Or does the ribosome 'read' the code from right to left? Very fortunately for Western scientists the first alternative has turned out to be correct.

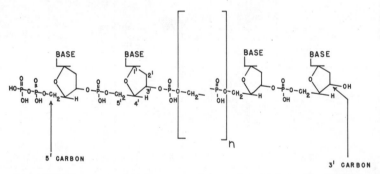

Fig. 14.11 The conventional manner of expressing the formula of RNA.

Before discussing some of the very interesting experimental work which has decided this problem, let us remind ourselves of the physical significance of the terms 'right' and 'left' in the nucleic acid script. Fig. 14.11 shows the conventional way of writing down the formula of RNA's polynucleotide chain.

The carbon atoms in the ribose moiety of each nucleotide are numbered from 1' to 5'. Primed numbers are used to distinguish

[1] Zipser (*J. Mol. Biol.*, **29**, 441 (1967)) has recently shown that UGA, like UAA and UAG, acts as a macromolecular full-stop, terminating the synthesis of a polypeptide chain. Thus all sixty-four codons have now been shown to be meaningful.

them from the unprimed numbers which are used to label the atoms of the bases. It is clear from fig. 14.11 that an RNA strand has a $C_{5'}$ end and a $C_{3'}$ end. It is also clear that if the message is read from left to right it will be read from the 5' end to the 3' end; vice versa, reading it from right to left will involve a progression from 3' to 5'.

Several pieces of evidence nowadays indicate that the direction of reading is from 5' to 3', that is from 'left' to 'right'. One of the initial and most interesting pieces of evidence emerged from a study of the lysozyme produced by the T4 phage. Chemical analysis of the primary structure of this enzyme has recently been completed.[1] Although the distribution of basic, acidic and hydrophobic residues seems to be similar to that found in egg-white lysozyme (fig. 7.16), the amino-acid sequence is otherwise quite dissimilar. This finding is interesting in the context of our discussions of the relation of the primary structure of proteins to their higher structure, and in the context of molecular evolution.

Terzaghi et al.[2] have, however, been able to relate the primary structure of this enzyme to the phage's nucleic acid code. First these workers were able to show that proflavin-induced mutations of the phage chromosome resulted in an enzyme with a slightly reduced activity. Second, this slight reduction in activity was traced to a block of five amino-acids which differed from those found in the normal enzyme.

Now it will be remembered from our discussion at the beginning of this chapter that proflavin is believed to either insert bases into, or delete bases from, the DNA double helix. Thus Terzaghi et al., knowing the primary structure of the normal and mutant protein, were able to show that their observations fitted the scheme shown in fig. 14.12.

Fig. 14.12 shows that adenine has been deleted from one end of the sequence, and either guanine or adenine inserted at the other. It is clear that the triplets following the deletion or insertion, depending on which way the code is read, will all be altered in the way shown in the figure. Because the translation mechanism may be regarded as a 'reading-frame' being moved from one codon to the next, this type of mutation is called a *frame-shift* mutation.

Now it has been known for some years that polypeptide chains are

[1] Inouye, M. and Tsugita, A. (1966), *J. Mol. Biol.*, 22, 193.
[2] Terzaghi, E., Okada, Y., Streisinger, G., Emrich, J., Inouye, M. and Tsugita, A. (1966), *Proc. Nat. Acad. Sci. Wash.*, 56, 500.

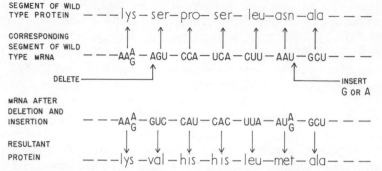

Fig. 14.12 Interpretation of certain proflavin-induced mutations observed in T4 lysozyme. For explanation see text. Modified from E. Terzaghi *et al.* (1966), *Proc.N.A.S.*, *56*, 500.

synthesised in the cell from the N-terminal to the C-terminal end.[1] In fig. 14.12 the amino-acids are written in the conventional manner with the N-terminal end at the left-hand side. It therefore follows that the mRNA strand must be read from the 5' end to the 3' end.

It is clear that these important experiments show not only that the code is read from 'left' to 'right', but also confirm Crick's interpretation of proflavin mutations as frame-shift mutations. Furthermore it is possible from this work to confirm the amino-acid meanings assigned to some of the codons.

19

Decipherment of the nucleic acid cryptogram has also opened up new vistas for the biochemist interested in organic evolution. We shall see in the next section that there is good evidence that the code is universal and that it was established very early in the history of life on this planet. It follows that it has governed the evolution of organisms for perhaps a billion years. In other words it is ultimately responsible for the vital variation on which, as we saw in Chapter 13, natural selection works. Consequently a deep knowledge of the mechanisms behind the code's mutability goes far to complete our understanding of the theory enunciated by Darwin in 1859.

A deep knowledge of the mutations to which the code is subject means, of course, a knowledge at the molecular level. We have already discussed, in the previous section, the molecular nature of

[1] Dintzis, H. M. (1961), *Proc. Nat. Acad. Sci. Wash.*, *47*, 247.

one type of mutation. Frame-shift mutations, we saw, are due to the insertion or deletion of one or a few bases. Now frame-shift mutations are particular cases of a class of mutations known, for obvious reasons, as *point mutations*. Two other types of point mutation are recognised: transitions and transversions. In these types of mutation a nucleotide is not deleted from or inserted into the chain but exchanged for another.

One avenue of approach to the study of transitions and transversions has already been alluded to in several parts of this book. This approach involves comparing the amino-acid sequences of homologous proteins obtained from different organisms. In Chapter 4 the structures of cytochromes c from a variety of organisms was discussed. In Chapter 6 the matter was referred to more explicitly when the evolution of haemoglobin was considered.

It is clear that, in many cases, the substitution of one nucleotide for another in a codon completely alters the meaning of that codon. For example fig. 4.17 shows the structure of five different β-MSH molecules. The principal difference between the five is the presence in position 6 of either lysine or arginine. Clearly lysine would be changed for arginine if AAA or AAG was altered to AGA or AGG, a difference of one base in both cases. It is worth noting, too, that both arginine and lysine are basic amino-acids, and that they, and also the other basic amino-acid—histidine—are coded by very similar triplets.

The fact that amino-acids with similar physico-chemical properties are coded by similar triplets is important. It means that point mutations are less likely to result in radical amino-acid substitutions. This term, it will be remembered, was introduced in Chapter 4 when the structure of cytochrome c was being discussed. It will be recalled that the primary structure of this molecule had been analysed for more than twenty different species. One notable feature was the conservation, presumably for structural reasons, of hydrophobic residues. In other words a position in the amino-acid chain occupied by a hydrophobic residue in one species was usually found to be occupied by a hydrophobic residue, not necessarily the same one, in another species. Inspection of Table 14.1 shows that the hydrophobic residues, for example phe, leu, ileu, val, all possess similar codons. Similarly the triplets coding for hydrophilic residues like asp, glu, asn, gln are all very much alike. It looks as though some of the structural features of protein molecules are reflected in the code.

As a final, and probably the best known, example of the substitution of amino-acids in the primary sequence of closely related proteins let us examine the various abnormal haemoglobins. These variations in primary structure are shown in fig. 6.5. Let us restrict our attention to the twelve alterations so far detected in the α-chain. Table 14.2 shows that if we use Table 14.1 to determine the changes in the codons responsible for each alteration it emerges that in each case only one nucleotide of the triplet has changed. The reader can satisfy himself that the same explanation holds for the sixteen alterations discovered in the β-chain. This is a remarkable confirmation of the validity of Table 14.1 for the cells of *H. sapiens*, and of the nature of certain point mutations.

TABLE 14.2

Amino-acid alterations in the α-chain of abnormal human haemoglobins A and presumptive nucleotide triplet alterations

Position in α-chain	Amino-acid alteration	Alteration in codon
5	ala → asp	GCb → GAb
6	gly → asp	GGb → GAb
16	lys → glu	AAe → GAe
22	gly → asp	GGb → GAb
30	glu → gln	GAe → CAe
47	asp → gly	GAb → GGb
54	gln → arg	CAe → CGe
54	gln → glu	CAe → GAe
57	gly → asp	GGb → GAb
58	his → tyr	CAb → UAb
68	asn → lys	AAb → AAe
87	his → tyr	CAb → UAb
116	glu → lys	GAe → AAe

b=C or U   e=A or G

(Adapted from T. H. Jukes, *Molecules and Evolution*, Columbia University Press, New York and London, 1966, p. 183)

It is clear that in all these cases—the melanophore-stimulating hormones, the cytochromes c, the haemoglobins—a single base change, not an insertion or a deletion, is responsible for the observed effect. The sixty-four dollar question is, therefore, how can bases change?

As long ago as 1953 Watson and Crick proposed one possible mechanism. They pointed out that each of DNA's four bases can

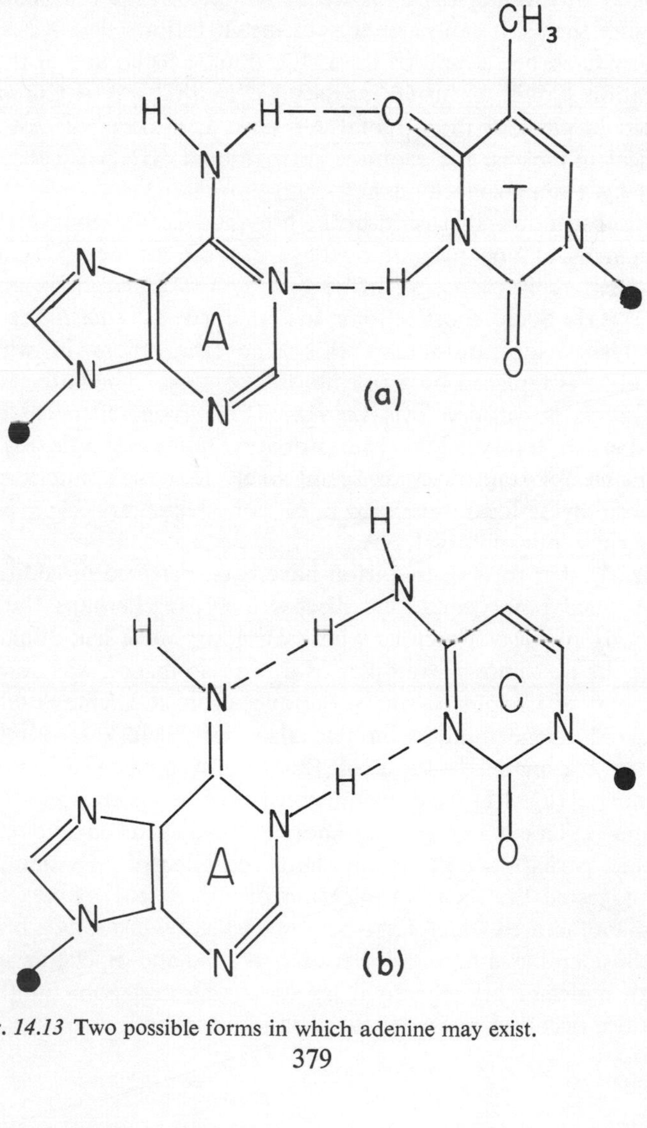

Fig. 14.13 Two possible forms in which adenine may exist.

379

exist in more than one form. This is due to the high degree of resonance which, as we have seen, is so marked a feature of the purines and pyrimidines. Adenine, for example, may exist in either of the two forms shown in fig. 14.13.

Fig. 14.13(a) shows the usual form of adenine (compare fig. 13.10), whilst fig. 14.13(b) shows another, far less common, form in which adenine may exist. It is clear that the adenine of fig. 14.13(b) is incapable of forming H-bonds with thymine; on the other hand, as the figure shows, it can partner cytosine. It follows that T is substituted by C on one strand of the DNA double helix, and at the next replication C will, as usual, specify G. In this way a CG pair is inserted in place of the original AT pair. It is believed that many chemical mutagens, for example nitrous acid (HNO_2), cause their effects by a similar mechanism.

The substitutions discussed in the previous paragraph result in the replacement of one pyrimidine base (T) by another (C) and, in subsequent replications, a purine base (A) is replaced by another purine (G). Such substitutions are defined as *transitions*. This distinguishes substitutions of this type from those in which a pyrimidine is replaced by a purine or vice versa. The latter type of substitution is called a *transversion*. The physico-chemical events lying behind transversions are probably not so simple as those responsible for transitions. It seems likely that such mutations are produced by a local breakdown of complementary base pairing during the replication of DNA.

Several other sorts of mutation have been detected in addition to the so-called point mutations discussed above. Perhaps the most interesting of these are cases where an entire gene has duplicated. One of the best known examples of this phenomenon was described at the end of Chapter 6 where the evolution of haemoglobin was considered. Gene duplication has also been held responsible for some of the major features of the insulin molecule. It will be remembered (fig. 4.11) that insulin consists of two polypeptide chains —A and B. To cut a long story short it is believed that the original molecule, perhaps a billion years ago, consisted of only one chain. It is suggested that gene duplication occurred so that two chains were manufactured which later became linked by disulphide bridges. The considerable differences between the A and B chains of the modern molecule are explained by supposing that point mutations have since occurred more or less at random in both chains.

DECIPHERING THE CODE

It is clear from the outline presented in this section that Table 14.1 is to the modern biochemist very much what the Rosetta stone was to the nineteenth-century Egyptologist.

20

In conclusion we may ask: is the code universal? It is true that a large proportion of the work done to establish Table 14.1 was done on *E. coli*. Nevertheless, Nirenberg-type experiments have now been carried out on protein-synthesising systems derived from quite a wide spectrum of organisms.[1] In all cases results very similar to those achieved with *E. coli* have been obtained. This is strong evidence for the universality of the code.

Supporting evidence comes from a study of the effects of mutation on the primary structures of proteins derived from various organisms. Some of this evidence was briefly reviewed in the previous section. In most cases the alteration can be accounted for if it is supposed that one or other of the three nucleotides in the appropriate codon has been altered.

However, perhaps the most telling reason for believing that the code is universal is the sheer difficulty of imagining how it could be altered during evolution. Once the code had become established, presumably very early in the evolution of life on Earth, it is hard to see how any major change could have occurred without disastrous results. Suppose, for example, that the meaning of the codon UUU were changed from phenylalanine to, say, lysine. Practically all the proteins in an organism's body contain these two amino-acids. In consequence the primary structure of each and every protein would be altered. It is not difficult to see that the results of this wholesale alteration might well be catastrophic.

[1] Marshall, R. E., Caskey, T. C. and Nirenberg, M. (1967), *Science*, *155*, 820.

15

Multicellularity

1

The mammalian body is composed of at least a hundred different types of cell.[1] Each is adapted to carry out a particular job. Each is dependent on its neighbours for survival. In this respect the great analogy which Plato and Hobbes drew between the body and the state may be reversed: the multicellular body is analogous to the closely-integrated nation states of the modern world. The cell population of the metazoan body comes closer than any modern society to the rather doubtful Utopia Auden envisaged in his *New Year Letter* where the individuals form a

> '. . . seamless live continuum
> Of supple and coherent stuff . . .
> Where in a unity of praise
> The largest publicum's a res
> And each least res a publicum'.

Yet each of the profoundly heterogeneous collection of cells forming the metazoan body has arisen from the same fertilised egg. Each, as we shall see, is believed to carry the same library of information in its nucleus. Each is built of a similar set of 'standard parts'—proteins, nucleic acids, and the molecular assemblies mentioned in Chapters 8 and 12. Each is a variation on a single theme, and from their billion-fold existence emerges a higher unity—the multicellular individual.

With the emergence of this higher unity we leave behind the field proper to molecular biology. The study of the innumerable interlocking mechanisms which ensure, in Claude Bernard's phrase, 'la fixité du milieu intérieur', and the study of the overall control and

[1] *The Cell*, edited by Brachet, J. and Mirsky, A. E., Academic Press, New York and London, 1960, Vol. 1, p. 448.

co-ordination of these and other systems is the province of the physiologist. The molecular approach, however, is beginning to prove effective in answering the question: how does the heterogeneity of cell form and function in the multicellular body arise? It is to this fundamental problem that the last chapter in this book is devoted.

2

The problem of how a differentiated organism arises from a single undifferentiated zygote has puzzled the understanding of biologists since biology began. Galen's words on this subject were quoted at the beginning of this book. Our survey of protein molecules, lipo-protein organellae and cells can only have increased our appreciation of the justice of his sentiments. Aristotle, some six hundred years before Galen's time, had thought much the same. Reflecting on the striking difference between chance events like a shower of rain in summer and the purposeful events of embryology, he writes: 'For teeth and all other natural things invariably and normally come about in a given way; but of not one of the products of chance or spontaneity is this true.'[1] It can indeed be argued that the impression that these ordered and apparently purposeful biological processes made on his mind coloured the whole of his philosophy.[2]

In the history of biological thought we find that the preformationists and the epigeneticists have championed the two extremes in the spectrum of possible explanation for the facts of embryological development. The former suggested that the adult is present, perhaps in the form of homunculus, ready made in the zygote and all that is necessary is enlargement. The latter that the adult's differentiated body crystallises under the influence of external forces working on a homogeneous jelly-like zygote. These are, of course, extreme views extremely stated. Neither is tenable. The truth, as usual, lies somewhere in between.

We have seen that the zygote's DNA carries all the information necessary to specify the principal characteristics of the emerging individual. These characteristics will, of course, be modified by the influence of the environment—'the thousand natural shocks the flesh is heir to'. But the information stored in the nucleotide base-sequences is adequate to ensure that offspring do not altogether

[1] *Physica*, 198ᵇ35. Translated by Hardie, R. P. and Gaye, R. K.
[2] See *Aristotle* by Marjorie Grene, Faber & Faber, London, 1963.

belie the name of the process to which they owe their origin: reproduction.

However, the molecular biologist is presented with a problem. Each cell of the adult body, with the exception of the germ cells, possesses at least the same amount of DNA as was present in the zygote. This is ensured by the very precise nature of the mitotic divisions which, as we mentioned in Chapter 13, are responsible for embryological and later development. Yet if each cell of the body contains an equivalent amount of DNA how is it that they vary so much? If the structure and function of a muscle cell, a nerve cell, a liver cell and a retinal cell, is determined by the same DNA how can they all be so different? In short, what is the molecular basis of differentiation?

3

It is possible to conceive that cell differentiation might arise because the DNA in the cell's nucleus had undergone some sort of structural deformation or mutation which had rendered parts of it inactive. The information available to one cell might then differ very significantly from that available to another cell in the same organism. If this were in fact the cause of cell differentiation we should feel bound to probe further and ask: what are the causes of these putative deformations and mutations? However, what evidence there is seems to point in another direction. It looks as though specialised cells carry a complete, and potentially functional, issue of the hereditary information. Two pieces of evidence which support this idea will be outlined in this section. First the work of J. B. Gurdon on the differentiation of amphibian cells; second the work of Beerman and Clever on the giant chromosomes of midges.

The essence of Gurdon's technique is to remove nuclei from unfertilised frog's eggs and to replace them by nuclei taken from specialised cells of the frog tadpole. It has long been known that unfertilised frog eggs can be caused to develop parthenogenetically if they are pricked with a sterilised glass needle. Gurdon was able to show that it was possible to cause the eggs possessing transplanted nuclei to develop parthenogenetically into fertile male and female frogs.[1] The specialised cells from which Gurdon obtained nuclei were fully developed intestinal cells. These cells were in every respect

[1] Gurdon, J. B. (1964), *Adv. in Morphogenesis*, 4, 1.

differentiated to carry out an absorbitive function. Yet Gurdon's experiment showed that their DNA complement was fully capable of programming the development of an entire organism. In other words the DNA of these intestinal cells retained the information necessary to control the synthesis of haemoglobin, insulin and myosin, and to specify the morphology of a blood cell, a pancreatic cell and a muscle cell.

Gurdon's work forces us to conclude that, in specialised cells, only certain of the items inscribed on DNA can be expressed. Information irrelevant to the cell's needs is in some way prevented from influencing the ribosomal protein manufactory.

That only certain regions of the DNA present in a differentiated cell are active is also the conclusion to be drawn from experiments[1] involving the midge—*Chironomus*. These experiments make use of the fact that this insect, and certain others, like *Drosophila*, possess, in some of their cells, unusually large chromosomes called 'giant chromosomes'. It will be recalled from Chapter 13 that chromosomes are not normally visible in the nuclei of undividing, or interphase, cells. This is, of course, awkward for the molecular biologist, for it is during this period of the cell's life that the programming of ribosomes, etc. takes place. Giant chromosomes, however, are easily visible in non-dividing, metabolically active, cells.

It seems that the cells[2] which contain giant chromosomes are able to grow without dividing. However, although the cell itself does not divide, its chromosomes replicate themselves. Each chromosome replicates in the normal manner by laying down alongside itself a duplicate. The original and its duplicate do not, however, fall apart as they would in normal cell division. Instead of being carried away to opposite poles of the cell to initiate the nuclei of daughter cells they remain firmly bound to each other. This process of abortive cell division and consequent chromosome replication recurs many times. It follows that the chromosomes become greatly increased in girth: several hundred times as thick as the usual chromosome. It is thus clear why these chromosomes are called giant chromosomes, and why they remain visible during interphase.

It has long been known that giant chromosomes are crossed by a series of bands (Plate X(c)). Chromosomes derived from the tissues of

[1] Beerman, W. and Clever, U., *Sci. Amer.* (April 1964), 1.
[2] In *Chironomus* giant chromosomes are to be found in the salivary glands, the malpighian tubules, and in the epithelium of the intestine.

a single insect all show a nearly identical band pattern. However, a very interesting differentiation does exist. It is found that the pattern of bands is disrupted at intervals by the development of 'puffs'. In these regions the otherwise strap-like chromosome appears to 'balloon' outwards. It can be shown that the position of these puffs on giant chromosomes differs from one tissue to another.

In the light of our discussion of molecular genetics in Chapter 14 we may immediately wonder whether the puffs might mark regions of the chromosome where the DNA is actively engaged in transcribing information on to mRNA. One way of testing this idea would be to label the cell's mRNA and observe whether the label attaches itself to the puffs.

This experiment is not too difficult to carry out. It is known that uridine is incorporated into RNA as the base uracil. This base, of course, does not form part of the structure of DNA; consequently if it can be shown to exist in the puffs its presence must indicate the presence of RNA.

The experimental procedure was thus to inject radioisotopically-labelled uridine into *Chironomus*, kill the insect after a few minutes, extract the giant chromosomes and examine them for radioactivity. Sure enough, radioactivity was found to be concentrated in the region of the puffs. Thus there is good evidence that the puffs are indeed regions where mRNA synthesis is occurring.

It follows that chromosomes which differ in puff pattern differ also in the information being expressed. There is some experimental evidence which supports this deduction. It is found that in two closely related midges—*C. pallidivitans* and *C. tentans*—the puff patterns of the salivary gland giant chromosomes differ slightly. It can be shown, for example, that the fourth chromosome of *C. pallidivitans* possesses a puff at a position which is puffless in *C. tentans*. Moreover, if the cells in which these giant chromosomes occur are carefully examined it is possible to see that the cytoplasm of *C. pallidivitans*' cells contains a number of secretory granules which are not to be found in similar cells of *C. tentans*. It looks as though the puffed region of *C. pallidivitans*' chromosome is responsible for programming the production of a protein which is lacking in *C. tentans*.

Some indication that this interpretation is correct is provided by experiments which involve crossing individuals belonging to the two species. It is found that the resultant hybrids inherit puffed or puff-less chromosomes according to the usual Mendelian rules. In other words the hybrids will possess one puffed and one puffless chromo-some. Examination of the cytoplasm of these cells reveals the presence of secretory granules—but far fewer than in the *C. palli-divitans* parent.

Thus we see that investigation of the giant chromosomes of chironomid midges points to the same general conclusion as did Gurdon's experiments on Amphibia. It looks as though only certain regions of the DNA in a differentiated cell are active. It seems that the genes specifying materials inappropriate to the cell's position in life remain 'switched off'. Our next question must therefore be: how does a cell switch on, or switch off, its genes?

4

In order to pick up the beginnings of an answer to this problem we have, once more, to turn to the world of the microbes. In particular we must re-acquaint ourselves with that most convenient and most well-known of micro-organisms—*Escherichia coli*.

It is found that micro-organisms in general, and *E. coli* in parti-cular, exhibit a phenomenon called *enzyme adaptation*. This means that when the environmental conditions in which the bacterium finds itself change, so does the bacterium's complement of enzymes. Moreover, the bacterium's enzymes change in such a way that it is more fitted to survive in the new conditions.

Clearly this phenomenon is of considerable value to the bacterium. But how is it achieved? We can hardly endow an organism so primitive as *E. coli* with high-grade powers of ratiocination. Instead a chemo-genetic mechanism has been proposed. It is suggested that factors present in the bacterium's environment are able to switch the genes which control enzyme production 'on' and 'off'.

These two alternatives are referred to as *enzyme induction* and *enzyme repression*. By means of these two mechanisms the bacterial enzymes vary with varying environmental conditions. It may well be that the 'internal environment' of a multicellular organism can exert a similar influence on the genes of a specialised cell. It is worthwhile, therefore, to examine the mechanisms which, it is believed, lie behind enzyme adaptation.

Let us, first, examine an instance of enzyme repression. It is known that the amino-acid tryptophan is essential to the well-being of the

E. coli cell. In the absence of externally supplied tryptophan *E. coli* can synthesise the amino-acid according to the following equation:

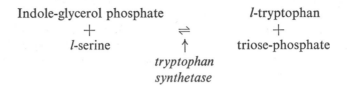

Fig. 15.1 The action of tryptophan synthetase.

Fig. 15.1 shows that the enzyme tryptophan synthetase is essential if the synthesis of tryptophan is to occur. Now it is found that if very little tryptophan is present in the environment, large numbers of tryptophan synthetase molecules are present in the bacterial cell. On the other hand, if the medium in, or on, which the bacterium is growing contains adequate supplies of tryptophan, it can be shown that very few molecules of tryptophan synthetase exist in the cell. It is said, in consequence, that the presence of tryptophan in the surrounding medium *represses* the synthesis of the enzyme tryptophan synthetase. It is as well for *E. coli* that the repression seems to be very specific: molecules chemically very similar to tryptophan have no effect on the synthesis of the enzyme.

Second, let us look at an example of enzyme induction. It can be shown that when *E. coli* is grown in the presence of a galactoside—for example, lactose—a hydrolytic enzyme, β-galactosidase, exists and is essential if the galactoside is to be utilised. In fact it is found that β-galactosidase is not sufficient on its own. If *E. coli* is to utilise galactosides they have first to pass through the cell membrane, for β-galactosidase is restricted to the bacterium's interior. Galactosides are largish molecules (fig. 15.2) and, in consequence, an enzyme is necessary to get them through the membrane. This enzyme is called galactoside-permease. Like β-galactosidase itself, this enzyme is also inducible. To begin with, however, let us concentrate our attention on β-galactosidase.

Now it is found that although several thousand molecules of β-galactosidase are present in an *E. coli* cell grown in the presence of a galactoside, this number is dramatically reduced when galactosides are removed from the environment. In consequence it is said that a galactoside, such as lactose, *induces* the synthesis of an appropriate

388

enzyme by the cell. As in the case of enzyme repression the action is, once again, very specific.

The biological advantage to the bacterium of induction and repression is clear. *E. coli*, striving to be economical, only synthesises an enzyme when it has to, or when the appropriate substrate is available. But how is the trick worked? How does the cell achieve this flexible response to environmental conditions?

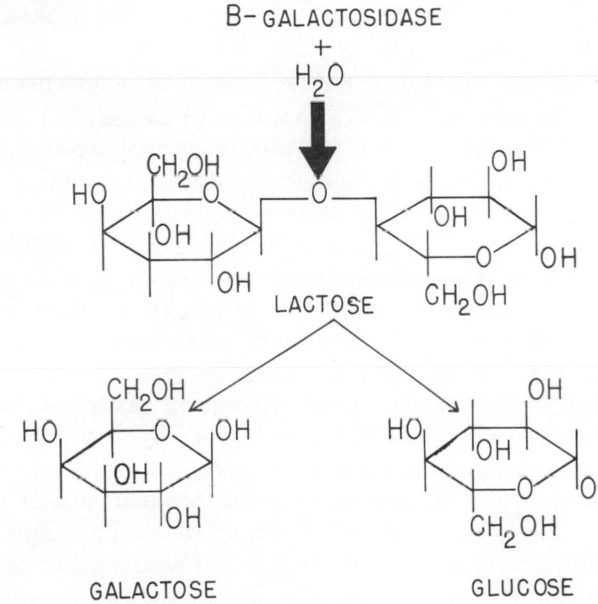

Fig. 15.2 The action of β-galactosidase.

It would be wrong to suggest that the mechanisms underlying enzyme induction and repression are yet completely understood. However, the interpretation first proposed by Jacob and Monod[1] and for which, in the main, they received the 1965 Nobel Prize in medicine is widely accepted. Hence it is Jacob and Monod's scheme which is outlined in the following brief account.

It will be recalled that in Chapters 13 and 14 we discussed how infection of an *E. coli* cell by T4 phage quickly resulted in the manufacture of phage protein by the bacterial ribosomes. In some ways this phenomenon is rather analogous to the case of enzyme induction

[1] Jacob, F. and Monod, J. (1961), *J. Mol. Biol.*, *3*, 318.

we have just considered. We could, if we liked, even say that the phage *induces* the *E. coli* cell to manufacture phage protein. In fact, of course, there is a very big difference between parasitism by phage and the induction of an enzyme by, say, a galactoside. It is clear that the main difference is that the bacteriophage injects a package of nucleic acid into *E. coli* and that this can reprogramme the bacterial ribosomes. There is no evidence that any nucleic acid adheres to the galactosides. In other words, if enzyme induction depends on reprogramming the cell's ribosomes the necessary nucleic acid must be provided by the bacterium itself.

We saw, in Chapter 14, that a cistron is able to control the type of polypeptide manufactured on the ribosomes by means of a messenger —mRNA. Perhaps the absence of a galactoside in some way inhibits the production of the mRNA controlling the synthesis of β-galactosidase. This is merely a more technical way of saying that the absence of a galactoside switches the β-galactosidase gene off. Is there any evidence that this, in fact, occurs?

The answer to this question seems to be *yes*. The evidence emerges from the genetics of *E. coli*. It is found, first, that certain mutant *E. coli* cells synthesise β-galactosidase whether galactosides are present in the environment or not. These mutants are called *constitutive mutants*. Vice versa, it is found, secondly, that other mutations, called *structural mutations*, destroy *E. coli*'s ability to manufacture the enzyme in all circumstances. By the techniques of genetic mapping discussed in Chapter 13 it can be shown that constitutive and structural mutations occur on different sites on the bacterial chromosome.

It is a comparatively simple matter to provide a molecular explanation for the structural mutation. We have only to suppose that certain nucleotide sequences in the appropriate gene, which we can call the *structural gene*, are altered or destroyed. It would then follow that the information transcribed on to mRNA would be faulty and that the ribosome, in consequence, would manufacture a faulty protein. It is unlikely that this faulty protein would retain its β-galactosidase activity, and hence the *E. coli* cell would be permanently deprived of this enzyme.

However, it is not so simple a matter to explain, in molecular terms, a constitutive mutation. The explanation put forward by Jacob and Monod suggests that the constitutive mutation inactivates a gene which normally *regulates* the activity of the structural gene.

Let us call this gene a *regulator gene*. Jacob and Monod suggest that
the regulator gene normally *inhibits* the activity of the structural gene.
They suggest, furthermore, as we shall see below, that this inhibitory
influence is blocked by galactosides. It follows, first, that when the
regulator gene is active (unmutated), galactosides, in blocking its
inhibitory influence, allow the structural gene to express itself.
Thus β-galactosidase is manufactured. On the other hand, it follows
that when the regulator gene is inactivated (mutated), its inhibitory
influence is permanently blocked and, in consequence, the structural
gene remains permanently switched on. β-galactosidase is manufactured whether galactosides are present in the environment or not.
Thus Jacob and Monod explain with one brilliant theory both the
phenomenon of enzyme induction and the phenomenon of constitutive mutation. Their ideas are schematised in fig. 15.3.

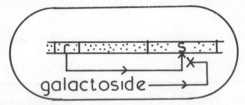

Fig. 15.3 Relation between a regulator and a structural gene. r=regulator
gene, s=structural gene, x=inhibition.

Next, we must ask: what is the nature of the inhibitory influence
produced by the regulator gene, and how does it act upon the
structural gene?

Let us take the second question first. Does the inhibitory influence
affect the whole of the structural gene, or only part of it? Strangely
enough it seems that it affects neither the whole nor a part of the
structural gene, but another gene immediately adjacent to it on the
chromosome. This gene is called an *operator gene*. It appears to
control the activity of the structural gene. Evidence for its existence
arises, once again, from studies on the genetics of *E. coli*.

We saw in Chapter 14 that *E. coli* enjoys a primitive form of sexual
reproduction. It will be remembered that the 'male' *E. coli* transfers
part of 'his' chromosome into the 'female' cell. It follows that the
resultant cell is, for a time, diploid. In addition to its own chromosome it contains a fragment of the male's. It is investigation of the
characteristics of these diploid cells which has enabled molecular
biologists to identify operator genes.

If operator genes exist they will be subject to mutation. It is reasonable to suppose that some mutations will render the operator immune to the influence of the regulator gene. The consequence of this will be that the structural gene will become uninhibitable by the regulator. β-galactosidase will be synthesised in all circumstances. But how are we to distinguish this type of mutant from the constitutive mutants described above? This is where use is made of diploid *E. coli.*

A diploid cell formed by the crossing of the original type of constitutive mutant with a normal cell will contain *two* regulator genes. The regulator gene derived from the constitutive mutant will, by definition, be inactive. Vice versa, that derived from the normal cell will, also by definition, be active. It will, in other words, be elaborating its normal inhibitory influence. In the absence of environmental galactosides this influence will be sufficient to inhibit the structural genes of both chromosomes. Hence the β-galactosidase enzyme will not be synthesised.

Next let us consider another possibility. Suppose we cross a normal *E. coli* with another possessing a mutated operator. In other words a normal *E. coli* is crossed with a constitutive mutant of the second type. It follows that the resulting diploid cell possesses two normally active regulator genes, but one inactive operator. The inhibitory influence is, by our hypothesis, unable to affect the inactive operator. Hence, even in the absence of environmental galactosides this diploid *E. coli* will produce β-galactosidase. These two different molecular-genetic situations are schematised in fig. 15.4.

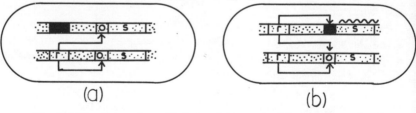

(a)   (b)

Fig. 15.4 Two types of constitutive mutant may be detected. Mutated and consequently non-functional regions of the chromosomes have been blacked out.

It is clear, therefore, that these two types of diploid *E. coli* are, in theory, distinguishable. If they can be shown to exist, the existence of operator genes is established. The necessary experiment was carried out by a group of investigators under the leadership of Jacob[1] in 1960.

[1] Jacob, F. *et al.* (1960), *C. R. Acad. Sci. (Paris)*, *250*, 1727.

The existence of operator genes was established. Fig. 15.5 summarises the relationships between regulator, operator and structural gene.

So far we have described the effect of the regulator on the operator as an inhibitory influence. In modern science the term 'influence' is little used; it is replaced by more precise notions. However, the

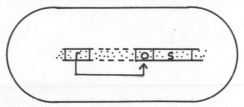

Fig. 15.5 Summary of Jacob and Monod's theory of the relationship between regulator (r), operator (o) and structural (s) genes.

precise way in which the regulator inhibits the operator is not at present known. It is thought[1] that the regulator gene serves as a template for the synthesis of a species of mRNA which, on reaching a ribosome, programmes the synthesis of a specific protein. This protein is believed to pass back on to the DNA where it inhibits the operator. These ideas, which are at present still rather speculative, are schematised in fig. 15.6.

Fig. 15.6 also shows the way in which inducer or suppressor molecules are believed to act on the system. Galactosides, as we have seen, are thought to inhibit the inhibitory influence of the regulator gene. In terms of fig. 15.6 it is suggested that the galactosides interact with the repressor protein in such a way that its activity is destroyed. The operator gene will then be able to activate the adjacent structural gene so that β-galactosidase is synthesised. It is conceivable that the galactoside acts as an allosteric effector (Chapter 7) altering, in some way, the repressor molecule's higher structure. These ideas are, at present, perforce rather speculative, as the precise nature of the repressor molecules has yet to be established. Recently, however, the first report of the isolation of a repressor molecule has appeared.[2] It seems to be a protein, and a protein, moreover, with a rather high molecular weight—150,000–200,000. This magnitude supports the idea that an allosteric mechanism may be operating (Chapter 8).

A similar explanation may be put forward to account for the phenomenon of enzyme repressors. It will be remembered that in the

1 Jacob, R. (1966), *Science, 152*, 1470.
2 Gilbert, W. and Muller-Hill, B. (1966), *Proc. U.S. Nat. Acad. Sci., 56*, 1891.

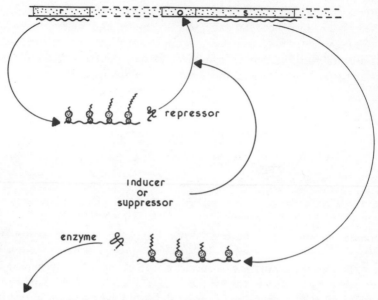

Fig. 15.6 Putative mechanism controlling the expression of *E. coli* genes.

presence of excess tryptophan the enzymes concerned in the synthesis of tryptophan are repressed. In this case Jacob and Monod propose that the regulator gene causes the synthesis of an inactive repressor. The presence of tryptophan, however, converts this inactive repressor into an active form. Once again an allosteric mechanism may be involved. The active repressor quickly inhibits the appropriate operator gene which, in turn, inactivates the structural gene. The manufacture of tryptophan synthetase abruptly ceases. Any of these enzymes already existing in the cell will, in the ordinary fluxes of metabolism, soon be broken down.

Finally, before leaving the topic of enzyme adaptation, it is worth noticing that an operator frequently controls more than one structural gene. This is in fact the case with the operator controlling the β-galactosidase gene. It is found that this operator also controls the activity of the galactoside-permease gene.[1] It will be remembered

[1] Yet another structural gene has been shown to be controlled by the β-galactosidase operator. This gene directs the synthesis of another enzyme—thiogalactoside transacetylase—which is also involved, though to a lesser extent in lactose metabolism. These three structural genes, because they are all concerned with the uptake and utilisation of lactose, are said in the shorthand of molecular biology to constitute the *lac* operon.

(p. 388) that both enzymes are necessary if *E. coli* is to utilise galactosides. It is thus an economical feature of *E. coli*'s genetic system to arrange matters so that both structural genes are governed by a single regulator. A number of structural genes activated by a single operator, and hence governed by a single regulator gene, is called an *operon*. An operon may consist of from one to ten, or perhaps more, structural genes. It seems that an operon manufactures a continuous strip of mRNA across all its structural genes. This is also an economical feature: it is pointless for the ribosomes to manufacture one enzyme if more than one are necessary to catalyse a biochemical process. The lengthy strip of mRNA moulded by an operon consisting of more than one structural gene is called, for obvious reasons, *polycistronic* mRNA.

5

The work on *E. coli* shows that a mechanism does exist, at least in bacteria, for the switching-on and switching-off of genes. Jacob[1] likens the information present in the DNA double helix to that present in the text of a book. The regulatory network, he suggests, 'determines which pages are read at a given time'.

In the earlier sections of this chapter some evidence was described which suggested that in the cells of higher organisms not all the DNA is active at any one time. It seems probable therefore that mechanisms for switching genes on and off, similar to those described for *E. coli*, exist. On the face of it such mechanisms, responsive as they are to external control, may well be responsible for the differentiation of cells observed in different parts of the body of a multicellular organism.

6

In conclusion it is important to notice that not only does the discovery of a system of cytoplasmic regulators indicate a way in which cells may become differentiated, but it also points to a decentralisation of the cell's control mechanism. Increasingly it is realised that there is not a one-way movement of information and command between nucleus and cytoplasm, but a continuous interchange and feedback from one to the other. Furthermore it has been shown that certain

[1] Jacob, F. (1966), *Science*, *152*, 1478.

cytoplasmic organelles, for example the mitochondria and chloroplasts, possess their own strands of DNA and, consequently, their own libraries of information.

The idea that the activity of the cytoplasm is rigorously and strictly controlled by the nucleus is thus giving way to a more sophisticated, albeit more complex, view. The cell is organised not so much on the lines of a totalitarian state as on the lines of a western-style democracy. Control is diffused throughout the whole community of molecules. By a delicate system of checks and balances (see also Chapter 7) the total system emerges as an harmonious unity, each part appearing to co-operate for the well-being of the whole; in short it is *alive*.

Similarly the properties which we recognise as being characteristic of life do not emerge from one particular type of molecular architecture but, as we emphasised at the end of Chapter 8, from the close juxtaposition and interaction of many. This jostling hive of macromolecules has its being, moreover, in an environment composed of water—itself a fascinating molecule—and numerous electrostatically charged ions. It is clear that this transient 'flickering' crowd of molecules and ions presents an outstanding challenge to the ingenuity and intellect of scientists. There is still much to be done.

Index

In this index an attempt has been made to help the reader by indicating the positions in the text where key words are first defined. The page numbers of illustrations are italicised.

INDEX

INDEX

402